THE COMPLEX j-PLANE

THE MATHEMATICAL PHYSICS MONOGRAPH SERIES

A. S. Wightman, Editor
Princeton University

George W. Mackey *(Harvard)*	THE MATHEMATICAL FOUNDATIONS OF QUANTUM MECHANICS
R. F. Streater *(Imperial College of Science and Technology)* and A. S. Wightman *(Princeton)*	PCT, SPIN AND STATISTICS, AND ALL THAT
R. G. Newton (*Indiana University*)	THE COMPLEX j-PLANE

THE COMPLEX j-PLANE

Complex Angular Momentum in Nonrelativistic Quantum Scattering Theory

ROGER G. NEWTON
Professor of Physics
Indiana University

W. A. BENJAMIN, INC.

New York *Amsterdam* *1964*

THE COMPLEX j-PLANE
Complex Angular Momentum in
Nonrelativistic Quantum Scattering Theory

Library of Congress Catalog Card Number 64-16072
Manufactured in the United States of America

The manuscript was put into production October 3, 1963;
this volume was published June 29, 1964

The publisher is pleased to acknowledge the assistance of Edith Miller, who composed the volume; Cecilia Duray-Bito, who prepared the art; and William Prokos, who designed the cover and dust jacket

W. A. BENJAMIN, INC.
One Park Avenue, New York, New York 10016

PREFACE

The present volume grew out of a number of journal articles (some written in collaboration with Dr. B. Desai) and lectures I gave at several universities, mostly in Europe, during 1962-63. Although it is concerned with a subject matter that has been of intense interest to a large number of physicists for about two years, my own taste is expressed both in the presentation and in the limitation of the material to the area in which mathematical proofs are possible, based on well-established dynamics. That eliminated the relativistic domain, where unquestionably the most important applications lie. As a partial remedy a number of reprints of papers on the relativistic aspects is included.

Our present state of knowledge concerning the Watson-Regge method in Schrödinger theory is remarkably detailed, in many ways more so than is likely to be of use in the future. This is a good time to write a monograph. On the other hand, there are important gaps, for instance, concerning the behavior of the S-matrix as Re $l \to -\infty$. The most important hole in our knowledge is that concerning the three- (or more) particle problem. Although some aspects of this are now understood and included here, a complete understanding of that complicated situation may well be the key to a more reliable transfer of this fruitful technique to the high-energy particle domain. Since this problem seems considerably more difficult than those we have faced up to now (in this area), it will probably take more time to solve. There was therefore no point in waiting for its solution before usefully summarizing what is known.

To Drs. A. Ahmadzadeh, A. O. Barut, P. G. Burke, F. Calogero, W. Carnahan, C. Lovelace, D. Masson, and C. Tate, I am grateful for allowing me to include in this volume curves based on their numerical calculations; to Drs. K. Bardakci, G. F. Chew, S. C. Frautschi, M. Gell-Mann, S. Mandelstam, P. T. Matthews, F. Zachariasen, and the editors of the *Physical Review* and of the *Proceedings of the Physical Society (London),* for permission to include reprints of their articles.

I should like to express my appreciation to the National Science Foundation, which financially supported part of the research contained in this book, most importantly in the form of a Senior Post-doctoral Fellowship. The hospitality of the Institute of Physics at the University of Rome, where this book was written, is also gratefully acknowledged.

R. G. Newton

Bloomington, Indiana
April 1964

CONTENTS

Preface v

1. Introduction 1
2. The Watson Transform 4
3. The Irregular Solutions 14
4. The Regular Solution ϕ 21
5. The Jost Function and the S-Matrix 30
6. Behavior as $|l| \to \infty$ 37
7. Regge Poles 48
8. Pole Trajectories 56
9. Threshold Behavior 64
10. The Residues 76
11. Representations of the S-Matrix 80
12. Examples 86
13. Exchange Potentials 103
14. Trajectories in the k-Plane 106
15. The Uniqueness Problem 114
16. Two Particles of Spin-½ 121
17. The Three-Body Problem 135
18. The Three-Body Problem *(Continued):* The Dynamical Branch Points 149

Appendix A. Bounds on the Green's Functions 161
Appendix B. Limitations on the Phase-Shift Derivative 165
Appendix C. Limitations on the Angular Momentum Matrix Elements of Potentials of the Yukawa Type 168

Bibliography 171

Reprints

S. C. Frautschi, M. Gell-Mann, and F. Zachariasen, *Phys. Rev.*, **126,** 2204-2218 (1962) 189
K. Bardakci, *Phys. Rev.*, **127,** 1832-1836 (1962) 204
G. F. Chew, S. C. Frautschi, and S. Mandelstam, *Phys. Rev.*, **126,** 1202-1208 (1962) 209
P. T. Matthews, *Proc. Phys. Soc. (London)*, **80,** 1-12 (1962) 216

Index 229

THE
COMPLEX j-PLANE

Chapter I

INTRODUCTION

The mathematical analysis of the results of scattering experiments has lately acquired a new tool. Whereas it used to be common practice to resolve scattering (or production) amplitudes into infinite series of contributions from each of the discrete, physically possible, angular momentum states, it has now been found useful to introduce an interpolation between the quantized states so as to make the amplitude an analytic function of the complex variable j, the angular momentum. Instead of discussing the energy dependence of each of the partial wave amplitudes for physical values of j, it has become advantageous for some purposes to discuss the amplitude as an analytic function of the two variables, energy and angular momentum, and specifically, to consider its singularities in the complex j-plane as functions of E.

None of this means, of course, that the quantization of the angular momentum has been given up. In fact, no new physics has been added. The new method is merely another mathematical device for analyzing scattering experiments and a new language in which to formulate more easily ideas which could also be expressed in the old, although less simply.

The replacement of an infinite series of discrete terms by a contour integral of an analytic function is not novel, and neither is the application of that procedure in physics. It was introduced by Poincaré[1] and Nicholson,[2] and first applied in its present form in electromagnetic theory by G. N. Watson.[3] After its resurrection, in electromagnetic wave problems, by Sommerfeld,[4] it has seen there a number of more recent applications.[5] In quantum scattering theory the Watson method was first used by T. Regge[6] in 1959 with the primary aim to prove the double dispersion relation in potential scattering. For about a year it did not find much favor among physicists. However in 1961 (strictly, from the end of 1960) it was speculatively taken over into the domain of relativistic particle physics[7] and from then on it saw a spectacular rise in interest. During the last 2 years it occupied the attention of a major fraction of the world's theoretical physicists; witness the bibliography of the present volume, which includes over 300 articles.

Within the confines of nonrelativistic quantum scattering theory the advantage of the new method consists primarily in the following. The customary procedure in the two-body problem, of making a partial wave analysis, computing the phase shift for each physically attainable angular momentum state, and adding the results to give the amplitude, makes full use of the rotational invariance of the interparticle forces; but for all that the procedure cares, these forces may be arbitrarily different in each angular momentum state. The fact that the usual interparticle potentials in nature are independent of the relative angular momentum state of the two particles, or at least depend on it in a very simple, explicitly given way, is not at all used in the "old-fashioned" method. Precisely that fact, in addition to rotational invariance, is exploited in the new procedure. Owing to this angular momentum independence (or simple given dependence) of the forces, there exist simple, continuous connections between the various partial wave amplitudes. It is true that for the purpose of analyzing these connections it is not necessary to make the angular momentum complex; it is sufficient to make it real and continuous. Many of the new results and insights can be obtained in that manner, as will be seen in Chapter 14. There are, nevertheless, some additional advantages to be gained from allowing the angular momentum to be a complex variable, as will be seen. Most of these have to do with its speculative use in high-energy physics. The step from a continuous real variable to a complex one is, of course, not nearly as radical as that from a discrete to a continuous one.

The method by which the physical partial wave amplitudes ought to be interpolated to yield an analytic function is a priori not uniquely defined. (The problem of uniqueness is discussed in Chapter 15.) There is, however, one class of interpolations, which we may call the "dynamical" one, and which on physical grounds is much to be preferred to any other. It is the one introduced by Regge and followed in this book. The three-dimensional Schrödinger wave function for two particles is analyzed in partial waves and the angular variables are eliminated. In this analysis the angular momentum is necessarily quantized. In the resulting radial Schrödinger equations, however, the angular momentum plays the role merely of a parameter, and it is at this stage that the quantization may be relaxed. The interpolation of the partial amplitudes, in other words, starts from a "natural" interpolation of the Schrödinger equations. Only in this manner do we gain the additional insights mentioned before, because of the angular momentum independence of the potential.

As a new tool in nonrelativistic scattering theory the present method has, no doubt, many uses and advantages. Nevertheless, it must be recognized that its greatest triumph, Pyrrhic as it might be, comes from its transfer to the relativistic domain. It is that transfer which made it suddenly so fashionable among high-energy physicists. The additional power of the Regge method in high-energy particle physics comes from two points inherent in the asymptotic behavior of the amplitude as the momentum transfer tends to infinity at fixed energy, given by (2-8'). As is discussed in more detail in Chapter 2, the "crossing relation" of relativistic quantum field theory thus allows that formula to be interpreted as an asymptotic high-energy formula (2-19), at fixed momentum transfer, for other, related physical processes. As such it has direct experimentally observable consequences which, moreover, appeared to be verified for a while in 1962. The second point, of a more technical theoretical nature, has to do with the oscillatory behavior of the asymptotic formula (2-19) and the resulting convergence of certain dispersion integrals. Although the first point, the apparent experimental verification of the "Regge pole prediction," has meanwhile disappeared, the second is still of importance in the theory of particle physics.

Now it should be noted that the use of the Regge method in high-energy physics involves a transfer from the nonrelativistic to the relativistic domain not merely of the procedure but of the results of that analysis. At that point we enter the realm of pure speculation, and not of a very plausible one at that. There appears to be no theoretical reason why the results of nonrelativistic two-particle theory should hold in the essentially many-particle relativistic theory, particularly in view of the possibly different results of the three-particle (or more) theory discussed in Chapter 18.

For these reasons the bulk of this book deals only with the nonrelativistic domain, where results are well grounded and, starting from known dynamics, can be proved. For those of a speculative turn of mind, who want to transfer the ideas to the high-energy domain, it is presumably important to know exactly what is known to be true in the less exciting nether regions and what it is based on. As for us, we may prefer the dictum of Sir Isaac Newton, "Hypothese non fingo."

The reprints are designed to lead the reader into the realm where the Regge method is used without proofs, but where the most interesting experimental consequences are to be found. Even if these turn out to be incorrect, they form an important part of the fabric of present-day, theoretical, high-energy physics.

Notes and References

1. (P10).
2. (N10).
3. (W4).
4. (S6), pp. 282 ff.
5. See, for example, (F14), (G21), (I5), and (P11).
6. (R1).
7. See Chew and Frautschi (C21), Chew (C28), and Gribov (G6).

Chapter 2

THE WATSON TRANSFORM

The scattering amplitude of two spinless particles interacting via a spherically symmetric potential is conventionally written as a series of partial waves

$$A(k, z) = (2ik)^{-1} \sum_{\ell=0}^{\infty} (2\ell + 1)[S_\ell(k) - 1] P_\ell(z) \tag{2-1}$$

where k is the wave number, $z = \cos\theta$, S_ℓ is the ℓth eigenvalue of the unitary S-matrix,

$$S_\ell = e^{2i\delta_\ell}$$

and P_ℓ is the Legendre polynomial. If every term in the series in (2-1) is considered as the value of an analytic function of λ at $\lambda = \ell + \frac{1}{2}$, $\ell = 0, 1, 2, \ldots$, the series may be replaced by an integral,

$$A(k, z) = (2k)^{-1} \int_C d\lambda\, \lambda[S(\lambda, k) - 1] P_{\lambda - 1/2}(-z) \sec \pi\lambda \tag{2-2}$$

where the contour C is indicated in Figure 2-1. The minus sign in the argument of the Legendre function compensates for the minus sign arising from the derivative of $\cos \pi\lambda$ at the poles.

If the functions in the integrand are sufficiently well behaved as $|\lambda| \to \infty$ we may add to C two quarter-circles at large distances in the first and fourth quadrant and then distort the contour to lie along the imaginary axis. In addition to the integral we then obtain a sum of terms coming from the residues of the poles of the integrand in the first and fourth quadrant; and if the integrand contains branch

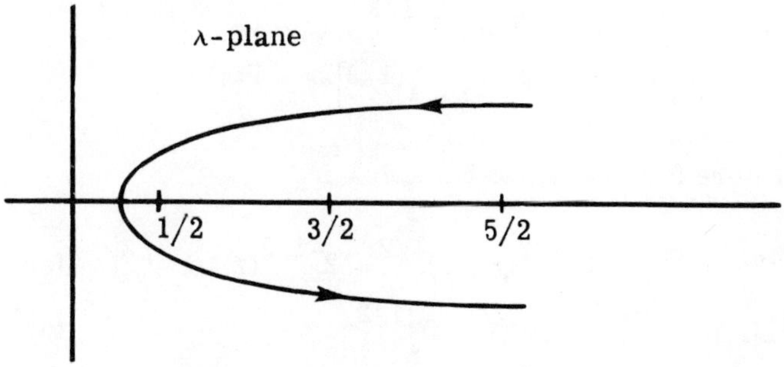

Figure 2-1
The contour C of integration in (2-2) for the Watson transform.

points, there will appear a sum of integrals over the discontinuities across the concomitant branch cuts. This procedure will be referred to as the "Watson transform."[1] If we use the standard interpolation of the Legendre functions[2] for nonintegral order they are free of singularities; the S-matrix of two particles interacting via a reasonable potential will be shown to have only poles in the relevant region say, at $\ell = \alpha_n$ with residues β_n. (The modifications necessary for three particles, where cuts may arise, are discussed in Chapter 18.) Thus we obtain for the amplitude

$$A(k, z) = (2k)^{-1} \int_{-\infty}^{\infty} d\lambda' \, \lambda' [S(i\lambda', k) - 1] P_{i\lambda' - 1/2}(-z)/\cosh \pi\lambda' + i\pi k^{-1} \sum_n (\alpha_n + \tfrac{1}{2}) \beta_n P_{\alpha_n}(-z)/\sin \pi\alpha_n \tag{2-3}$$

In order to justify each step in the Watson transform a number of conditions have to be met. A given interpolation of the functions involved, primarily of the Legendre polynomials and of the S-matrix, may or may not satisfy them. The arising uniqueness question for the interpolation is discussed in Chapter 15. For the Legendre functions there is a "standard" extension away from the integers, based on Legendre's differential equation. It is "optimal" for the present purpose. The resulting functions $P_\nu(z)$ are, for fixed z, entire analytic functions of ν with the asymptotic behavior[3]

$$P_\nu(z) \simeq (2\pi)^{-1/2} \nu^{-1/2} (z^2 - 1)^{-1/4} e^{\xi} \tag{2-4}$$

as $|\nu| \to \infty$ for[4] $\mathrm{Re}\, \nu \geq 0$, where

$$\xi(z) = \ln 2^{-1/2 - \nu}\left\{\left[(z+1)^{1/2} + (z-1)^{1/2}\right]^{2\nu+1} + i\left[(z+1)^{1/2} - (z-1)^{1/2}\right]^{2\nu+1}\right\}$$

and therefore for real z, with $\nu = \nu_1 + i\nu_2$

$$\xi(z) = \begin{cases} (2\nu_1 + 1)\ln\left[2^{-1/2}(z+1)^{1/2} + 2^{-1/2}(z-1)^{1/2}\right] & \text{for} \quad z > 1 \\ 2|\nu_2|\tan^{-1}\left[(1-z)/(1+z)\right]^{1/2} & \text{for} \quad z^2 < 1 \end{cases}$$

For fixed ν, $P_\nu(z)$ is an analytic function of z regular everywhere in the finite z-plane cut from $z = -\infty$ to $z = -1$ with the asymptotic behavior[5]

$$P_{\nu - 1/2}(z) \simeq \pi^{-1/2} 2^{\nu - 1/2} z^{\nu - 1/2}\Gamma(\nu)/\Gamma(\nu + \tfrac{1}{2}) \tag{2-5}$$

as $|z| \to \infty$ for Re $\nu \geq 0$.

The problem of justifying the Watson transform, therefore, reduces to finding a suitable interpolation of the S-matrix elements with the required properties. Most of the remainder of this book is concerned with the study of the properties of a specific kind of interpolation procedure, based on the radial Schrödinger equation. It is an analog of the extension of the Legendre polynomials via Legendre's differential equation. Physically speaking, this is the most appealing method because it is based on an equation that incorporates the dynamics of the scattering process. Ultimately, of course, the proof of the pudding is in the eating. In the case of two interacting particles, the dynamical procedure does yield the requisite properties for a large class of potentials. The uniqueness problem in the interpolation will be discussed in more detail in Chapter 15.

If the interparticle force is due to a superposition of Yukawa potentials, as written in (3-8), then the asymptotic behavior of the S-matrix as Re $\lambda \to \infty$ is given by (6-16). Insertion of this together with (2-4) in (2-2) shows that the integral in (2-2) converges absolutely for values of z in the region

$$\left|(z+1)^{1/2} \pm (z-1)^{1/2}\right| < 2^{1/2}C \qquad C = \left|\frac{\mu_0}{2k} + \left(1 + \frac{\mu_0^2}{4k^2}\right)^{1/2}\right|$$

The boundary of this domain is an ellipse with foci at $z = \pm 1$ and semimajor axis[6]

$$z_0 = \tfrac{1}{2}(C^2 + C^{-2})$$

For positive energies, i.e., real k, this simplifies to

$$z_0 = 1 + \frac{\mu_0^2}{2k^2}$$

Since $P_{\lambda - 1/2}(-z)$ has a cut from $z = 1$ to $z = \infty$, A appears, according to (2-2), to have a cut starting at $z = 1$ too. This, however, is not the case, as is immediately seen by evaluating the discontinuity of A across the positive real z-axis. Since the discontinuity of P is[7]

$$\Delta P_{\lambda - 1/2}(-z) = 2i \cos \pi\lambda \; P_{\lambda - 1/2}(z) \tag{2-6}$$

we may, for $z < z_0$, use (2-2) and obtain

$$\Delta A(k, z) = ik^{-1} \int_C d\lambda \; \lambda[S - 1]P_{\lambda - 1/2}(z) = 0$$

the contour containing no singularities. Thus, the cut really starts at the branch point $z = z_0$, beyond which the representation (2-2) breaks down. As a function of the negative square of the momentum transfer,

$$t \equiv -\Delta^2 = 2k^2(z - 1) \tag{2-7}$$

the cut of A starts at $t = \mu_0^2$.

In view of (2-4) and (6-16), the Watson transform can be completed for $z < z_0$, and since by (6-5) and (6-10) for potentials of the Yukawa type (3-8), as $\text{Im}\,\lambda \to \pm\infty$[8]

$$S - 1 = O\left(|\lambda|^{-1/2}\right)$$

whereas by (2-4), $P_\lambda(z)$ increases at most as $\exp[|\text{Im}\,\lambda| \arg z]$, the "background" integral in (2-3) converges absolutely for all z not lying between $z = +1$ and $z = +\infty$. Thus (2-3) may be analytically continued and used even for values of z for which (2-1) or (2-2) fail to converge absolutely.[9]

The virtue of (2-3) compared to (2-1) is that it allows us to extract the asymptotic behavior as a function of z very simply. According to (2-5), the background term in (2-3) is of order $z^{-1/2}$ as $|z| \to \infty$. Assuming that the S-matrix has only a finite number of poles in the right half λ-plane (it will be shown later that that is the case for large classes of potentials, but not always), we obtain the leading term as $|z| \to \infty$ from the pole term in (2-3) with the largest real part. Suppose that that "leading" pole occurs at $\ell = \alpha$. Then (2-3) and (2-5) show that

$$A(k, z) \underset{|z| \to \infty}{\sim} F(k) z^{\alpha(k)} \tag{2-8}$$

where

$$F(k) = i\pi^{1/2} k^{-1} (\alpha + \tfrac{1}{2})\beta \csc(\pi\alpha) 2^{\alpha} \Gamma(\alpha + \tfrac{1}{2}) / \Gamma(\alpha + 1)$$

Both the pole position α and the residue β will, in general, of course, depend on k, and hence on the energy. In terms of the momentum transfer we may also write, with $\alpha = \alpha_R + i\alpha_I$,

$$A \underset{|t| \to \infty}{\sim} G(E) t^{\alpha_R(E)} e^{i\alpha_I(E) \ln t} \tag{2-8'}$$

Since for fixed k, A(k, z) has no singularities in the finite z-plane cut from $z = z_0$ to ∞, and asymptotically it behaves according to (2-8), it satisfies a "subtracted" dispersion relation in the z-variable[10]:

$$A(z) = \sum_{j=1}^{n} A(z_j) \prod_{i \neq j} \frac{z - z_i}{z_j - z_i} + \frac{1}{2\pi i} \int_{z_0}^{\infty} dz' \frac{\Delta A(z')}{z' - z} \prod_{i=1}^{n} \frac{z - z_i}{z' - z_i} \tag{2-9}$$

ΔA being the discontinuity of A across the cut from $z = z_0$ to $z = \infty$, and the n points z_i may be chosen arbitrarily (but not on the cut); n is a finite integer, $n > \text{Re}\,\alpha$. Next, the behavior of A in the energy plane may be exploited in order to write dispersion relations in E for ΔA and the $A(z_j)$ in (2-9), and the result is the celebrated double dispersion relation or Mandelstam representation.

In the derivation of (2-9) it was of great importance that the number of poles of S for $\text{Re}\,\lambda > 0$ be finite,[11] which in turn implies the existence of a "leading pole" in S. It is, therefore, imperative to determine whether, or for what potentials, the number of poles of S in the right-hand half of the λ-plane is finite. Moreover, since the pole position α depends on the energy, it is important for the subsequent energy dispersion relation to see if there exists an integer n to the right of all the poles in the λ-plane, for all energies. If there are poles that move toward infinity in the right-hand direction, i.e., $\text{Re}\,\alpha(E) \to \infty$ as $E \to \infty$, then this will not be the case, and no double dispersion relation can be written down.

Turning to other uses of (2-3), we may recover the "physical" S-matrix elements from it by the integral

$$(S_\ell - 1)/ik = \int_{-1}^{1} dz\, A(k, z) P_\ell(z) \tag{2-10}$$

Using the fact that[12]

$$\int_{-1}^{1} dz\, P_\ell(z)P_\alpha(-z) = \frac{2}{\pi}\frac{\sin \pi\alpha}{(\ell - \alpha)(\ell + \alpha + 1)} \tag{2-11}$$

we get from the insertion of the nth pole term of (2-3) into (2-10)

$$S_\ell^{(n)} - 1 = \frac{\beta_n(2\alpha_n + 1)}{(\ell - \alpha_n)(\ell + \alpha_n + 1)} \tag{2-12}$$

When α_n is close to the integer ℓ, we can expect (2-12) to give the contribution that varies most strongly with the energy. The result will be a resonance. Expanding $\alpha_n(E)$ about the energy E_0 at which Re $\alpha_n = \ell$ we obtain

$$[\ell - \alpha_n(E)]^{-1} = (\alpha_n')^{-1}[E - E_0 + \Delta E + (i/2)\Gamma]^{-1} \tag{2-13}$$

where

$$\Delta E = \frac{\text{Im}\, \alpha_n\, \text{Im}\, \alpha_n'}{(\text{Re}\, \alpha_n')^2 + (\text{Im}\, \alpha_n')^2}$$

$$\Gamma = \frac{2\, \text{Im}\, \alpha_n\, \text{Re}\, \alpha_n'}{(\text{Re}\, \alpha_n')^2 + (\text{Im}\, \alpha_n')^2} \tag{2-14}$$

and the primes indicate derivatives with respect to E, evaluated at $E = E_0$. Insertion of (2-13) into (2-12) yields a standard Breit-Wigner formula for the scattering cross section, ΔE being the shift from the energy E_0 at which the pole passes the angular momentum ℓ to the real part of the apparent pole in the E-plane, and Γ, the resonance width. It should be particularly noticed that according to (2-14) the width depends not only on the nearness of the pole to the real axis, i.e., Im α_n, but also on its energy dependence. Only if Γ is small relative to the scale on which all other quantities in the amplitude change significantly, is the "resonance" really visible as a peak in the cross section. In addition, ΔE must be small too in order for the result to be meaningful. If ΔE is not small then no resonance occurs near E_0, and near $E_0 - \Delta E$ the terms neglected in the expansion in (2-13) become important.

It will be shown in Chapter 7 that Im $\alpha_n > 0$. Hence the width in (2-13) is positive if the pole moves toward the right as a function of the energy, and negative, if it moves toward the left. Only in the former case can we speak of a physical resonance because only then is the outgoing flux of particles delayed with respect to the incoming flux. The return part of the motion of a pole past an integral ℓ thus at most corresponds to the downward passage of the phase shift through $\frac{1}{2}\pi$ at higher energies. In Chapter 14 it will be seen that this retrograde motion has no separate correspondence with poles in the E-plane.

The trajectories of the Regge poles in the ℓ-plane, as functions of E, thus allow us, via (2-3) and (2-12), to connect various resonances that appear at different angular momenta to come from the same origin, or to have the same "cause." In addition the resonances may be connected to bound states, since a negative energy pole of S_ℓ, at integral ℓ, has that physical significance (see Chapter 7). The ensuing picture has a great deal of intuitive appeal. At the same time, as will be discussed in Chapter 14, these virtues of the complex, angular momentum method can also be achieved by considering merely continuous real ℓ-values, but going to complex energies.

There are certain additional points that are worth considering in (2-3). The first is that each individual pole term contains a cut in the z-plane that starts at $z = 1$. It is only after the cooperative cancellations of the background term and the pole terms that the cut disappears from $z = 1$ to $z = z_0$. Indeed, it is possible to combine parts of the background term with the pole terms in such a way that each has a cut that starts at $z = z_0$.[13]

An interesting question that arises when the Watson transform is carried out is whether the path of integration of the background integral in (2-3) can be pushed further toward the left. If so, further pole terms from the left-hand half of the λ-plane will contribute to the sum, but the new integral will asymptotically, as $|z| \to \infty$, tend to zero faster than before. In order to accomplish this we substitute[14]

$$P_{\lambda - 1/2}(-z) = (1/\pi) \cot \pi\lambda [Q_{-\lambda - 1/2}(z) - Q_{\lambda - 1/2}(z)] \qquad (2\text{-}15)$$

in (2-2) and get

$$A(k, z) = (2\pi k)^{-1} \int_C d\lambda\, \lambda [S(\lambda, k) - 1] Q_{-\lambda - 1/2}(z)/\sin \pi\lambda$$
$$+ (k\pi i)^{-1} \sum_{\lambda=1}^{\infty} (-)^\lambda \lambda [S(\lambda, k) - 1] Q_{\lambda - 1/2}(z) \qquad (2\text{-}16)$$

If the contour C is now shifted toward the left, to become C_M, which connects the upper with the lower branch between $\lambda = -M + 1$ and $\lambda = -M$, the resulting pole contributions

$$(i/k\pi) \sum_{\lambda=-1}^{-M+1} (-)^\lambda \lambda [S(\lambda, k) - 1] Q_{-\lambda - 1/2}(z)$$

must be subtracted out. By the symmetry (5-21) these are just equal to the first M-1 terms of the sum in (2-16) and we have

$$A(k, z) = (2\pi k)^{-1} \int_{C_M} d\lambda\, \lambda[S - 1] Q_{-\lambda - 1/2}(z)/\sin \pi\lambda$$

$$+ (i\pi k)^{-1} \sum_{\lambda=M}^{\infty} (-)^{\lambda} \lambda[S(\lambda, k) - 1] Q_{\lambda - 1/2}(z)$$

The contour C_M may now be distorted to run parallel to the imaginary axis from $\lambda = -M + \frac{1}{2} - i\infty$ to $\lambda = -M + \frac{1}{2} + i\infty$, and we get instead of (2-3)[15]

$$A(k, z) = -(2\pi k)^{-1} \int_{-M - i\infty}^{-M + i\infty} d\ell\, \ell[S_{\ell}(k) - 1] Q_{-\ell - 1}(z) \sec \pi\ell$$

$$+ (i\pi k)^{-1} \sum_{\lambda=M}^{\infty} (-)^{\lambda} \lambda[S(\lambda, k) - 1] Q_{\lambda - 1/2}(z)$$

$$+ (ik)^{-1} \sum_{n} (\alpha_n + \tfrac{1}{2})\beta_n Q_{-\alpha_n - 1/2}(z) \sec \pi\alpha_n \qquad (2\text{-}17)$$

where the last sum runs over all the S-matrix poles to the right of $\ell = M$. As $|z| \to \infty$,

$$Q_{\lambda - 1/2}(z) = O(z^{-\lambda - 1/2}) \qquad (2\text{-}18)$$

Consequently the integral in (2-17) is $O(z^{-M})$, whereas the leading term of the "background sum" is $O(z^{-M - 1/2})$. The asymptotic value of the "pole sum" in (2-17) is, of course, the same as that of (2-3), but it now holds even when the leading pole lies in the left half-plane.

In order for the argument leading to (2-17) to be correct, the S-matrix must tend to unity, or at least be less singular than $\exp[|\frac{1}{2}\pi \text{ Im } \lambda|]$ when $\text{Im } \lambda \to \pm\infty$ and $\text{Re } \lambda < 0$. According to (6-5), (6-5'), and (6-10) this is the case for superpositions of Yukawa potentials, and (2-17) is justified.

It is at this point very tempting to suppose[16] that the "background integral" can be pushed all the way to minus infinity, that is, M might be taken to be infinite. The first two terms in (2-17) would then disappear, it seems, and only the pole sum would remain. It should be noted, though, that the same equations of Chapter 6 that justify (2-17), also indicate that the integral increases in magnitude as it is translated leftward. There is, therefore, no evidence that the background integral can be entirely eliminated in favor of an infinite series of pole contributions.[17]

Before turning to the proofs of the various properties of the interpolated S-matrix necessary for the Watson transform, as well as to an investigation of the motion of its poles in the ℓ-plane as functions of the energy, we ought to mention the most interesting aspect of the speculative use of the complex angular momentum method referred to in the Introduction. Suppose that the results of two-particle Schrödinger theory could be taken over to the relativistic domain and (2-8') were to hold there too for the scattering of two particles by one another. It would then immediately give us an asymptotic formula for the amplitude in the "crossed channel" as the energy tends to infinity. That is, because the "substitution law" of relativistic field theory allows us to obtain an amplitude in which an incoming particle is replaced by an outgoing antiparticle, and vice versa, in a very simple manner from the original one. The main difference, in the case of two-particle - to - two-particle amplitudes, is the exchange of significance of the square of the energy and the negative of the square of the momentum transfer.[18] In other words, writing s for the square of the total relativistic energy and assuming that (2-8') holds also in the relativistic domain, it reads

$$A^{(1)} \underset{|t| \to \infty}{\sim} f(s) t^{\alpha_R(s)} e^{i\alpha_I(s) \ell n\, t} \tag{2-8''}$$

for an amplitude describing a process in which particles I and II collide and III and IV emerge. The "crossing relation" then tells us that the amplitude for another process, say, for I and anti-III colliding and IV and anti-II emerging are the same, except that s and t must be interchanged:

$$A^{(2)} \underset{|s| \to \infty}{\sim} f(t) s^{\alpha_R(t)} e^{i\alpha_I(t) \ell n\, s} \tag{2-19}$$

[Of course, (2-19) and (2-8'') with s and t interchanged are not both physically possible for the same ranges of the variables. In order for an amplitude to be physical, s must be positive and t, negative.] In contrast to (2-8''), equation (2-19) has direct physical significance. It says that at high energies the cross section should be proportional to a power of the energy, which power in turn varies with the momentum transfer. The smaller the momentum transfer (i.e., the larger t) the larger we expect α_R to be (in a region where the leading pole in the crossed channel moves toward the right). Hence the ratio of a cross section at one momentum transfer to the same at a larger momentum transfer should increase with energy and thus the width of the forward diffraction peak should shrink.

The "prediction" (2-19) appeared for a short euphorious while to be born out by high-energy scattering experiments, and as a result the complex angular momentum method received a great boost in popularity among physicists. Recently the bubble burst and the diffraction peak no longer appears to shrink. This result, of course, need surprise no one, since there is no theoretical reason to suppose that the simple relation (2-8'), which has been proved in nonrelativistic quantum mechanics of two particles only, should hold in the relativistic domain where production processes are not only possible but very likely. Indeed, in view of the results in the three-body problem, described in Chapters 17 and 18, it appears most unlikely that (2-8''), and hence (2-19), should be true.

We now return from our brief jaunt into the realm of speculation.

Notes and References

1. As mentioned in the Introduction, it is due to Watson (W4), was resurrected by Sommerfeld (S6), p. 282, and used for the present purpose by Regge (R1).
2. The "standard interpolation of the Legendre functions" is based on Legendre's differential equation for unrestricted values of the parameters; see, for example, Chapter III of the Bateman Project (B22), Vol. 1. It can be written in terms of the hypergeometric function; see Eq. (3) on p. 122, loc. cit.
3. See Bateman Project (B22), Vol. 1, p. 142, Eq. (21).
4. Re ν and Im ν stand for the real and imaginary parts of ν, respectively.
5. See (B22), Vol. 1, p. 126, Eq. (23).
6. This is called the "small Lehmann ellipse."
7. From (B22), Vol. 1, p. 140, Eq. (10). The function $Q_\nu(z)$ has a cut from $z = -\infty$ to $z = +1$.
8. $f(z) = O(g(z))$ as $z \to 0$ (or $z \to \infty$) means that $|f/g|$ is bounded as $z \to 0$ (or $z \to \infty$).
9. Moreover, (2-4) can be used for negative energies, where the region of convergence of (2-2) is small.
10. Or, correspondingly, a dispersion relation in the momentum transfer. Equation (2-9) is proved by writing ΔA out explicitly, completing the contour of integration at infinity, and using Cauchy's theorem.
11. In the electromagnetic case there are infinitely many poles. If in the present case the number of poles is infinite, the validity of the results below depends on their asymptotic distribution, and on the asymptotic values of the residues.
12. See (B22), Vol. 1, p. 170, Eq. (7). In order for (2-11) to hold ℓ must be an integer.
13. See Khuri (K5) and Jones (J3).
14. From (B22), Vol. 1, p. 140, Eqs. (9) and (10).
15. This formula is due to Mandelstam (M1).
16. As Mandelstam conjectured in (M1).
17. For other arguments against the possibility of eliminating the background integral, see Kaufman (K1).
18. For further details of the introduction of the most convenient variables in relativistic theory, and their use, see Chew (C28).

Chapter 3

THE IRREGULAR SOLUTIONS

The radial Schrödinger equation for the ℓth partial wave can be written[1]

$$-\psi'' + (\lambda^2 - \tfrac{1}{4})r^{-2}\psi + V\psi = k^2\psi \tag{3-1}$$

it being convenient to put it in terms of $\lambda \equiv \ell + \frac{1}{2}$. Two linearly independent solutions f_+ and f_- are defined by the boundary conditions

$$\lim_{r \to \infty} f_{\pm} \, e^{\pm ikr} = 1 \tag{3-2}$$

Indicating explicitly all the variables on which f depends, we have

$$f_+ \equiv f(\lambda, k; r) = f(-\lambda, k; r) \tag{3-3}$$

because the differential equation (3-1) depends on λ^2 only, and the boundary condition (3-2) is independent of λ.

The differential equation (3-1) and the boundary condition (3-2) can be combined and replaced by the integral equation

$$f_+(r) = f_{0+}(r) - \int_r^{\infty} dr' \, g(r, r')V(r')f_+(r') \tag{3-4}$$

in which the λ and k variables are not explicitly shown. The Green's function is given by

$$\begin{aligned} g(r, r') &= \tfrac{1}{2}\pi(rr')^{1/2}\left[J_\lambda(kr')Y_\lambda(kr) - J_\lambda(kr)Y_\lambda(kr')\right] \\ &= -i\tfrac{1}{2}\pi(rr')^{1/2}\left[J_\lambda(kr)H_\lambda^{(2)}(kr') - J_\lambda(kr')H_\lambda^{(2)}(kr)\right] \\ &= \tfrac{1}{2}\pi(rr')^{1/2}\left[J_\lambda(kr)J_{-\lambda}(kr') - J_\lambda(kr')J_{-\lambda}(kr)\right]/\sin \pi\lambda \\ &= i\tfrac{1}{4}\pi(rr')^{1/2}\left[H_\lambda^{(2)}(kr)H_\lambda^{(1)}(kr') - H_\lambda^{(1)}(kr)H_\lambda^{(2)}(kr')\right] \end{aligned} \tag{3-5}$$

in terms of the Bessel functions of the first and second kind, or alternatively in terms of Hankel functions. The inhomogeneous term in (3-4) is

$$f_{0+}(r) = e^{-i\frac{1}{2}\pi(\lambda + \frac{1}{2})}\,(\tfrac{1}{2}\pi kr)^{1/2}H_\lambda^{(2)}(kr) \tag{3-6}$$

The integral equation (3-4) can be solved by successive approximations under the standard conditions[2] of the existence of the second absolute moment of $V(r)$. The proof is no different from that for the half-integral λ (integral ℓ). For fixed λ and $r \neq 0$, f_+ is an analytic function of k, regular in the open, lower half of the complex plane and continuous on the real axis, except at $k = 0$. For $\text{Im } k \leq 0$ we have

$$\lim_{|k| \to \infty} f_+ e^{ikr} = 1 \tag{3-7}$$

The reason why f is not an even function of k, even though the differential equation is a function only of k^2, is that the boundary condition at infinity <u>necessarily</u> depends on k. That, in turn, is so because infinity is an (irregular) singular point and k^2 multiplies the term of highest singularity of the differential equation. The entire distinction between the behavior of the solution f, defined by a boundary condition at infinity, in the upper and the lower halves of the k-plane comes from this circumstance, and the fundamental reason why f_+ is regular in the lower half of the k-plane but not necessarily so in the upper, is that the boundary condition (3-2) defines f_+ uniquely only when $\text{Im } k \leq 0$. For $\text{Im } k > 0$ the other solution, f_-, is asymptotically smaller and hence the boundary condition does not prevent the addition of an arbitrary multiple of it.

Suppose that the potential admits an analytic continuation into the complex r-plane,[3] with no singularities in the region $-\frac{1}{2}\pi \leq -\sigma \leq \arg r \leq \sigma \leq \frac{1}{2}\pi$ and so that for real x

$$V_\varphi(x) \equiv e^{2i\varphi}V(xe^{i\varphi})$$

is absolutely integrable near $x = \infty$ and has a finite first absolute moment near $x = 0$:

$$\int_0 dx\, x\left|V_\varphi(x)\right| < \infty \qquad \int^\infty dx\left|V_\varphi(x)\right| < \infty$$

We shall refer to such potentials as "analytic" (in the σ-class).

We then write $r = xe^{i\varphi}$, $k = \kappa e^{-i\varphi}$, and

$$f_\varphi(\lambda, \kappa; x) \equiv f(\lambda, \kappa e^{-i\varphi}; xe^{i\varphi})$$

f_φ satisfies the differential equation

$$-f''_\varphi + (\lambda^2 - \tfrac{1}{4})x^{-2} f_\varphi + V_\varphi f_\varphi = \kappa^2 f_\varphi \tag{3-1'}$$

where the primes now denote differentiation with respect to x. Equation (3-1') together with the boundary condition

$$\lim_{x \to \infty} f_\varphi e^{i\kappa x} = 1$$

can be replaced by the integral equation

$$f_\varphi(\lambda, \kappa; x) = f_0(\lambda, \kappa; x) - \int_x^\infty dx'\, g(x, x')V_\varphi(x')f_\varphi(\lambda, \kappa; x') \tag{3-4'}$$

from which it follows that $f_\varphi(\lambda, \kappa; x)$ is an analytic function of κ regular in the open lower half of the κ-plane. But that implies that $f(\lambda, k; xe^{i\varphi})$ is regular as a function of k in the region $\varphi - \pi < \arg k < \varphi$ for all φ in $-\sigma \leq \varphi \leq \sigma$. We may now let the variable x in (3-4') be complex, say with $\arg x = -\varphi$, without changing the fact that the integration runs to ∞ asymptotically along the real axis. It is then found that $f(\lambda, k; r)$ for real r is also regular as a function of k in the region $-\pi - \sigma < \arg k < \sigma$. Moreover, (3-4') directly gives it to us there.

The foregoing suppositions are fulfilled if V is a superposition of Yukawa potentials[4,5]

$$V(r) = \int_{\mu_0}^\infty d\mu\, \rho(\mu)e^{-\mu r}/r \qquad \mu_0 > 0 \tag{3-8}$$

σ is then any angle between zero and $\frac{1}{2}\pi$. Furthermore, for real r, V asymptotically decreases at least as exp $-\mu_0 r$. Thus f_+ is, for half-integral values of λ, regular everywhere in the finite k-plane cut along the imaginary axis from $k = \frac{1}{2}i\mu_0$ to $k = i\infty$. This is the so-called "Yukawa cut" or "left-hand cut" [in the $E = k^2$ $(0 \leq \arg k < \pi)$ plane].

For general values of λ the Hankel function, as a function of k, has a branch point at k = 0. As a result so does f_{0+}, and consequently so does f_+; the Green's function g is an entire function of k. The nature of the branch point is characterized by the circuit relation

$$H_\lambda^{(2)}(ze^{-2\pi i}) = -H_\lambda^{(2)}(z) + 2\cos\pi\lambda H_\lambda^{(2)}(ze^{-i\pi}) \tag{3-9}$$

which entails

$$f_{0+}(\lambda, ke^{-2\pi i}; r) = f_{0+}(\lambda, k; r) - 2i\cos\pi\lambda f_{0+}(\lambda, ke^{-i\pi}; r)$$

In order to draw a corresponding conclusion for f_+ it must first be ascertained that there are no other intervening cuts in the k-plane. It then follows that

$$f_+(\lambda, ke^{-2\pi i}; r) = f_+(\lambda, k; r) - 2i\cos\pi\lambda f_+(\lambda, ke^{-i\pi}; r) \tag{3-10}$$

If, for example, the potential is of the Yukawa type (3-8), then (3-10) holds only in the circle $|k| < \frac{1}{2}\mu_0$.

It should be remembered at this point that the boundary condition (3-2) for f_+ serves to define a solution of (3-1) uniquely only when Im $k < 0$. That is the reason why $f_+(\lambda, ke^{-2\pi i}; r)$ need not equal $f_+(\lambda, \bar{k}; r)$. For positive k and $0 < \varphi < \pi$, $f_+(\lambda, ke^{-i\varphi}; r)$ is uniquely defined by the differential equation (3-1) and the boundary condition (3-2), and if we set $\varphi = \pi$, f_+ satisfies both (3-1) and (3-2) of f_-. Consequently, for $k > 0$,

$$f_-(\lambda, k; r) = \lim_{\varphi \to \pi} f_+(\lambda, ke^{-i\varphi}; r) \equiv f_+(\lambda, ke^{-i\pi}; r) \tag{3-11}$$

which equation may be analytically continued into the upper half of the k-plane, and into that part of the lower half where f_+ is regular. Needless to say, (3-11) holds for f_0.

For real λ and k, the reality of (3-1) and the conjugate nature of the two conditions (3-2) imply that[6]

$$f_-(\lambda, k; r) = f_+^*(\lambda, k; r) \tag{3-12}$$

Since $f^*(k^*)$ is an analytic function of k regular at $k = k_1^*$ if f(k) is regular at $k = k_1$, it follows[7] that for real λ and complex k

$$f_-(\lambda, k; r) = f_+^*(\lambda, k^*; r) \tag{3-12'}$$

provided that k^* lies in the region of analyticity of f_+. For k in the first quadrant, (3-11) and (3-12') together imply that when $\mathrm{Im}\, k_0 < 0$ then

$$f_+(\lambda, -k_0^*; r) = f_+^*(\lambda, k_0; r)$$

and hence f_+ is <u>real</u> on the negative imaginary k-axis (for real λ). On the positive imaginary k-axis the same conclusion cannot be drawn, no matter how well behaved the potential is, except for half-integral λ, when $k = 0$ is not a branch point.[8]

Assuming now that the potential is, say, of the type (3-8) and thus produces no intervening cuts, we get from (3-10) for $|k| < \frac{1}{2}\mu_0$

$$f_+\left(\lambda, |k|\, e^{i(1/2)\pi}; r\right) - f_+\left(\lambda, |k|\, e^{-i(3/2)\pi}; r\right)$$
$$= 2i \cos \pi\lambda f_+\left(\lambda, |k|\, e^{-i(1/2)\pi}; r\right) \tag{3-13}$$

the right-hand side of which is purely imaginary. If the branch cut of f_+, which leads from $k = 0$ to $k = \infty$, is put along the <u>positive imaginary</u> axis alongside the Yukawa cut (but starting at $k = 0$), then the <u>real</u> part of f_+ is continuous across that cut while its imaginary part equals one-half the discontinuity and is given by (3-13) in terms of f_+ on the negative imaginary axis[9]:

$$\mathrm{Im}\, f_+\left(\lambda, |k|\, e^{i(1/2)\pi}; r\right) = \cos \pi\lambda f_+\left(\lambda, |k|\, e^{-i(1/2)\pi}; r\right) \tag{3-14}$$

We shall from now on assume that the cut lies there.

At $k = 0$ the functions $f_\pm$ are not only singular, but in general infinite. It follows from (3-4) and (3-6) that for $\mathrm{Re}\, \lambda \geq 0$,

$$f(\lambda, k; r) = O\left(k^{(1/2) - \lambda}\right) \quad \text{as} \quad k \to 0 \tag{3-15}$$

so that if we define

$$\bar{f}(\lambda, k; r) \equiv k^{\lambda - (1/2)} e^{i(1/2)\pi[\lambda - (1/2)]} f(\lambda, k; r) \tag{3-16}$$

then $\bar{f}$ is finite when $k \to 0$ for Re $\lambda \geq 0$. When Re $\lambda < 0$, however, $\bar{f}$ does not possess a finite limit as $k \to 0$, nor does the factor $k^{\lambda - (1/2)}$ remove the singular nature of the point $k = 0$, even when Re $\lambda \geq 0$. (It must be remembered that $H_\lambda(z)$ contains not only z^λ but also $z^{-\lambda}$.)

The exponential factor in (3-16) is designed to retain the reality of $\bar{f}$ when $k = |k|\, e^{-i(1/2)\pi}$. Hence if $\bar{f}_-$ is defined by the analog of (3-11)

$$\bar{f}_-(\lambda, k; r) \equiv \bar{f}_+(\lambda, ke^{-i\pi}; r) = k^{\lambda - (1/2)} e^{-i(1/2)\pi[\lambda - (1/2)]} \times f_-(\lambda, k; r) \tag{3-17}$$

then it satisfies the analog of (3-12'). It follows that the real part of $\bar{f}$ is continuous across the cut along the positive imaginary k-axis, and the discontinuity is still purely imaginary. However, the circuit relation (3-10) becomes

$$\bar{f}_+\left(\lambda, ke^{-2\pi i}; r\right) = -e^{-2\pi i\lambda}\bar{f}_+(\lambda, k; r) + \left(1 + e^{-2\pi i\lambda}\right)\bar{f}_-(\lambda, k; r) \tag{3-18}$$

and there is no simple analog of (3-14).

The series of successive approximations to (3-4) being uniformly convergent in any closed region in the λ-plane, the functions f_+ and f_-, for fixed real $k \neq 0$ and $r \neq 0$, are entire functions of λ. When k is not real we must be in a region where (3-4) still holds. That means for f_+, that k must lie in the lower half-plane, unless sufficiently strong assumptions are made concerning the potential. If V decreases asymptotically like an exponential, k may lie in a certain strip in the upper half-plane. If V is of the Yukawa type (3-8), taking r into the complex plane shows that (3-4) is good everywhere in the complex plane, except on the imaginary axis with $-ik > \frac{1}{2}\mu_0$. Thus for any fixed k not on the Yukawa cut, f_+ is an entire function of λ.

Equation (3-12') implies that for general values of λ and k^* in the region of analyticity of f_+,

$$f_+^*(\lambda^*, k^*; r) = f_-(\lambda, k; r) \tag{3-12''}$$

The functions f_+ and f_- are always linearly independent of one another (as functions of r), except when $k = 0$. That fact follows from the evaluation of the Wronskian [by means of (3-2)]

$$W(f_+, f_-) \equiv f_+f'_- - f'_+f_- = 2ik \tag{3-19}$$

which vanishes only when $k = 0$. Consequently, every solution $\psi(\lambda, k; r)$ of (3-1) may be expressed as a linear combination of f_+ and f_-:

$$\psi = Af_+ + Bf_-$$

The coefficients A and B can be evaluated by means of (3-19) as

$$A = W(\psi, f_-)/2ik$$

$$B = -W(\psi, f_+)/2ik$$

i. e.,

$$\psi = (2ik)^{-1}[f_+ W(\psi, f_-) - f_- W(\psi, f_+)] \tag{3-20}$$

Because of the boundary conditions (3-2) this amounts to a separation of the outgoing and the incoming wave parts of ψ, and

$$W(\psi, f_+)/W(\psi, f_-)$$

is the ratio of the outgoing to incoming wave amplitudes in the solution ψ.

Notes and References

1. We use units in which the reduced mass equals one-half.
2. The general technique used here and in the following is standard, see for example (N8).
3. This technique is due to Regge (R1), (R2), and (B7).
4. Potentials of the form (3-8) are suggested by field theory. There is no theoretical reason why interparticle potentials in nature must be of this form. There are, however, similarities between the properties of the S-matrix calculated with such a potential and the S-matrix of field theory.
5. The first and second absolute moments of V(r) are finite provided that $|\rho(\mu)|\,\mu^{-1}$ is integrable.
6. We use an asterisk to indicate complex conjugation.
7. The argument here is, of course, nothing but a simple extension of Schwartz's reflection principle.
8. For potentials of type (3-8), f_+ is real on the positive imaginary k-axis for half-integral λ and $-ik < \frac{1}{2}\mu_0$.
9. For potentials of type (3-8), equation (3-14) holds only when $|k| < \frac{1}{2}\mu_0$.

Chapter 4

THE REGULAR SOLUTION ϕ

A regular solution ϕ of (3-1) for Re $\lambda \geq 0$ is defined by the boundary condition

$$\lim_{r \to 0} r^{(-1/2) - \lambda} \phi(\lambda, k; r) = 1 \tag{4-1}$$

Again the differential equation with boundary condition may be replaced by an integral equation[1]

$$\phi(r) = \phi_0(r) + \int_0^r dr' \, g(r, r') V(r') \phi(r') \tag{4-2}$$

where g(r, r') is given by (3-5), and

$$\phi_0(r) = r^{1/2} (k/2)^{-\lambda} \Gamma(1 + \lambda) J_\lambda(kr)$$

Alternatively, we may write down another integral equation, also satisfied by ϕ:

$$\phi(r) = r^{(1/2) + \lambda} + \int_0^r dr' \frac{(rr')^{1/2}}{2\lambda} \left[\left(\frac{r}{r'}\right)^\lambda - \left(\frac{r'}{r}\right)^\lambda \right] \times [V(r') - k^2] \phi(r') \tag{4-3}$$

which for some purposes is more convenient than (4-2).

The series of successive approximations to (4-2) and (4-3) converge under the standard conditions[1] of finiteness of the first absolute moment of V, as for half-integral values of λ. For fixed r and λ with $\mathrm{Re}\,\lambda \geq 0$, ϕ is an entire function of k, and it clearly satisfies the relations

$$\phi(\lambda, -k; r) = \phi(\lambda, k; r) \tag{4-4}$$

$$\phi^*(\lambda^*, k^*; r) = \phi(\lambda, k; r) \tag{4-5}$$

For fixed k and r, ϕ is an analytic function of λ, regular in the whole region $0 < \mathrm{Re}\,\lambda < \infty$.

In the left half-plane, $\mathrm{Re}\,\lambda < 0$, a possible analytic continuation of ϕ is an "irregular" solution of (3-1). Since it dominates the regular one, the boundary condition (4-1) fails to make the solution unique. Because the integral diverges at $r = 0$, the integral equation (4-2) breaks down in that region. In order to obtain the properties of ϕ in the domain $\mathrm{Re}\,\lambda < 0$ we must, therefore, work with its analytic continuation from $\mathrm{Re}\,\lambda > 0$; we cannot use (4-2) directly.[2,3]

It should be noticed that the fundamental reason for the distinction between the behavior in the left and right halves of the λ-plane of the solution defined by a boundary condition at the origin, is entirely analogous to the distinction between the upper and lower halves of the k-plane for a solution defined by a boundary condition at infinity. The point $r = 0$ is a (regular) singular point of the differential equation and λ multiplies the term of highest singularity. As a consequence the boundary condition at $r = 0$ must depend on λ.

The discussion of the analytic extension[4] of the integral equation (4-2) is based on the circumstance that, although an integral of the form

$$\int_0^y dx\, x^{\alpha} f(x)$$

diverges when $\mathrm{Re}\,\alpha \leq -1$, repeated integration by parts shows that, if the necessary derivatives of f exist, the integral considered as a function of α is analytic in the region $\mathrm{Re}\,\alpha < -1$ with the exception of simple poles at the negative integers.

More precisely, what we need is the following

Lemma: Let f(x) and its first m derivatives exist for $0 \leq x \leq x_0$. Then

$$g(\alpha, y) \equiv y^{-\alpha - 1} \int_0^y dx\, x^{\alpha} f(x)$$

and its first m partial derivatives with respect to y are analytic functions of α for $0 \leq y \leq x_0$, regular in the region $\mathrm{Re}\,\alpha > -m - 1$, except for simple poles at $\alpha = -1, -2, \ldots$. Furthermore, the residue of g at[5] $\alpha = -N$ is proportional to y^{N-1}.

Proof: The existence of f and of its first m derivatives implies that for $0 \leq x \leq x_0$ it can be written

$$f(x) = \sum_{N=0}^{m-1} C_N x^N + x^m \bar{f}(x)$$

where

$$x^m \bar{f}(x) = \int_0^x dx_1 \int_0^{x_1} dx_2 \ldots \int_0^{x_{m-1}} dx_m \, f^{(m)}(x_m)$$

and hence $\bar{f}(x)$ is bounded in $0 \leq x \leq x_0$. Insertion in g yields

$$g(\alpha, y) = \sum_{N=0}^{m-1} \frac{C_N y^N}{\alpha + N + 1} + y^{-\alpha - 1} \int_0^y dx \, x^{m + \alpha} \bar{f}(x)$$

The first term and all its y-derivatives are analytic functions of α everywhere, except for simple poles at the negative integers, $\alpha = -N - 1$, where the residues are proportional to y^N. The second term and its first m y-derivatives are analytic functions of α regular for $\mathrm{Re}\,\alpha > -m - 1$ and for all y in $0 \leq x \leq x_0$; Q. E. D.

Now then let us isolate the r dependence near the origin of all the functions appearing in (4-2). We write, not showing the k dependence explicitly,

$$g_\lambda(r) \equiv (\tfrac{1}{2}\pi)^{1/2} (kr)^{-\lambda} J_\lambda(kr)$$

$$u_\lambda(r) \equiv (\tfrac{1}{2}\pi)^{1/2} 2^{-\lambda} r^{(-1/2) - \lambda} \phi(\lambda, k; r)/\Gamma(1 + \lambda)$$

$$h_\lambda(r, r') \equiv (rr')^{(-1/2)} (r'/r)^\lambda g(r, r')$$

$$= \left[g_\lambda(r) g_{-\lambda}(r') - (r'/r)^{2\lambda} g_\lambda(r') g_{-\lambda}(r)\right] / \sin \pi\lambda$$

The function $g_\lambda(r)$ is, for each fixed λ, an entire analytic function of r; and for each fixed r, it is an entire analytic function of λ, with the property

$$g_{-N}(r) = (-)^N r^{2N} g_N(r) \tag{4-6}$$

As a result

$$h_{-N}(r, r') = h_N(r, r') = \frac{1}{\pi}\left[\bar{g}_{-N}(r)g_N(r') - (r/r')^{2N}\bar{g}_{-N}(r')g_N(r)\right]$$

$$- \frac{2}{\pi}(-)^N g_N(r)g_N(r')r^{2N}\ln(r'/r) \qquad (4\text{-}7)$$

where

$$\bar{g}_\lambda(r) \equiv \partial g_\lambda(r)/\partial\lambda$$

The integral equation (4-2) becomes

$$u_\lambda(r) = g_\lambda(r) + \int_0^r dr'\, U(r')r'^{p+1}h_\lambda(r, r')u_\lambda(r') \qquad (4\text{-}2')$$

if we write

$$V(r) \equiv U(r)r^p \qquad p \geq -1 \qquad (4\text{-}8)$$

We shall assume that p is an integer and that U(r) is continuous and m times differentiable at r = 0. That implies that rV(r) and its first m derivatives are continuous in some region $0 \leq r \leq r_0$, and if $p > -1$, rV(r) and its first p derivatives at r = 0 are zero. If V is of the Yukawa form (3-8) then these assumptions amount to

$$\left|\int_{\mu_0}^{\infty} d\mu\,\sigma(\mu)\mu^n\right| < \infty \qquad \text{for} \qquad 0 \leq n \leq m$$

$$= 0 \qquad \text{for} \qquad 0 \leq n \leq p$$

We solve (4-2') by iteration:

$$u_\lambda(r) = \sum_{n=0}^{\infty} u_\lambda^{(n)}(r)$$

$$u_\lambda^{(0)}(r) = g_\lambda(r)$$

$$\bar{u}_\lambda^{(n+1)}(r) \equiv r^{-1-n}u_\lambda^{(n+1)}(r)$$

$$= r^{-1}\int_0^r dr'\,(r'/r)^n r'^{\,p+1}U(r')h_\lambda(r, r')\bar{u}_\lambda^{(n)}(r') \qquad (4\text{-}9)$$

From the mentioned properties of $g_\lambda(r)$ and $h_\lambda(r, r')$ it follows that $\bar{u}_\lambda^{(1)}(r)$ and its first m derivatives with respect to r are analytic functions of λ (in some $0 \leq r \leq r_0$), regular in the region Re $2\lambda > -m - p - 2$, except for the points $2\lambda + p = -2, -3, \ldots$. However, it will be seen that because of (4-6) and (4-7) there are no poles at $\lambda = -N$, and that

$$\bar{u}_{-N}^{(1)}(r) = O(r^{2N}) \qquad \text{as} \qquad r \to 0$$

At $\lambda = -\frac{1}{2} - N$, $N \geq \frac{1}{2}(p + 1)$, $\bar{u}_\lambda^{(1)}(r)$ has simple poles, whose residues, by our lemma, are $O(r^{2N})$ as $r \to 0$.

We now proceed by induction. Assume that $n \geq 1$, $\bar{u}_\lambda^{(n)}(r)$ and its first m r-derivatives are analytic functions of λ for Re $\lambda > -\frac{1}{2}(m + p + 2)$ (for $0 \leq r \leq r_0$) except for simple poles at $\lambda = -N - \frac{1}{2}$, $N \geq \frac{1}{2}(p + 1)$, where the residue of $\bar{u}_\lambda^{(n)}$ is $O(r^{2N})$ as $r \to 0$; and that

$$\bar{u}_{-N}^{(n)}(r) = O(r^{2N}) \qquad \text{as} \qquad r \to 0 \tag{4-10}$$

Then it will be seen from (4-9), (4-7), and our lemma that $\bar{u}_{-N}^{(n+1)}(r)$ and its first m derivatives with respect to r are analytic functions of λ regular for Re $\lambda > -\frac{1}{2}(m + p + 2)$, except for poles at $\lambda = -N - \frac{1}{2}$, $N \geq \frac{1}{2}(p + 1)$. The poles for $\lambda \geq -\frac{1}{2} - \frac{1}{2}p - \frac{1}{2}n$ are simple because they come from $\bar{u}_\lambda^{(n)}$ only; those for $\lambda < -\frac{1}{2} - \frac{1}{2}p - \frac{1}{2}n$ appear at first sight to be double, coming as they do both from $\bar{u}_\lambda^{(n)}$ and from the integration. But since the residue of $\bar{u}_\lambda^{(n)}$ at $\lambda = -N - \frac{1}{2}$ is proportional to r'^{2N}, the integration does not introduce a further divergence as $\lambda \to -N - \frac{1}{2}$. The poles are thus simple. Moreover, the residue of $\bar{u}_\lambda^{(n+1)}$ at $\lambda = -\frac{1}{2} - N$ is $O(r^{2N})$ as $r \to 0$. That there are no poles at $\lambda = -N$ can be seen from (4-7) and (4-10), which show at the same time that (4-10) holds also for $\bar{u}_\lambda^{(n+1)}$.

This proves that each term in the series of successive approximations to $u_\lambda(r)$, for all fixed k and r in $0 \leq r \leq r_0$, is an analytic function of λ regular for Re $\lambda > -\frac{1}{2}m - \frac{1}{2}p - 1$ except for simple poles at $\lambda = -\frac{1}{2} - N$, $N \geq \frac{1}{2}(p + 1)$. We must now consider the convergence of the series.

We keep $u_\lambda^{(0)} + \cdots u_\lambda^{(m+p)}$ explicitly and start summing the series for $n > m + p + 1$. Then for $n \geq m + p + 2$

$$\tilde{u}_\lambda^{(n+1)} \equiv r^{-m-p-2} u_\lambda^{(n+1)}(r)$$

$$= \int_0^r dr_n\, U(r_n)(r_n/r)^{m+p+2} h_\lambda(r, r_n) \tilde{u}_\lambda^{(n)}(r_n)$$

and, therefore, for Re $2\lambda > -m - p - 2$,

$$\left|\tilde{u}_\lambda^{(n+1)}(r)\right| \leq C\int_0^r dr_n \left|U(r_n)\right| \left|\tilde{u}_\lambda^{(n)}(r_n)\right| \leq \ldots$$

$$\left|\tilde{u}_\lambda^{(m+p+2+q)}(r)\right| \leq C^q \int_0^r dr_1 \int_0^{r_1} dr_2 \ldots \int_0^{r_{q-1}} dr_q$$

$$\times \left|U(r_1)\right| \ldots \left|U(r_q)\right|$$

$$\times \left|\tilde{u}_\lambda^{(m+p+2)}(r_q)\right|$$

$$\leq C\Gamma(\tfrac{1}{2}+\lambda)\left[C\int_0^r dr' \left|U(r')\right|\right]^q / q!$$

since $\tilde{u}_\lambda^{(m+p+2)}(r)/\Gamma(\frac{1}{2}+\lambda)$ is bounded in $0 \leq r \leq r_0$. It follows that the series converges absolutely. Thus, $u_\lambda(r)$ is for each k and r $(0 < r \leq r_0)$ an analytic function of λ for Re $\lambda > -1 - \frac{1}{2}m - \frac{1}{2}p$, except for simple poles at negative half-integral values of $\lambda \leq -1 - \frac{1}{2}p$ (negative integral $\ell \leq -\frac{3}{2} - \frac{1}{2}p$). Because of the factor $\Gamma(1+\lambda)$, $\phi(\lambda, k; r)$ is an analytic function of λ in the same region, except for simple poles at the negative integral values of λ and at negative half-integral values for $\lambda \leq -1 - \frac{1}{2}p$.

In the region where $\phi_+ \equiv \phi(\lambda, k; r)$ and $\phi_- \equiv \phi(-\lambda, k; r)$ both exist we may evaluate their Wronskian by means of (4-1),

$$W(\phi_+, \phi_-) = -2\lambda \tag{4-11}$$

Since the right-hand side vanishes for $\lambda = 0$ only, that is the only value of λ for which ϕ_+ and ϕ_- are not linearly independent solutions of (4-2).

We may readily remove the simple poles of ϕ at the negative integers and half-integers by defining a new solution

$$\bar{\phi}(\lambda, k; r) \equiv \phi(\lambda, k; r)/\Gamma(1+2\lambda) \tag{4-12}$$

which, if rV is continuous and infinitely many times differentiable at $r = 0$, is an entire analytic function of λ for each (finite) fixed k and r in $0 \leq r \leq r_0$. However, since

$$W(\bar{\phi}_+, \bar{\phi}_-) = -\frac{1}{\pi}\sin 2\pi\lambda \tag{4-13}$$

the functions $\overline{\phi}_+$ and $\overline{\phi}_-$ are not linearly independent when $\lambda = \frac{1}{2}N$, $N = 0, 1, 2, \ldots$. In other words,

$$\overline{\phi}(-\tfrac{1}{2}N, k; r) = C_N(k^2)\overline{\phi}(\tfrac{1}{2}N, k; r) \tag{4-14}$$

What is more, the function $C_N(k^2)$ may, for specific values of k^2, vanish, or it may even be identically zero as a function of k^2. In contrast to the functions $\phi(\lambda, k; r)$, which for all values of k and λ, and $\overline{\phi}(\lambda, k; r)$, which for all values of k and Re $\lambda \geq 0$, are prevented by their boundary condition from vanishing identically as functions of r, $\overline{\phi}(\lambda, k; r)$ for $\lambda = -\frac{1}{2}N$, $N = 1, 2, \ldots$ may be identically zero (in r), either for specific values of k only, or else for all values of k.

Indeed, if rV and its first p derivatives vanish at r = 0, then ϕ has no poles at the half-integers $\lambda > -1 - \frac{1}{2}p$; hence

$$\overline{\phi}(-N - \tfrac{1}{2}, k; r) \equiv 0 \qquad 0 \leq N < \tfrac{1}{2} + \tfrac{1}{2}p$$

A special, well-known case is that in which $V \equiv 0$. The Bessel functions have no poles, and, therefore, in that case

$$C_N(k^2) \equiv 0 \qquad \text{for all odd N}$$

A similar situation exists for the square well potential; in that case the regular solution is again essentially a regular Bessel function and, therefore, has no poles. Thus the poles of ϕ at the negative half-integral values of λ are missing and $C_N \equiv 0$ for all odd N. The same is true for any potential which is constant in the region $0 \leq r \leq r_0$ for some r_0.

Another example is the Coulomb potential. In that case

$$\overline{\phi}(\lambda, k; r) = r^{(1/2) + \lambda} e^{ikr} F(\tfrac{1}{2} + \lambda + i\eta, 1 + 2\lambda, -2ikr)/\Gamma(1 + 2\lambda)$$

F being the confluent hypergeometric function, and $\eta = c/2k$ (c is the strength of the Coulomb potential). F has simple poles at $2\lambda = -N$, and as $2\lambda \to -N$, $\overline{\phi}$ is a multiple of its value at $2\lambda = +N$. However, if $\frac{1}{2} + \lambda + i\eta$ assumes a negative integral value too, then $\overline{\phi}$ vanishes, i.e., $C_N = 0$ for that specific value of k.

It will be recognized that the foregoing arguments, demonstrating the possibility of continuing $\phi(\lambda, k; r)$ analytically into the left half of the λ-plane, are easily generalized to cases where the number p of (4-8) is not an integer, and where V is a sum of terms such as (4-8) with different, nonintegral p. ϕ then contains poles at nonintegral values of -2λ which are easily obtainable in the same manner.

We now turn to the high-energy behavior of ϕ.

As $|k| \to \infty$ it is readily shown by means of the series of successive approximations to (4-2) that[6]

$$\phi(\lambda, k; r)/\Gamma(1+\lambda) = \pi^{1/2} 2^{\lambda - (1/2)} k^{-(1/2) - \lambda} \sin(kr + \tfrac{1}{4}\pi - \tfrac{1}{2}\pi\lambda) + o\left(|k|^{-(1/2) - \lambda} \exp[r|\mathrm{Im}\, k|]\right) \qquad (4\text{-}15)$$

when Re $\lambda \geq 0$. When $-\frac{1}{2}m - \frac{1}{2}p - 1 < \mathrm{Re}\,\lambda < 0$, $0 < r \leq r_0$, the same result is easily shown, using the analytic continuation of the series of successive approximation, except for the points $\lambda = -N - \frac{1}{2}$, $\lambda \leq -1 - \frac{1}{2}p$.

Because of the linear independence of ϕ_+ and ϕ_- we may express any solution ψ of (3-1) as a linear combination of ϕ_+ and ϕ_-. Analogously to (3-20) we obtain

$$\psi = [\phi_- W(\psi, \phi_+) - \phi_+ W(\psi, \phi_-)]/2\lambda \qquad (4\text{-}16)$$

which may be said to pick out the "regular" and "irregular parts" of the solution ψ.

Notes and References

1. Again the technique used here and in the following is standard, except that it is convenient here to normalize the regular solution differently from (N8), for example.
2. If the potential has a "hard core," i.e., $V \equiv \infty$ for $r < r_0$, $r_0 > 0$, then ϕ must vanish at $r = r_0$. Hence the singularity of the differential equation (3-1) at $r = 0$ never comes into play, and the boundary condition can be made independent of λ. The solution ϕ is then an even function of λ, and the left-hand λ-plane presents no problem at all. The same is true if the potential is more singular than r^{-2} at $r = 0$ (if it can be handled). For discussions of such potentials see Predazzi and Regge (P2), Berendt (B3), Brander (B9), and Challifour and Eden (C7).
3. If the potential contains a term such as $\gamma^2 r^{-2}$, the latter may be combined with the centrifugal term, and a new variable $\Lambda = (\lambda^2 + \gamma^2)^{1/2}$ takes the place of the old variable λ. As a result there appear two fixed branch points in the λ-plane, at $\lambda = \pm i\gamma$. If the cuts are placed from $\lambda = i\gamma$ to $i\infty$ and from $\lambda = -i\gamma$ to $-i\infty$, ϕ is again an even function of λ. The left-hand half of the thus cut λ-plane then presents no difficulties. But there is no continuous transition from this situation to that when $\gamma = 0$. In order to be able to make that transition, we must connect the two branch points directly by a cut from $\lambda = -i\gamma$ to $\lambda = +i\gamma$. In the plane cut in this manner, ϕ is not an even function of λ, and all the difficulties that arise when $\gamma = 0$ are already present

for $\gamma \neq 0$. For a discussion of such potentials, see Barut and Calogero (B1); see also Challifour and Eden (C7).

4. There are several papers on the analytic continuation to the left half of the λ-plane. Those by Squires (S2), Mandelstam (M1), and Bethe and Kinoshita (B4), use a power series expansion of the potential about r = 0 and derive recursion relations for the expansion coefficients of the wave function; those by Cheng (C13), Froissart (F3), and Newton (N1) use integral equations, which do not require the existence of a whole power series expansion and are thus more general. In contrast to (C13) and (F3), (N1) continues not only the S-matrix to Re $\lambda < 0$, but also the entire "regular" solution of (3-1). Here we follow (N1), correcting at the same time some simple errors in the details of that proof.
5. Here and below we shall always mean by N a nonnegative integer.
6. $f(z) = o(g(z))$ as $z \to 0$ (or $z \to \infty$) means that f/g tends to zero as $z \to 0$ (or $z \to \infty$).

Chapter 5

THE JOST FUNCTION AND THE S-MATRIX

We express the solution ϕ in terms of the two solutions f_+ and f_- and obtain by (3-20)

$$\phi = (2ik)^{-1}(f_+ F_- - f_- F_+) \tag{5-1}$$

where

$$F_{\pm}(\lambda, k) \equiv W(\phi, f_{\pm})$$
$$= -2\lambda \lim_{r \to 0} r^{\lambda - (1/2)} f_{\pm}(\lambda, k; r) \qquad \text{if Re } \lambda > 0 \tag{5-2}$$

is a generalized Jost function.[1] The properties of F follow from those established for f in Chapter 3 and for ϕ, in Chapter 4.

For fixed λ, $F_+ = F$ is an analytic function of k regular in the lower half of the k-plane and, except for the point k = 0, continuous on the real axis. For that property it is sufficient to assume that V has finite first and second absolute moments. If V is of the Yukawa type (3-8) then F has an analytic continuation into the upper half of the k-plane cut from $\frac{1}{2}\mu_0 i$ to $i\infty$. At k = 0 there is an additional singularity of the branch point type and we put the concomitant cut along the positive imaginary axis. For half-integral values of λ this cut is absent and the singularity at k = 0 is either absent or a pole. The branch point at k = 0 is characterized by the circuit relation

$$F\left(\lambda, ke^{-2\pi i}\right) = F(\lambda, k) - 2i \cos \pi\lambda F(\lambda, ke^{-i\pi}) \tag{5-3}$$

which follows from (3-10) and holds with the restrictions discussed there. For real λ and k* in the region of analyticity of F_+, F satisfies

$$F_+^*(\lambda, k^*) = F_+\left(\lambda, ke^{-i\pi}\right) = F_-(\lambda, k) \tag{5-4}$$

It follows that for real λ and k on the negative imaginary axis, F is real; across the positive imaginary axis its real part is continuous and its imaginary part, discontinuous, with

$$F\left(\lambda, |k|e^{-i(3/2)\pi}\right) = F^*\left(\lambda, |k|e^{i(1/2)\pi}\right) \tag{5-5}$$

If, for example, the potential is of the Yukawa type (3-8), then for $|k| < \frac{1}{2}\mu_0$,

$$\text{Im } F\left(\lambda, |k|e^{i(1/2)\pi}\right) = \cos \pi\lambda \; F\left(\lambda, |k|e^{-i(1/2)\pi}\right) \tag{5-6}$$

For complex λ and k* in the region of analyticity of F_+, we have

$$F_+^*(\lambda^*, k^*) = F_-(\lambda, k) = F_+\left(\lambda, ke^{-i\pi}\right) \tag{5-4'}$$

For fixed k in the region discussed near the end of Chapter 3 for f, F(λ, k) is an analytic function of λ, regular in the right-hand half of the λ-plane, Re $\lambda \geq 0$. If V is of the form (4-8), with the properties there stated, then F can be analytically continued to the left half[2] of the λ-plane as far as Re $\lambda > -\frac{1}{2}m - \frac{1}{2}p - 1$. It has no singularities there, except for simple poles at the negative integral values of λ and at negative half-integral values with $\lambda < -1 - \frac{1}{2}p$.

Insertion of (5-1) into (4-11) leads to the following symmetry property for F:

$$F_-(\lambda, k)F_+(-\lambda, k) - F_-(-\lambda, k)F_+(\lambda, k) = 4i\lambda k \tag{5-7}$$

For many purposes a more convenient Jost function is defined by

$$\begin{aligned} \underline{f}_+ \equiv \underline{f}(\lambda, k) &\equiv (\tfrac{1}{2}\pi)^{1/2} k^{\lambda - (1/2)} e^{i(1/2)\pi[\lambda - (1/2)]} \\ &\quad \times 2^{-\lambda} F(\lambda, k)/\Gamma(\lambda + 1) \\ &= W(\phi, \overline{f})(\tfrac{1}{2}\pi)^{1/2} 2^{-\lambda}/\Gamma(\lambda + 1) \\ &= W(\overline{\phi}, \overline{f}) 2^{\lambda - (1/2)} \Gamma(\lambda + \tfrac{1}{2}) \end{aligned} \tag{5-8}$$

and

$$\underline{f}_-(\lambda, k) \equiv \underline{f}(\lambda, ke^{-i\pi})$$
$$= (\tfrac{1}{2}\pi)^{1/2} k^{\lambda - (1/2)} e^{-i(1/2)\pi[\lambda - (1/2)]}$$
$$\times 2^{-\lambda} F_-(\lambda, k)/\Gamma(\lambda + 1) \tag{5-9}$$

Although $\underline{f}$ still has a singularity at $k = 0$ (except when λ is half-integral), it is generally finite there when $\operatorname{Re}\lambda > 0$.[3] It has all the analyticity properties of F, including the symmetry for k^* in the domain of analyticity of $\underline{f}_+$,

$$\underline{f}_+^*(\lambda^*, k^*) = \underline{f}_-(\lambda, k) = \underline{f}_+(\lambda, ke^{-i\pi}) \tag{5-4''}$$

and the reality on the negative imaginary axis. Instead of (5-3) we have[4] for sufficiently small $|k|$

$$\underline{f}_+\left(\lambda, ke^{-2\pi i}\right) = -e^{-2\pi i\lambda}\underline{f}_+(\lambda, k) + \left(1 + e^{-2\pi i\lambda}\right)\underline{f}_-(\lambda, k) \tag{5-10}$$

and although (5-5) is true for $\underline{f}$:

$$\underline{f}\left(\lambda, |k|e^{-i(3/2)\pi}\right) = \underline{f}^*\left(\lambda, |k|e^{i(1/2)\pi}\right) \tag{5-6'}$$

(5-6) has no simple analog. The symmetry (5-7) becomes for $\underline{f}$

$$\underline{f}_-(\lambda, k)\underline{f}_+(-\lambda, k)e^{i\pi\lambda} - \underline{f}_-(-\lambda, k)\underline{f}_+(\lambda, k)\, e^{-i\pi\lambda} = 2i \sin \pi\lambda \tag{5-11}$$

As a function of λ, for fixed k, $\underline{f}$ has the same region of analyticity as F, except that the poles at negative integral values of λ are absent. For $\operatorname{Re}\lambda > -\frac{1}{2}m - \frac{1}{2}p - 1$, $\underline{f}$ is regular everywhere, except for simple poles at the negative half-integers $\lambda \leq -1 - \frac{1}{2}p$. The discussion below (4-14) shows that in specific cases (e.g., the square well) some, or all, of these poles may be missing.

We obtain useful integral representations for $\underline{f}$ if we insert the integral equations (3-4) and (4-2) into (5-2). Depending on whether the Wronskian is evaluated as $r \to \infty$ or as $r \to 0$, we get

$$\underline{f}(\lambda, k) = 1 - i(\pi/2k)^{1/2} e^{i(1/2)\pi[\lambda + (1/2)]} \int_0^\infty dr\, r^{1/2} V(r)$$
$$\times J_\lambda(kr) f(\lambda, k; r)$$
$$= 1 - i\tfrac{1}{2}\pi \frac{(\frac{1}{2}k)^\lambda}{\Gamma(\lambda + 1)} \int_0^\infty dr\, r^{1/2} V(r) H_\lambda^{(2)}(kr)\phi(\lambda, k; r) \tag{5-12}$$

$$\underline{f}_{\pm}(\lambda, k) = 1 - \tfrac{1}{2}\pi \frac{(\frac{1}{2}k)^{\lambda}}{\Gamma(\lambda + 1)} \int_0^{\infty} dr\, r^{1/2} V(r)[Y_{\lambda}(kr) \pm iJ_{\lambda}(kr)] \times \phi(\lambda, k; r) \qquad (5\text{-}12')$$

From (3-7) and the first form of (5-12) it follows immediately that when Im $k \leq 0$, Re $\lambda \geq 0$

$$\lim_{|k| \to \infty} \underline{f}(\lambda, k) = 1 \qquad (5\text{-}13)$$

When Im $k > 0$ this is in general not true, even if $\underline{f}$ is otherwise well behaved there. In the region Re $\lambda < 0$ the integral representations (5-12) break down. (Depending on the nature of V near $r = 0$ they may continue to hold further to the left.) But we may continue the integral analytically, say, in the second form of (5-12). Split the integral into two pieces, from 0 to r_0, and from r_0 to ∞. The second piece is directly seen to vanish in the limit as $|k| \to \infty$ (for Im $k \leq 0$) by the use of (4-15). In the first piece we insert the series of successive approximations to ϕ and find that each term vanishes in the limit, except at the points $\lambda = -\frac{1}{2} - N$, $\lambda \leq -1 - \frac{1}{2}p$. As a result (5-13) holds in the entire region Re $\lambda > -\frac{1}{2}m - \frac{1}{2}p - 1$ except on the poles at the negative half-integral values of λ in Re $\lambda \leq -1 - \frac{1}{2}p$.[5]

The S-matrix is, except for a phase factor, the ratio of the amplitudes of the outgoing to the incoming waves in a regular solution of the radial Schrödinger equation (3-1). For integral values of ℓ the phase factor is $(-)^{\ell}$.[6] Now by (5-1), (5-8), and (5-9), we have

$$\phi = -i\pi^{-1/2} 2^{\lambda - (1/2)} k^{-(1/2) - \lambda} \Gamma(\lambda + 1)\Big[e^{i(1/2)\pi[\lambda - (1/2)]} \times f_{+}\underline{f}_{-} - e^{-i(1/2)\pi[\lambda - (1/2)]} f_{-}\underline{f}_{+}\Big]$$

The function

$$S(\lambda, k) \equiv \underline{f}_{+}(\lambda, k)/\underline{f}_{-}(\lambda, k) \qquad (5\text{-}14)$$

therefore, equals the S-matrix when ℓ is an integer, and the analytic continuation of the phase has been so chosen that according to (5-13)

$$\lim_{k \to \pm\infty} S(\lambda, k) = 1 \qquad (5\text{-}15)$$

for real k and all values of λ with Re $\lambda > -\frac{1}{2}m - \frac{1}{2}p - 1$, except for the negative half-integers in Re $\lambda \leq -1 - \frac{1}{2}p$.

The properties of S as a function of λ and k follow directly from those of $\underline{f}$. Since physically S is considered as a function of $E = k^2$, we describe them in the E and λ planes. (The mapping of the k-plane onto the E surface is such that the upper half of the k-plane is mapped onto the first or "physical" sheet.)

If we know nothing about the potential, except that its first and second absolute moments are finite, nothing can be said about an analytic extension of S off the real axis. But if we assume that V is of the Yukawa form (3-8), then such an extension is possible. For fixed λ, S is then an analytic function of E regular in the finite complex plane cut from $E = 0$ to $E = \infty$ along the positive real axis (this is the "right-hand cut"), except for those points where $\underline{f}_-(\lambda, k) = 0$; there S has poles. (It can be shown that those are simple.[7]) When λ is a half-integer then the plane is cut further along the negative real E-axis from $E = -\frac{1}{4}\mu_0^2$ to $E = -\infty$ (this is the "left-hand cut"); for general values of λ there is an additional, kinematic left-hand cut along the negative real axis from $E = 0$ to $E = -\infty$. The plane thus cut is referred to as the "physical sheet" of the resulting Riemann surface. Under the stated assumptions there exists an analytic continuation to the "second sheet," accessible through the right-hand cut. There too the S-matrix is regular, except for poles where $\underline{f}_-$ vanishes in the lower half of the k-plane (or $\underline{f}_+$, in the upper), and except for the left-hand cuts.

The generalized unitarity relation is obtained from (5-4'). If both k and k* lie in the region of analyticity of f_+, then

$$S^*(\lambda^*, k^*) = 1/S(\lambda, k) \tag{5-16}$$

which connects the behavior of S on the second sheet of the E surface to that on the physical sheet.

The circuit relation (5-10) yields for S, if no other cuts intervene,

$$S(\lambda, k)e^{-2\pi i\lambda} + S^{-1}\left(\lambda, ke^{-i\pi}\right) = 1 + e^{-2\pi i\lambda} \tag{5-17}$$

For potentials of type (3-8) this holds when $|k| < \frac{1}{2}\mu_0$. It connects, for example, the behavior of S on the upper half of the first sheet with that on the upper half of the sheet reached through the kinematic left-hand cut of the second sheet. For half-integral values of λ, (5-17) goes over into the well-known relation

$$S_\ell(k) = 1/S_\ell(-k) \tag{5-17'}$$

It follows from (5-16) and (5-17') that for half-integral values of λ, S is real on the negative E-axis, on both sheets [for $-E < \frac{1}{4}\mu_0$ if the potential is of the form (3-8)]; for other values of λ this is no longer the case.

Since by (5-8), (5-9), and (5-14)

$$S(\lambda, k) = e^{i\pi[\lambda - (1/2)]}F_+/F_- \tag{5-18}$$

and for sufficiently small $|k|$ we have (5-6), it follows that, correspondingly,

$$\mathrm{Im}\left[e^{-i\pi[\lambda - (1/2)]}S\left(\lambda, |k|e^{i(1/2)\pi}\right)\right] = \cos \pi\lambda \tag{5-19}$$

F_- being real there. It must be remembered, though, that for a potential of the type (3-8) this holds only below the onset of the "Yukawa cut," $|k| < \frac{1}{2}\mu_0$.

For fixed k, $S(\lambda, k)$ is an analytic function of λ, regular in the right half of the λ-plane, except for poles where $\underline{f}_-$ vanishes. If V is of the form (4-8), with the properties there stated, then S can be analytically continued to the left half of the λ-plane as far as Re $\lambda > -\frac{1}{2}m - \frac{1}{2}p - 1$, and it has no singularities there except for poles at the zeros of $\underline{f}_-$. The fixed poles of $\underline{f}$ at the negative half-integers cancel out. The symmetry (5-11) implies

$$S(-\lambda, k)e^{i\pi\lambda} - S(\lambda, k)e^{-i\pi\lambda} = \frac{2i \sin \pi\lambda}{\underline{f}_-(\lambda, k)\underline{f}_-(-\lambda, k)} \tag{5-20}$$

For integral values of λ the right-hand side vanishes unless either one of the $\underline{f}_-$ does. For half-integral values of λ, $|\lambda| \geq 1 + \frac{1}{2}p$, the right-hand side generally vanishes because one of the $\underline{f}_-$ has a pole. Hence, in general,

$$S(-\tfrac{1}{2}N, k) = (-)^N S(\tfrac{1}{2}N, k) \tag{5-21}$$

for $N \geq p + 2$, and for even N also in $N < p + 2$. This equation, however, breaks down if $\underline{f}_-$ has a zero at a positive or negative integral value of λ, or if it does not have a pole at a half-integral value.

Let us pause to note that it is no accident that the S-matrix distinguishes both between the upper and the lower halves of the k-plane (i.e., first and second E-sheets) and between the left and right halves of the λ-plane, in spite of the fact that the Schrödinger equation does not. Physics demands that the wave function be regular at $r = 0$ and that the scattering amplitude be defined in terms of the behavior of the wave function at $r = \infty$. It was discussed at the beginnings of Chapters 3 and 4 why reference to these points introduces the ensuing distinctions between the k and λ half-planes.

Notes and References

1. The general technique used here and in the following is standard, see for example (N8). The main ambiguity in the generalization of the Jost function to nonintegral ℓ-values lies in a phase assignment; see below.
2. See footnotes 2 and 3 of Chapter 4 for discussions of the continuation to the left half λ-plane when the potential has a hard core or a term such as $\gamma^2 r^{-2}$. The remarks apply equally to the Jost function.
3. When Re $\lambda < 0$, $\underline{f}$ is generally infinite at $k = 0$; remember that F contains terms such as $k^{(1/2) + \lambda}$ as well as $k^{(1/2) - \lambda}$.
4. That is, below the Yukawa cut.
5. See (N1) for a somewhat more detailed discussion of this point.
6. See, for example, (N8).
7. The proof is the same as that for integral ℓ; see, for example, (N8).

Chapter 6

BEHAVIOR AS $|\ell| \to \infty$

We now want to approach the question of how the S-matrix, or the Jost function, behaves as $|\lambda| \to \infty$ at fixed energy. The answer is important for several reasons. In the first place, the distortion of the contour of integration in the Watson transform (see Chapter 2) depends critically on the assumption that S approaches unity as $|\lambda| \to \infty$ in all directions with $-\frac{1}{2}\pi \leq \arg \lambda \leq \frac{1}{2}\pi$. It should be specifically noted that $\arg \lambda = \pm\frac{1}{2}\pi$, in other words, $\operatorname{Im} \lambda \to \pm\infty$ with fixed $\operatorname{Re} \lambda > 0$, is of great importance, for without it we cannot get the contour to lie on the imaginary λ-axis or parallel to it, but only to tilt at least slightly to the right. But then the asymptotic behavior (2-8) does not follow.

Another reason for the importance of the study of S as $|\lambda| \to \infty$ is the bearing of the answer on the distribution of poles in the λ-plane. Again the directions parallel to the imaginary axis are important in order to rule out the possibility of finding poles further and further up and closer and closer to the right of the imaginary axis. If, at a fixed energy, the poles were distributed that way, the Watson transform could be carried out only at the expense of an infinite sum of pole contributions in (2-3), and hence the asymptotic behavior (2-8') as a function of the momentum transfer again would not follow.

A knowledge of the behavior of S as $|\lambda| \to \infty$ in the left half-plane is of importance also for two reasons. One is the question of whether it is possible to push the integral in (2-3) further to the left and hence to improve the asymptotic behavior when there are no poles on the right. The other is again the repercussions of the answer on the pole distribution and the subsequent possibility of representations of the S-matrix in terms of its poles, as discussed in Chapter 11.

The study of $\underline{f}$ as $|\lambda| \to \infty$ is complicated by the nonuniform behavior (with respect to their argument) of the Bessel and Hankel functions as the magnitude of their order tends to infinity. For example, as $|\lambda| \to \infty$ with $\operatorname{Re} \lambda \geq 0$ for a fixed value of x,

$$J_\lambda(x) \simeq (\tfrac{1}{2}x)^\lambda/\Gamma(\lambda+1) \simeq (2\pi\lambda)^{-1/2}(\tfrac{1}{2}x)^\lambda e^{\lambda - \lambda \ln \lambda}$$

$$J_{-\lambda}(x) \simeq (\tfrac{1}{2}x)^{-\lambda}/\Gamma(1-\lambda) = (1/\pi)(\tfrac{1}{2}x)^{-\lambda} \sin \pi\lambda \, \Gamma(\lambda)$$

$$\simeq (\tfrac{1}{2}\pi\lambda)^{-1/2}(\tfrac{1}{2}x)^{-\lambda} \sin \pi\lambda \, e^{\lambda \ln \lambda - \lambda} \qquad (6\text{-}1)$$

while for $x = \lambda$ we have only[1]

$$J_\lambda(\lambda) = O(\lambda^{-1/3})$$

For fixed x, $J_\lambda(x)$ very strongly decreases toward the right and increases toward the left. If x increases along with λ, the decrease is much less rapid. In order to facilitate the argument here the necessary preliminary estimates for the Bessel function and Green's function have been relegated to Appendix A.

We want, then, to estimate ϕ, the solution of (4-2), which is obtainable by successive approximations. Writing

$$S(r) \equiv \phi(\lambda, k; r) r^{-\eta - 1/2} e^{-|k|r}$$

(with $\lambda = \eta + i\nu$), using (A-2), (A-9), and Stirling's formula, we arrive at

$$|S(r)| \leq C + C'|\lambda|^{-1} \int_0^r dr' \, r' |V(r')| \, |S(r')|$$

iteration of which yields

$$|S(r)| \leq C \exp\left[C'|\lambda|^{-1} \int_0^r dr' \, r'|V(r')|\right]$$

This shows that if the first absolute moment of V exists, then S(r) is uniformly bounded in all its three variables, with $|\lambda| \geq c > 0$, and $\operatorname{Re} \lambda \geq 0$, or

$$|\phi(\lambda, k; r)| \leq C r^{(1/2) + \eta} e^{|k| r} \qquad (6\text{-}2)$$

An estimate without the exponential growth in r can be had in any vertical strip. Suppose that $0 \leq \eta < \frac{1}{2} + n$. Then (A-5) yields in the same way as above,

$$|\phi(\lambda, k; r)| \leq C r^{(1/2) + \eta}[1 + (\tfrac{1}{2}kr)^{2n}] \exp\left\{C'|\lambda|^{-1} \int_0^r dr' \, r'|V(r')| \times [1 + (\tfrac{1}{2}kr')^{2n}]\right\}$$

Assuming, then, that <u>all</u> the absolute moments of V are finite, we find that for $0 \leq \eta < \frac{1}{2} + n$

$$|\phi(\lambda, k; r)| \leq C r^{(1/2) + \eta}[1 + (\tfrac{1}{2}kr)^{2n}] \tag{6-3}$$

Notice, though, that C will generally increase without bounds when $n \to \infty$. In other words, the increase as Im $\lambda \to \pm\infty$ is nonuniform with respect to Re λ.

We can similarly use (A-5) and (A-6) to obtain a bound for $f(\lambda,k;r)$. The result is that if the first $6n + 1$ absolute moments of V are finite and $0 < k \leq k_0$, $|\eta| < \frac{1}{2} + n, |\nu| \geq \nu_0 > 0$, then

$$|f(\lambda, k; r)| \leq e^{(1/2)\pi(\nu - |\nu|)}(kr/|\lambda|)^{1/2}[1 + (\tfrac{1}{2}kr)^{2n}]$$
$$\times [C_1 e^{-\pi\nu}(kr/2|\lambda|)^{\eta} + C_2(kr/2|\lambda|)^{-\eta}] \tag{6-4}$$

Somewhat more precise estimates are obtained if (6-3) and (6-4) are reinserted in the integral equations. The conclusion then is that (in the stated regions), ϕ and $r^{\lambda - (1/2)}f$ approach their "unperturbed" values asymptotically as Im $\lambda \to \pm\infty$ <u>uniformly</u> in r; the remainders tend to zero <u>relative</u> to the asymptotic values. According to (6-2), the approach of $V\phi$ to $V\phi_0$, as Re $\lambda \to \infty$, has been shown to be uniform in r only if the potential decreases asymptotically at least as fast as an exponential, say as $\exp(-\mu_0 r)$, and if $|k| < \mu_0$. That inconvenient fact is due to the exponentials appearing in the estimate (A-9) of the Green's function. However, it has no serious consequences.

Our primary concern, of course, is with the Jost function. From (A-2), (A-4), (6-4), and the first form of (5-12) we get for $|\eta| < \frac{1}{2} + n$, $|\nu| \geq \nu_0 > 0$,

$$|\underline{f}(\lambda, k) - 1| \leq \frac{e^{-(1/2)\pi|\nu|}}{|\lambda||\Gamma(\frac{1}{2} + \lambda)|}\int_0^\infty dr\, r|V(r)|\,[1 + (\tfrac{1}{2}kr)^{2n}]^2$$
$$\times [C_1 e^{-\pi\nu}\left(\frac{k^2r^2}{4|\lambda|}\right)^{\eta} + C_2|\lambda|^{\eta}]$$

Furthermore, by Stirling's formula, as $\nu \to \pm\infty$,

$$\Gamma(\tfrac{1}{2} + \lambda) \simeq |\lambda|^{\eta}e^{-(1/2)\pi|\nu|}$$

Consequently we learn that if all the absolute moments of V are finite then for $k > 0$

$$\underline{f}(\lambda, k) = \begin{cases} 1 + O(\nu^{-1}) & \text{as} \quad \nu \to +\infty, \\ 1 + O(\nu^{-1-2\eta} e^{-\pi\nu}) & \text{as} \quad \nu \to -\infty \end{cases} \tag{6-5}$$

and because of (5-4''),

$$\underline{f}_-(\lambda, k) = \begin{cases} 1 + O(\nu^{-1}) & \text{as} \quad \nu \to -\infty \\ 1 + O(\nu^{-1-2\eta} e^{\pi\nu}) & \text{as} \quad \nu \to +\infty \end{cases} \tag{6-5'}$$

In other words, as Im $\lambda \to -\infty$, $\underline{f}_-$ tends to unity, but in general we cannot say the same when Im $\lambda \to +\infty$. In the case of superpositions of Yukawa potentials, however, the situation is considerably better. Since this is a problem of importance we shall look into it in some detail.

The "Born approximation" to $\underline{f}$ is by (5-12)

$$\underline{f}^{(B)}(\lambda, k) = 1 - \tfrac{1}{2}\pi i \int_0^\infty dr\, rV(r) H_\lambda^{(2)}(kr) J_\lambda(kr) \tag{6-6}$$

and since

$$H_\lambda^{(2)}(kr) = \frac{e^{i\pi\lambda} J_\lambda(kr) - J_{-\lambda}(kr)}{i \sin \pi\lambda}$$

as $\nu \to -\infty$, the leading term in $\underline{f}^{(B)}$ is, by a factor of $e^{\pi\nu}$,

$$\underline{f}^{(B)}(\lambda, k) \simeq 1 - \tfrac{1}{2}\pi\, e^{i\pi\lambda} \csc \pi\lambda \int_0^\infty dr\, rV(r)[J_\lambda(kr)]^2 \tag{6-7}$$

If we insert here the Yukawa form for V, the integral can be performed[2]:

$$\int_0^\infty dr\, e^{-\mu r}[J_\lambda(kr)]^2 = \frac{1}{\pi k} Q_{\lambda - (1/2)}\left(1 + \frac{\mu^2}{2k^2}\right)$$

$Q_{\lambda - (1/2)}$ being the Legendre function of the second kind. Since this is $O(|\lambda|^{-1/2})$ as $\nu \to -\infty$, the integral, because of the rapid oscillations in the integrand, tends to zero, instead of increasing as it should if only the magnitude of J_λ entered. But that fortuitous circumstance occurs only for Yukawa potentials or superpositions of such. We must, in that case, construct a separate proof that the result holds not only for $\underline{f}^{(B)}$, but for all of $\underline{f}$, because the demonstrated fact that ϕ (or f) approaches ϕ_0 (or f_0) asymptotically as $\nu \to -\infty$ is not sufficient to assure that the remainder tends to zero, the oscillations and not the magnitude of the asymptotic value being responsible for the anomalous decrease.

Writing

$$\varphi(r) \equiv \phi(r)(\tfrac{1}{2}k)^{\lambda} r^{-1/2}/\Gamma(\lambda + 1)$$

we have for the leading term (by an exponential) in $\underline{f}_-$ as $\nu \to +\infty$

$$\underline{f}_-^{(\ell)} = 1 - \tfrac{1}{2}\pi e^{-i\pi\lambda} \csc \pi\lambda \int_0^{\infty} dr\, rV(r)J_{\lambda}(kr)\varphi(r) \tag{6-8}$$

By (4-2) and (3-5)

$$\varphi(r) = J_{\lambda}(kr) + \tfrac{1}{2}\pi r \csc \pi\lambda \int_0^1 dt\, (tr)V(tr)\varphi(tr)\,[J_{\lambda}(kr)J_{-\lambda}(krt) - J_{\lambda}(krt)J_{-\lambda}(kr)]$$

which may be solved by iteration. We now insert the form (3-8) for V, and Hankel's integral[3]

$$J_{\lambda}(z) = \frac{(\frac{1}{2}z)^{\lambda}}{\Gamma(\frac{1}{2} + \lambda)\Gamma(\frac{1}{2})} \int_{-1}^{1} ds\, e^{izs}(1 - s^2)^{\lambda - (1/2)} \tag{6-9}$$

for each of the Bessel functions. This can be done provided that $|\eta| < \frac{1}{2}$. The series generated by the integral equation for φ is then inserted into (6-8), and the nth term is of the form

$$\left[\int_0^{\infty} dr\, rVJ_{\lambda}\varphi\right]_n = CI_{st\mu}^{(n)} k^{2\lambda} \int_0^{\infty} dr\, r^{n + 2\lambda} e^{-r(\overline{\mu} + i\overline{st})}/[\Gamma(\tfrac{1}{2} + \lambda)]^2$$

where $I_{st\mu}^{(n)}$ stands for the relevant integrals over the variables s, t, and μ; $\overline{\mu}$ is the sum of the μ's and, therefore, $\overline{\mu} > n\mu_0$; and $\overline{st}$ is a bilinear combination of s and t variables. Use has also been made of the fact that

$$\Gamma(\tfrac{1}{2} + \lambda)\Gamma(\tfrac{1}{2} - \lambda) \sin \pi\lambda = \pi \tan \pi\lambda \to \pi \qquad \text{as} \qquad \nu \to \infty$$

The r-integral yields

$$(\bar{\mu} + i\bar{s}\bar{t})^{-1-n-2\lambda}\Gamma(1+n+2\lambda)$$

each of the 2n + 2 s-integrals yields a factor of $|\lambda|^{-1/2}$, and there is the outside factor of $1/[\Gamma(\frac{1}{2}+\lambda)]^2$. Using Stirling's formula and collecting exponential factors, we get

$$\exp\left[-\tfrac{1}{2}\ln|\lambda| - n\ln n + (\tfrac{1}{2} + n + 2\lambda)\ln\left|2 + n\lambda^{-1}\right|\right]$$

Thus the terms are seen to tend to naught (uniformly) as $\nu \to \infty$; the series is $O(\nu^{-1/2})$, and (6-8) tells us that[4]

$$\underline{f}_-(\lambda, k) = 1 + k^{2\eta}O\left(\nu^{-1/2}\right) \quad \text{as} \quad \nu \to \infty \tag{6-10}$$

When $\frac{1}{2} \leq \eta < \frac{3}{2}$, (6-9) can still be used for J_λ, but for $J_{-\lambda}$ we insert (6-9) into the recurrence formula

$$J_{-\lambda}(z) = 2(1-\lambda)z^{-1}J_{1-\lambda}(z) - J_{2-\lambda}(z)$$

When $-\frac{3}{2} < \eta \leq -\frac{1}{2}$, each of the t-integrals must, of course, be analytically continued from its value at $\eta > -\frac{1}{2}$. Provided the potential is sufficiently regular at r = 0, as discussed in Chapter 4, the result is that (6-10) is found to hold also when $-\frac{3}{2} < \eta < \frac{3}{2}$. Repetition of this procedure proves (6-10) for all η, as far to the left as the potential allows us to go. It should be re-emphasized, though, that this conclusion holds only for potentials of the Yukawa type (3-8).

As far as the k dependence is concerned, (6-10) shows that the approach of $\underline{f}_-$ to unity as $\nu \to \infty$ is not uniform. The larger k, the larger must ν be taken in order for $\underline{f}_-$ to be in a given neighborhood of 1. However, for $\eta = 0$, that is not so. Along the imaginary axis $\underline{f}_-$ approaches unity <u>uniformly</u> in k.

The next question is how $\underline{f}(\lambda, k)$ behaves as Re $\lambda \to \infty$. Assuming that the potential decreases asymptotically at least as fast as $e^{-\mu_0 r}$, and that $|k| < \mu_0$, we may insert ϕ_0 for ϕ in the second version of (5-12); as $\eta \to \infty$, $\underline{f}$ then approaches its Born approximation (6-6). Furthermore, as $\eta \to +\infty$, the leading term in $H^{(2)}_\lambda$ is $J_{-\lambda}$:

$$\underline{f}(\lambda, k) \simeq 1 + \tfrac{1}{2}\pi \csc \pi\lambda \int_0^\infty dr\, rV(r)J_{-\lambda}(r)J_\lambda(kr) \tag{6-11}$$

whereas by (5-12')

$$\underline{f}_+(\lambda, k) - \underline{f}_-(\lambda, k) \simeq -i\pi\int_0^\infty dr\, rV(r)\left[J_\lambda(kr)\right]^2 \tag{6-12}$$

If the potential decreases asymptotically sufficiently rapidly we can insert the limiting values of the Bessel functions as Re $\lambda \to \infty$, without regard to uniformity. That would yield

$$\underline{f}(\lambda, k) \simeq 1 + (2\lambda)^{-1}\int_0^\infty dr\, rV(r) \tag{6-13}$$

and

$$S - 1 \simeq \underline{f}_+ - \underline{f}_- \simeq -i\pi(\tfrac{1}{2}k)^{2\lambda}[\Gamma(\lambda + 1)]^{-2}\int_0^\infty dr\, V(r)r^{1 + 2\lambda} \tag{6-14}$$

This argument is correct if the potential vanishes beyond a point, but otherwise we are not sure how rapid an asymptotic decrease is necessary to make it work.

If V is of the Yukawa type (3-8), then we may insert Bessel's integral in (11)[5]

$$J_{-\lambda}(z) = (2\pi)^{-1}\int_{-\pi}^{\pi} d\theta\, e^{-i\lambda\theta - iz\sin\theta} + \pi^{-1}\sin\pi\lambda \times \int_0^\infty d\theta\, e^{\lambda\theta - z\sinh\theta}$$

and perform the resulting Laplace transform[6]

$$k\int_0^\infty dr\, e^{-pr}J_\lambda(kr) = (1 + p^2)^{-1/2}e^{-\lambda\sinh^{-1}p}$$

where in one case $p = (\mu/k) + i\sin\theta$ and in the other, $p = (\mu/k) + \sinh\theta$. Now letting λ tend to infinity along any ray with $0 < |\arg\lambda| < \pi/2$ we find that the second term in (6-11) vanishes.

When Re $\lambda \to \infty$ with Im $\lambda = 0$ (or fixed), we use, instead of (11),

$$\underline{f}(\lambda, k) \simeq 1 - \tfrac{1}{2}\pi\int_0^\infty dr\, rV(r)J_\lambda(kr)Y_\lambda(kr) \tag{6-11'}$$

and insert[7]

$$Y_\lambda(z) = \pi^{-1}\cos\pi\lambda\int_0^\pi d\theta\,\sin(\lambda\theta + z\sin\theta) + \pi^{-1}\int_0^\infty d\theta\, e^{-z\sinh\theta} \times (e^{\lambda\theta} - \cos\pi\lambda\, e^{-\lambda\theta})$$

It is then similarly found that the second term in (6-11') vanishes in the limit. As a result,[8]

$$\lim_{\text{Re}\,\lambda \to \infty} \underline{f}_{\pm}(\lambda, k) = 1 \tag{6-15}$$

both for potentials of finite range and for those of Yukawa type (3-8). In (6-15), λ may tend to infinity along any ray with $-\frac{1}{2}\pi < \arg \lambda < \frac{1}{2}\pi$.

For Yukawa-type potentials (3-8) we may also carry out the integral in (6-12), getting

$$\underline{f}_{+} - \underline{f}_{-} \simeq -ik^{-1} \int d\mu\, \rho(\mu) Q_{\lambda - (1/2)}\left(1 + \frac{\mu^2}{2k^2}\right)$$

Insertion of the asymptotic form of Q for Re $\lambda \to \infty$ yields[9]

$$\begin{aligned} S - 1 &\simeq -i(\pi/2k\lambda)^{1/2} \int_{\mu_0}^{\infty} d\mu\, \mu^{-1/2} \rho(\mu) \left(1 + \frac{\mu^2}{4k^2}\right)^{-1/4} \\ &\quad \times \left[\frac{\mu}{2k} + \left(1 + \frac{\mu^2}{4k^2}\right)^{1/2}\right]^{-2\lambda} \\ &= O(\lambda^{-1/2} e^{-2\lambda a}) \qquad \text{as} \qquad \text{Re}\,\lambda \to \infty \end{aligned} \tag{6-16}$$

with

$$a = \ln \left[\frac{\mu_0}{2k} + \left(1 + \frac{\mu_0^2}{4k^2}\right)^{1/2}\right]$$

It should be recalled, however, that (6-15) has been proved here only when $|k| < \mu_0$. Since that suffices for our most important purposes, we shall content ourselves with it. The weaker statement, that $S \to 1$ as Re $\lambda \to \infty$, can, nevertheless, be shown to be true without that restriction.[10]

The most difficult question is, of course, how the Jost function behaves as Re $\lambda \to -\infty$. For this we have no rigorous proofs but must be satisfied with arguments of a more heuristic nature.[11]

Let us suppose that the potential decreases "sufficiently rapidly" at infinity so that the nonuniform limits of the Bessel functions as $|\lambda| \to \infty$ may be inserted in the various integrals. The precise nature of the asymptotic decrease necessary for that is not clear, nor is it even sure that exponential decrease suffices. Then it is easily seen that $f(\lambda, k; r)$ approaches $f_0(\lambda, k; r)$ and thus $\underline{f}$ approahces its Born approximation (6-6). Furthermore, as Re $\lambda \to -\infty$ it is again the J_λ that dominates in $H_\lambda^{(2)}$, and we get (6-7). Next we assume that the potential is of the Yukawa form (3-8). We then obtain

$$\underline{f}_{\pm}(\lambda, k) \simeq 1 \mp \tfrac{1}{2}k^{-1} e^{i\pi\lambda} \csc \pi\lambda \int_{\mu_0}^{\infty} d\mu\, \rho(\mu) Q_{\lambda - (1/2)}\left(1 + \frac{\mu^2}{2k^2}\right)$$

which defines the integral in (6-7) even when Re $\lambda < 0$. The asymptotic value of $Q_{\lambda - (1/2)}$ as Re $\lambda \to -\infty$ (or as Im $\lambda \to \pm\infty$ with Re $\lambda < 0$) then yields[12]

$$\underline{f}_{\pm}(\lambda, k) \simeq 1 \pm \tfrac{1}{2} e^{i\pi\lambda} \sec \pi\lambda \int_{\mu_0/2k}^{\infty} d\alpha\, \rho(2k\alpha) \times \left(\frac{\pi}{-\alpha\lambda}\right)^{1/2} (1 + \alpha^2)^{-1/4} \Lambda^{-2\lambda} \tag{6-17}$$

where

$$\Lambda = \alpha + (1 + \alpha^2)^{1/2} > 1$$

It is useful to describe our results in terms of a "growth rate." First, in order to remove the poles of $\underline{f}$ at the negative half-integral values of λ, we define

$$\overline{\underline{f}}(\lambda, k) \equiv \underline{f}(\lambda, k)/\Gamma(\tfrac{1}{2} + \lambda)$$

That, however, grows strongly as Re $\lambda \to -\infty$. So we consider the function (suppressing the k dependence)[13]

$$\begin{aligned} g_{\pm}(\lambda) &\equiv \pi \overline{\underline{f}}_{\pm}(\lambda, k) \overline{\underline{f}}_{\pm}(-\lambda, k) \\ &= \underline{f}_{\pm}(\lambda, k) \underline{f}_{\pm}(-\lambda, k) \cos \pi\lambda \end{aligned} \tag{6-18}$$

which, for suitable potentials (Chapter 4) is an <u>entire</u> analytic function of λ; moreover, it is <u>even</u> in λ. By (6-17) and (6-15), then, as Re $\lambda \to \infty$

$$g_{\pm}(\lambda) \simeq \cos \pi\lambda \pm \tfrac{1}{2} e^{-i\pi\lambda} \int_{\mu_0/2k}^{\infty} d\alpha\, \rho(2k\alpha) \times \left(\frac{\pi}{\lambda\alpha}\right)^{1/2} (1 + \alpha^2)^{-1/4} \Lambda^{2\lambda} \tag{6-19}$$

On the other hand, when Re $\lambda = 0$ and Im $\lambda \to \infty$ we have by (6-5) and (6-18)

$$g_{\pm}(\lambda) = O(|\lambda|^{-1} e^{2\pi|\lambda|}) \tag{6-20}$$

and for potentials of Yukawa type by (6-10),

$$g_{\pm}(\lambda) = O(e^{\pi|\lambda|}) \tag{6-20'}$$

Suppose, then, that the potential is a simple Yukawa one [and that the heuristic derivation of (6-19) is applicable to it]. Then $g(\lambda)$ grows exponentially for large $|\lambda|$. Its order,[14] defined by

$$\rho \equiv \lim_{r \to \infty} \frac{\ln \ln M(r)}{\ln r}$$

$M(r)$ being the maximal value of the function on a circle of radius $|\lambda| = r$, is, therefore, $\rho = 1$. Its type,[14] defined by

$$\tau \equiv \lim_{r \to \infty} r^{-\rho} \ln M(r)$$

is $\tau < \infty$. The entire function g is thus said to be "of exponential type." The same results hold if V is either a finite sum or a proper integral of Yukawas.

If V is a general superposition of Yukawas, such as (3-8), we cannot say as much. If all the moments of $\rho(\mu)$ are finite, g is an entire function. Its asymptotic behavior for large $|\lambda|$ depends primarily on the asymptotic behavior of $\rho(\mu)$ for large μ. Suppose that $\rho(\mu)$ decreases exponentially for large μ:

$$\rho(\mu) \simeq ce^{-\beta\mu}$$

then the behavior of the α-integral in (6-19) for large Re λ is determined by the integrand for large α, which is

$$\lambda^{-1/2} \int^{\infty} d\alpha\, e^{-2k\alpha\beta} \alpha^{2\lambda - 1} \propto \lambda^{-1} \exp\{2\lambda [\ln (\lambda/k\beta) - 1]\} \qquad (6\text{-}21)$$

It follows that g is of order $\rho = 1$ and type $\tau = \infty$.

If the potential is of the square well variety, the arguments leading to the Born approximation for f̲ are certainly correct and we may insert the asymptotic value of J_λ in (6-7). The Γ-function then leads to an order $\rho = 1$ and type $\tau = \infty$, with

$$\ln g = O(\eta \ln \eta) \qquad \text{as} \qquad \eta \to \infty \qquad (6\text{-}22)$$

just as in the case of Yukawa-type potentials. That can, therefore, be expected to be the general growth rate of g for a wide class of potentials.

Notes and References

1. See Watson (W5), p. 232.
2. See (W5), p. 389.
3. See Whittaker and Watson (W6), p. 366.
4. The first proof that the S-matrix approaches unity as $\nu \to \pm\infty$, with fixed $\eta \geq 0$, was given by Calogero (C2). That given here is different and more general, since it allows also $\eta < 0$. A subsequent proof was given by de Alfaro et al. (D1).
5. See Whittaker and Watson (W6), p. 362.
6. See Bateman Project (B23), Vol. 1, p. 182, Eq. (1).
7. This follows from Bessel's integral.
8. That the S-matrix approaches unity as Re $\lambda \to +\infty$ was first established by Bottino et al. (B7), by a generalization of the WKB method. The necessary assumptions on the potential are not clear in that proof. Subsequently proofs were given by Desai and Newton (D4) (where the necessary assumptions are also unclear), Jaffe and Kim (J2), Calogero (C1), and de Alfaro et al. (D1).
9. See Bateman Project (B22), Vol. 1, p. 136, Eq. (44).
10. See the references mentioned in footnote 8.
11. These follow (D4).
12. See Bateman Project (B22), Vol. 1, p. 143, Eq. (22).
13. The argument follows (D4).
14. See Boas (B25).

Chapter 7

REGGE POLES

We now want to study the nature and position of the singularities of the S-matrix in the complex λ-plane, and their motion as functions of the energy. Although one may profitably investigate S as a function of two complex variables, energy and angular momentum,[1] it is of prime interest to search for singularities either in the E-plane, keeping λ real, or in the λ-plane, keeping E real. For the present we shall do the latter.[2]

Since for real $k \neq 0$, $F(\lambda, k)$ is an analytic function of λ in the right half-plane, $\operatorname{Re} \lambda \geq 0$, the S-matrix for positive energy can have singularities there only where F_- vanishes. S then has a pole. The study of the poles of S in the λ-plane is thus equivalent to the study of the zeros of F_- or $\underline{f}_-$, which is simpler. A zero of F_- with $k > 0$ produces a pole on the upper rim of the right-hand cut in S, a zero with $k < 0$, on the lower rim. We are interested in the upper rim.

When the energy is negative, sufficiently strong suppositions concerning the potential have to be made in order to rule out singularities in S caused by singularities of F_+. Assumption (3-8) is certainly sufficient. For E to the right of the left-hand cut that need not be true any longer, though. But if we follow only those singularities that, for some value of λ, appear to the right of the left-hand cut, the "wrong" ones are eliminated. For more general potentials it will be taken for granted that we are interested only in those singularities of S that, for some value of λ, appear at $E > 0$ as poles. That implies that we are <u>always</u> looking for the zeros of F_-, both for $k \geq 0$ and for $-ik \geq 0$.[3]

In order to find the region where zeros of F_- can occur, we evaluate the Wronskian of ϕ^* with ϕ by means of the differential equation (3-1) in the standard way. We get for real k^2

$$\frac{d}{dr} W(\phi^*, \phi) = 2i \operatorname{Im} \lambda^2 r^{-2} |\phi|^2$$

Assuming that Re $\lambda > 0$, this may be integrated from zero to infinity:

$$2i \operatorname{Im} \lambda^2 \int_0^\infty dr\, r^{-2} |\phi|^2 = \lim_{r \to \infty} W(\phi^*, \phi) \tag{7-1}$$

Consider first the case of purely positive imaginary k and assume that λ and k are such that $F_-(\lambda, k) = 0$. Then ϕ is a multiple of f_- and, therefore, vanishes exponentially at infinity. Thus the right-hand side of (7-1) vanishes. The integral being positive, it follows that Im $\lambda^2 = 0$. In the region Re $\lambda > 0$ and for negative energy (on the first sheet, i.e., $-ik > 0$), F_- can, therefore, vanish on the real λ-axis only. When it does, ϕ is regular at $r = 0$ and decreases exponentially with r at infinity. Hence it is square integrable and we have a discrete eigenvalue of (3-1). Thus, when a negative energy zero of F_- moves through a half-integral value of λ, there is a bound state at the corresponding binding energy and angular momentum.

In the region Re $\lambda \leq 0$ the proof that a negative energy zero of F_- must lie on the real λ-axis breaks down. But it is, nevertheless, true that for purely imaginary $\lambda \neq 0$ and negative energy, F_- cannot vanish either. That can be seen by dividing (5-7) by $2F_- F_+$ and using (5-4'):

$$\frac{1}{2}\left[\frac{F_+(-\lambda, k)}{F_+^*(-\lambda, k)} - \frac{F_-(-\lambda, k)}{F_-^*(-\lambda, k)}\right] = \frac{2ik\lambda}{F_-(\lambda, k)F_+(\lambda, k)} \tag{7-2}$$

The left-hand side having a magnitude not exceeding unity, $F_-(\lambda, k)$ cannot vanish, and hence neither can $F_-^*(\lambda, k) = F_-(-\lambda, k)$.

It is worth pointing out that the absence of negative energy zeros of F_- on the imaginary λ-axis is, from an unguarded point of view, surprising. If we were to think of the centrifugal term in (3-1) as a "potential" in the ordinary sense, that potential would become more and more attractive when λ moves up along the imaginary axis. One would, therefore, expect to find an unlimited number of "bound states," and consequently, negative energy zeros of F_-, along the imaginary λ-axis. That this is entirely incorrect shows the danger of regarding the centrifugal term in the Schrödinger equation, with its special r^{-2} dependence, as a "potential." Most of the complications of the nature of the λ dependence in $S(\lambda, k)$ come, of course, from the fact that that parameter multiplies an r^{-2} term, and the boundary condition refers to $r = 0$.

If, for example, the potential has a "hard core," i.e., $V = \infty$ for $r < r_0$, so that the regular solution must vanish at $r = r_0$, the special nature of the centrifugal term at once disappears.[4] The foregoing reasoning is then correct; F_- indeed has infinitely many, negative, energy zeros on the imaginary λ-axis, and it is an even function of λ.[5] As the radius of the hard core shrinks to zero, these zeros all move toward $\lambda = 0$, and in the limit of no core, the structure of F_- is entirely changed, including especially its zero distribution.[6]

In the left half of the λ-plane, Re $\lambda < 0$, negative energy zeros may appear off the real axis. It then follows from (5-4') that they must occur in complex conjugate pairs. That is to say, if F_- has a zero at λ, then it must at the same energy also have one at λ^*. Such complex, negative, energy zeros are explicitly known to exist in specific cases, and they are not to be regarded as exceptional.[7] The pairing is accounted for by the circumstance that two zeros "collide" in their motion along the real axis and then move symmetrically into the complex plane.

The negative energy zeros of F_- in Re $\lambda > 0$ are always simple. That is established by differentiating (5-2) with respect to λ and using the fact that when $F_- = 0$ then

$$f_- = c\phi$$

so that

$$\frac{\partial F_-}{\partial \lambda} = cW(\frac{\partial \phi}{\partial \lambda}, \phi) - \frac{1}{c}W(\frac{\partial f_-}{\partial \lambda}, f_-)$$

Differentiation of the differential equation (3-1) with respect to λ yields

$$\frac{d}{dr} W(\frac{\partial \psi}{\partial \lambda}, \psi) = -2\lambda r^{-2}\psi^2 \tag{7-3}$$

where ψ may be either φ or f. It follows that

$$\frac{\partial F_-}{\partial \lambda} = -2\lambda c \int_0^\infty dr\ r^{-2}\phi^2 \tag{7-4}$$

when $F_- = 0$. Since φ is real for real λ and k^2, the right-hand side cannot vanish, and the zero of F_- as a function of λ is simple. [As is well known,[8] the zero of F_- considered as a function of k, is also simple. That follows from

$$\frac{\partial F_-}{\partial k} = 2kc \int_0^\infty dr\ \phi^2$$

which is derived in perfect analogy with (7-4).]

We now take the energy to be positive, i.e., $k > 0$. In that case (7-1) together with (5-1) yields

$$8k \operatorname{Re} \lambda \operatorname{Im} \lambda \int_0^\infty dr\, r^{-2} |\phi|^2 = |F_+|^2 - |F_-|^2 \tag{7-5}$$

If Re $\lambda > 0$ and Im $\lambda < 0$ it follows that F_- cannot vanish; nor can it vanish when Im $\lambda = 0$, for F_+ cannot be zero at the same point. That would imply $\phi = 0$, by (5-1), and thus it would contradict the boundary condition (4-1). A positive energy zero of F_- in the right half λ-plane, therefore, cannot lie on the real axis or below, but it must lie in the first quadrant. Again, in the left half of the λ-plane this need not be true; a zero may lie either in the second or in the third quadrant. It may be situated on the real axis, however, only at especially privileged points. The argument which generally prohibits zeros of F_- on the real λ-axis holds also in the left half-plane, but F_+ and F_- have fixed poles there. The absence, at a specific energy, of one of these poles of F_- and its presence in F_+ has the same effect as a zero of F_-. The privileged points at which S-matrix poles may occur on the real λ-axis are thus those points where F has its "fixed" poles (fixed, that is, except for isolated values of k). Under the conditions discussed in connection with (4-8), these are the negative integral values of λ and at negative half-integral values $\lambda \leq 1 - \frac{1}{2}p$.[9]

The positive energy zeros of F_- need not necessarily be simple. In the region Re $\lambda > 0$, (7-4) still holds, but since ϕ is not real, the right-hand side may vanish. It is clear that if a zero is not simple, it is to be regarded as fortuitous. In other words, it may possibly happen at isolated points that a zero of F_- is multiple, either as a function of λ or as a function of k. But in general it will be simple, since it necessarily starts so in the negative energy region.

Having established that a negative energy pole of S in the right half λ-plane must lie on the real axis, a positive energy pole, off the real axis in the first quadrant, and that in the left half λ-plane these restrictions are not valid, we now look for other restrictions on the positions of poles of S.

Consider first the number of zeros of F_- in the right half of the λ-plane. For $E < 0$ they must all lie on the real axis; hence all the zeros in the first quadrant at a fixed positive energy fall into three categories according to where they go as the energy decreases to naught: those which move to the real positive λ-axis, those which move to $\lambda = 0$, and those which cross the positive imaginary λ-axis at some $E > 0$. Among them, only those in the first category can be connected with physical bound states. Those in the second category are of the special class discussed in Chapter 9; their number increases without bounds as the energy decreases or it may even be infinite in some cases at a fixed energy. Those of the third category are presumably of a rather exceptional kind. We do not usually expect to see poles of S in the right half-plane that are not also there at a lower energy.

For potentials of the Yukawa type (3-8) it follows from (6-10) and (6-15) that the number of poles of S in the right half-plane must, for each fixed $k < \mu_0$ be finite. Otherwise there would have to be a finite accumulation point of zeros of $\underline{f}_-$ there, which would contradict its analyticity. As k increases, their number grows without bounds (see Chapter 9). For potentials of finite range (i.e., which vanish identically beyond a finite point), though, the number of poles of S on the right may be infinite, since for these (6-10) does not hold.

It is possible to derive an upper bound on the number n of zeros of $\underline{f}(\lambda, 0)$ with $\mathrm{Re}\,\lambda > 0$, and thus on the number of zeros of $\underline{f}(\lambda, k)$ in the first category. This limitation is a generalization of that for the number of bound states of angular momentum ℓ. The result being of a somewhat special nature, we give here only the inequality, without derivation[10]:

$$n \leq 1 + \frac{\int_0^\infty dr \int_0^r dr'\, rr'\, \mathcal{V}(r)\mathcal{V}(r') \ln (r/r')}{\int_0^\infty dr\, r\mathcal{V}(r)} \tag{7-6}$$

where

$$\mathcal{V}(r) = \begin{cases} -V(r) & \text{if} \quad V(r) < 0 \\ 0 & \text{if} \quad V(r) > 0 \end{cases}$$

No matter how weakly attractive a potential is, there is always at least one zero of $\underline{f}(\lambda, 0)$ with a positive real part.[11] Only if the potential is everywhere repulsive need this not be true.

Simple limitations on the position of zeros of F_- in the right half λ-plane are obtained as follows.

Suppose that the potential is "analytic" [see below (3-7)].[12] We may then use (3-1') to derive the Wronskian

$$\frac{1}{2i}\frac{d}{dr} W(f^*_{\varphi-}, f_{\varphi-}) = (x^{-2}\, \mathrm{Im}\,\lambda^2 + \mathrm{Im}\, V_\varphi - \mathrm{Im}\,\kappa^2)|f_{\varphi-}|^2 \tag{7-7}$$

Suppose now that $F_-(\lambda, k) = 0$. We may then make r complex, $r = xe^{i\varphi}$ (x real), and the Wronskian F_- remains zero. Thus

$$f_{\varphi-}(\lambda, ke^{i\varphi}; x) = f_-(\lambda, k; xe^{i\varphi})$$

decreases exponentially at infinity if $\mathrm{Im}\,(ke^{i\varphi}) > 0$, and it vanishes at $r = 0$. We may, therefore, integrate (7-7) and obtain for real k^2

$$\int_0^\infty dx |f_{\varphi-}|^2 A(x, \varphi, \lambda, k) = 0 \tag{7-8}$$

where

$$A = x^{-2} \operatorname{Im} \lambda^2 + \operatorname{Im} V_\varphi - k^2 \sin 2\varphi$$

Similarly, by adding (3-1') for $f_{\varphi-}$ multiplied by $f^*_{\varphi-}$ to its complex conjugate, we get

$$\frac{1}{2}\frac{d}{dx}\left(\frac{1}{x}|f_{\varphi-}|^2 - \frac{d}{dx}|f_{\varphi-}|^2\right) + \left|f'_{\varphi-} - \frac{1}{2x}f_{\varphi-}\right|^2 + |f_{\varphi-}|^2 B(x, \varphi, \lambda, k) = 0$$

where

$$B = x^{-2} \operatorname{Re} \lambda^2 + \operatorname{Re} V_\varphi - k^2 \cos 2_\varphi$$

Integration yields

$$-\int_0^\infty dx \left|f'_{\varphi-} - (2x)^{-1} f_{\varphi-}\right|^2 = \int_0^\infty dx |f_{\varphi-}|^2 B(x, \varphi, \lambda, k) \qquad (7\text{-}9)$$

Now multiply (7-9) by $\cos \alpha$, (7-8) by $\sin \alpha$, with $0 \leq \alpha < \frac{1}{2}\pi$, and add the results. The ensuing equation can be satisfied only if for some value of x

$$x^{-2}(\cos \alpha \operatorname{Re} \lambda^2 + \sin \alpha \operatorname{Im} \lambda^2) - k^2 \cos (\alpha - 2\varphi)$$
$$+ \cos \alpha \operatorname{Re} V_\varphi + \sin \alpha \operatorname{Im} V_\varphi < 0 \qquad (7\text{-}10)$$

Suppose now that the potential is such that for $\varphi = \frac{1}{2}\pi$ there exists a constant M so that

$$|V_{(1/2)\pi}(x)| = |V(ix)| < Mx^{-1} \qquad (7\text{-}11)$$

Then (7-10) says, for $\varphi = \frac{1}{2}\pi$, with $\lambda = \eta + i\nu$,

$$x^{-2}[(\eta^2 - \nu^2) \cos \alpha + 2\eta\nu \sin \alpha] + k^2 \cos \alpha < \sqrt{2}\, Mx^{-1}$$

or, since $AB \leq \frac{1}{2}(A + B)^2$

$$[(\eta^2 - \nu^2) \cos \alpha + 2\eta\nu \sin \alpha] \cos \alpha < M^2/k^2 \qquad (7\text{-}12)$$

In other words, every zero $\eta + i\nu$ of $\underline{f}_-$ in the right half-plane must lie to the left of each of the hyperbolas

$$\eta^2 - \nu^2 + 2\eta\nu \tan\alpha - M^2k^{-2} \sec\alpha = 0$$

with $\tan\alpha > 0$. Hence it must lie to the left of the envelope of this family of curves, which is given by $\eta = M/k$:

$$\mathrm{Re}\,\lambda(k) \leq Mk^{-1} \tag{7-13}$$

All poles of S in the right half of the λ-plane must satisfy (7-13).

A somewhat stronger statement for small values of k is obtained directly from (7-9) if we assume that for fixed φ there exists a constant N_φ so that

$$|V_\varphi(x)| = |V(xe^{i\varphi})| < N_\varphi x^{-2} \tag{7-14}$$

Specifically, setting $\varphi = \frac{1}{4}\pi$, the fact that B must be negative for some value of x implies that

$$\eta^2 - \nu^2 < N_{(1/4)\pi} \tag{7-15}$$

that is, all zeros of $\underline{f}_-$ must lie to the left of the hyperbola $\eta^2 - \nu^2 = N_{(1/4)\pi}$.

It should be remembered that the results (7-13) and (7-15) require an "analytic" potential of class $\sigma = \frac{1}{2}\pi$ that, in addition, satisfies (7-11) and (7-14). A simple Yukawa potential is in that category; but a square well potential, for instance, or any other which vanishes beyond some distance, is not—such potentials never possess the necessary analytic continuation.[13]

In order to obtain a simple limitation on the position of negative energy poles of S no analytic continuation of V is required. Assuming simply (7-14) for $\varphi = 0$ we immediately obtain

$$\lambda^2 < N_0 \tag{7-16}$$

from (7-9). This, of course, is an obvious inequality for bound states.

A well-known example in which V does not satisfy (7-11) and (7-16) is not true, is that of the Coulomb potential. In that case negative energy poles of S exist along the whole real λ-axis, as a physical consequence of which there are (infinitely many) bound states for each angular momentum.

In the left half-plane the number of poles of S is usually infinite. That fact follows from the consideration of the function g in Chapter

6, which is an entire function of λ^2. As such it is of order $\rho = \frac{1}{2}$, and entire functions of nonintegral order must have infinitely many zeros.[14] It also follows from the threshold behavior discussed in Chapter 9.[15]

Notes and References

1. For a general discussion of this, see Bottino and Longoni (B8).
2. The most important results of this Chapter concerning the right half of the λ-plane were first obtained by Regge (R1) and (R2); see also (B7).
3. It may be well to keep in mind that for general potentials, not in the class (3-8), S may have poles (and other singularities) which are not zeros of F_-. Such singularities need not follow the rules established for the positions of zeros of F_-.
4. See footnote 2 of Chapter 4.
5. See Berendt (B3) for a demonstration that, when there is a hard core, there are infinitely many poles on the right. The Watson transformation cannot then be carried out; see Brander (B9).
6. It is simpler to understand the analogous transition in case the potential contains $\gamma^2 r^{-2}$, as discussed in footnote 3 of Chapter 4. If the cuts in the λ-plane have been placed in their most "natural" position so that F is an even function of λ, then the left-hand λ-plane for $\gamma = 0$ is that reached through the cuts.

   The infinity of poles which, in the absence of a core, move toward $\lambda = 0$ as $E \to 0$ (see Chapter 9), are the "ghosts" of the infinity which, for $E \to 0$, lie on the imaginary axis.
7. The possibility of such poles was mentioned in (N1), but it was there dismissed as presumably exceptional. Their existence can be seen in Figure 2 of (B1) (Figure 12-8 of this book) but they were not mentioned there. They were then discussed explicitly in (D4), (L1), and (K2).
8. This proof is entirely analogous to the one for integral ℓ; see, for example (N8).
9. For examples, see Chapter 12.
10. See Newton (N1).
11. This was concluded in (F5) and shown in (N1).
12. The techniques used are due to Regge (R2), and Bottino and Longoni (B8).
13. It is known explicitly that these limitations on the poles are violated by square well potentials; see Barut and Calogero (B1) and Bollini and Giambiagi (B6).
14. See Boas (B25) p. 24.
15. Neither of these two arguments, however, is rigorous. The first is not, because the arguments of Chapter 6 which establish that g is of order $\rho = \frac{1}{2}$, are only heuristic. The second is not rigorous either, as discussed in the paragraph below (9-9).

Chapter 8

POLE TRAJECTORIES

We are now interested in the behavior of the pole positions of S in the λ-plane, as functions of the energy. Where the equation

$$F_-(\lambda, k) = 0$$

has a solution, it defines λ(k) as an analytic function of k in the complex k-plane regular where F_- is regular, and where, furthermore,

$$\frac{\partial F_-}{\partial \lambda} \neq 0$$

Since F_- has its "left-hand cut" on the <u>second</u> sheet of the E-plane [i.e., if the potential is of the form (3-8), its "Yukawa cut," is in the <u>lower</u> half of the k-plane], so will λ(k).[1] Considered as a function of E, then, the pole position λ of S, is regular on the first sheet wherever it is finite, except possibly for isolated points.[2] One singularity of λ(k) always lies at k = 0, except when $\lambda(0) = \frac{1}{2}$. That is because F is singular there, containing terms of the form $k^{(1/2)+\lambda}$ and $k^{(1/2)-\lambda}$. It is for this reason that the threshold behavior is special and is separately discussed in Chapter 9. Another singular point of λ(k) is, of course, k = ∞.

We cannot conclude without further ado, though, that λ(k) may not tend to infinity at some value of k. The behavior of F_- as $|\lambda| \to \infty$ is complicated and unknown in detail. Poles or much less innocuous singularities, or regions of singularity, of λ(k) cannot, therefore, be ruled out.

Our primary interest lies in λ(k) not for general complex values of k, but only for either real positive or positive imaginary values. In other words we are interested in the motion of the poles of S in the λ-plane as a function of the <u>real</u> energy. The curve described by an individual pole, as E varies from $-\infty$ to $+\infty$, is referred to as the pole trajectory. It has been established in the last chapter that the negative energy part of a pole trajectory in the right half-plane stretches along the real axis. Furthermore, for potentials that satisfy (7-11) for $\varphi = 0$, there always is a value of λ beyond which no more negative energy poles of S can exist. As such a pole passes through an integral ℓ-value, it is responsible for a physical bound state. At E = 0 it must arrive at a finite value of λ[if (7-11) holds] and then leave the real axis, turning into the first quadrant of the λ-plane. The precise manner in which it leaves will be discussed in the next chapter.

Let us first consider the motion of a negative energy zero of F_- along the real positive λ-axis. Suppose that we "sit" on a zero $\lambda = \lambda(k)$ defined by

$$F_-(\lambda, k) = 0$$

Differentiating (3-1) with respect to k^2 then yields in the standard way for the Wronskian

$$\frac{d}{dr} W\left(\frac{\partial f}{\partial k^2}, f\right) = \left(1 - \frac{d\lambda^2}{dk^2} r^{-2}\right) f^2$$

Since $F_- = 0$, this may be integrated from 0 to ∞, the left-hand side giving zero. Consequently,

$$\frac{d\lambda^2}{dk^2} = \frac{\int_0^\infty dr\, f_-^2}{\int_0^\infty dr\, r^{-2} f_-^2} = \frac{1}{\langle r^{-2} \rangle} \tag{8-1}$$

where the expectation value on the right must, of course, be evaluated at the same energy and angular momentum as the left.

An immediate consequence of (8-1) is that, since the right-hand side is necessarily positive, a negative energy zero must move toward the right with increasing energy. This is nothing but the familiar fact that the binding energies of "corresponding" bound states of different angular momenta must decrease with increasing ℓ. In the left half of the λ-plane, however, it is not necessary that a negative energy zero of F_- moves toward the right. We shall return to this point below.

When $E > 0$, then (8-1) no longer holds. The wave function not being normalizable, the expectation value does not exist. We may, however, imagine (8-1) to be derived for any k in the lower half-plane, Im $k < 0$, and specifically just below the real axis. The integrals in (8-1) then have a well-defined limit as k becomes real. Of course, they no longer define an expectation value, because f is not real. Thus (8-1) becomes complex when $E > 0$ (and its real part need not be positive).

It will be shown in the threshold discussion, Chapter 9, that if a zero of F_- leaves the real axis at a point $\lambda_0 > \frac{1}{2}$, it does so toward the right. The question now is whether it may continue to move to the right, or whether it will turn around.

In order to get useful limitations upon the trajectories on the right, we must again assume that the potential is "analytic," as discussed below (3-7). It was shown in Chapter 7 that for such potentials which in addition satisfy (7-11), each zero of F_- must satisfy (7-13). Hence as the energy increases, a zero of F_- can do only one of three things: either it remains in (or repeatedly returns to) a finite region with Re $\lambda \geq 0$; or it tends to infinity along the positive imaginary axis; or it crosses over into the left half-plane. It will be shown below that the first alternative is not true; the second is ruled out by the fact that $\underline{f}_-$ approaches unity uniformly in k as Im $\lambda \to \infty$ and Re $\lambda = 0$, as shown by (6-10). Therefore, it follows that every pole of S must eventually turn over and cross the imaginary λ-axis into the left half-plane.

The assumptions on the potential that had to be made in order to reach this important conclusion must not be forgotten, though. The requisite analyticity is not satisfied, for example, by any potential that vanishes beyond a finite point, and the conclusion specifically does not hold for square well potentials. In that case it is explicitly known that some pole trajectories lead to infinity on the right.[3]

It should also be remarked parenthetically that the result need not hold if the "potential" depends upon either the energy or the angular momentum since then M in (7-11) may increase without bounds when $|\lambda|$ or k increases.

Although for a large class of potentials each trajectory in the right half-plane must eventually turn back, it must not be concluded that this turning necessarily happens only once. In the case of a simple Yukawa potential it is known that some trajectories describe simple loops (see Chapter 12), but there appears to be no reason why in general a trajectory may not oscillate, loop several times, and cross itself. Nor is there any reason why two trajectories may not cross one another.[4]

The physical significance of the turning of a trajectory is the assurance, via the Watson transform, that the asymptotic behavior of the scattering amplitude as a function of the momentum transfer does not get worse and worse as the energy increases. Thus it makes a double dispersion relation possible (with a finite number of subtractions).[5] On the backward part of a trajectory, if it passes an integer sufficiently close to the real axis, the width of the ensuing "resonance" is negative, by (2-14). Hence it is not associated with a time delay, but instead with an advance of the outgoing wave. Thus the peak in the cross section is not a resonance in the proper physical sense at all, but instead, at best, it comes from the downward passage of a phase shift through $\frac{1}{2}\pi$. Such a downward passage is, of course, necessary for any phase shift that has caused a resonance.

At the turning point of a trajectory, if it can be associated with a resonance, the width is zero, as seen from (2-14). Presumably, therefore, it is impossible for the turning point to occur sufficiently close to the real λ-axis for the shift term ΔE in (2-14) to be small. A sharp resonance is then prevented from occurring.

The possibility that a trajectory may lead to infinity at a finite energy can be ruled out in the right half-plane, at least for potentials of the Yukawa type (3-8). That follows from (6-10) and (6-15). Hence all trajectories (for such potentials) are continuous there, though not necessarily free of cusps.

It has been shown in Chapter 7 that for potentials of Yukawa type the number of poles of S in the right half of the λ-plane, at a fixed energy is finite. Since for (7-11) each pole eventually disappears toward the left, we should be tempted to conclude that there always exists an energy beyond which the right half-plane is free of poles. That conclusion, however, cannot be drawn in the absence of proof that there may not be an unlimited number of poles that, on some part of their journey, cross the imaginary axis toward the right, and then return again to the left. That may not appear as a very likely possibility, but it cannot be ruled out.

Once a trajectory has crossed the positive imaginary λ-axis toward the left, it may do things that cannot happen on the right. It may, for example, cross the real axis at negative integral or certain half-integral values of λ, if the potential satisfies the necessary conditions for the discussion below (7-5) to be applicable. If the potential has certain simple kinds of singularities at $r = 0$ (e.g., r^{α}), then it may cross at other specific, easily calculable points. Furthermore, trajectories may lead to infinity on the left, at finite energies.

We may also follow a trajectory that appears at some energy on the right by tracing it backward, i.e., by following the pole as the energy decreases. In that direction too, each trajectory must eventually cross over into the left half-plane. That follows immediately from (7-9), where for $k^2 < 0$ we may take $\varphi = 0$, and Re $\lambda^2 > 0$. If the potential is everywhere repulsive (positive), then (7-9) is impossible and no negative energy zeros of F_- ever appear in the right half-plane. If the potential is somewhere attractive, and its attractive part is bounded, then (7-9) shows that there always exists a negative energy below which F_- has no zeros on the right. Consequently, *a fortiori*, each pole must cross over to the left at some negative energy.

In the left half-plane the negative energy poles need not remain on the real axis. There are infinitely many such poles that move toward $\lambda = 0$ as $E \to 0-$, and they do so along complex trajectories (as will be shown in Chapter 9). Furthermore, two poles may "collide" along the real axis and rebound in conjugate pairs into the complex plane. In contrast to the situation on the right, a negative energy pole on the left may move in either direction as the energy decreases.

A curious connection between poles on the left and right follows from the symmetry relation (5-11). Suppose that $\underline{f}_-$ has a zero at some positive integer, $\lambda = N$. Then (5-11) says that either $\underline{f}_-(-N, k) = 0$ or $\underline{f}_+(N, k) = 0$ for the same k. But $\underline{f}_+$ cannot vanish at the same point where $\underline{f}_-$ does when Re $\lambda > 0$, because that would imply by (5-1) that $\phi \equiv 0$ and thus it would contradict the boundary condition (4-1). Consequently, whenever a pole of S moves through a positive integral value of λ, the residue cannot vanish and another pole must, at the same energy, move through the corresponding negative integer.

Suppose similarly that a zero of $\underline{f}_-$ moves through a negative integer, $-\lambda = N$. Then (5-11) again implies that either $\underline{f}_-(N, k) = 0$, or $\underline{f}_+(-N, k) = 0$. But now we cannot conclude that $\underline{f}_+(-N, k) \ne 0$, because (5-8) and (5-1) show that ϕ need not vanish when $\underline{f}_+(-N, k) = \underline{f}_-(-N, k) = 0$, because of the Γ-function in (5-8). Thus a zero of F_- may move through a negative integral value of λ without forcing another zero to move through the corresponding positive integer. But if that right-hand zero is missing, then we must instead have $F_+ = 0$ on the left, and hence S really does not have a pole at $\lambda = -N$. Clearly, then, what is happening is that a zero of F_- and a zero of F_+, i.e., a zero and a pole of S on the left, coincide on a negative integral value of λ. There being a limitation on the positive integers through which a trajectory can move (for reasonable potentials), this must happen almost every time that a pole of S moves through a negative integral value of λ: it must coincide with a zero and thus at this point of the trajectory, the residue vanishes.[6,7]

A similar argument applies to the half-integral values of λ, i.e., integral ℓ values. When for $\lambda < -1 - \frac{1}{2}p$ [for potentials of the form (4-8)] $-\lambda$ takes on a half-integral value, then $\underline{f}_-$ and $\underline{f}_+$ both have generally simple poles. Hence (5-11) shows that when for $\lambda > 1 + \frac{1}{2}p$, a zero of $\underline{f}_-$ moves through a half-integer, then the pole of $\overline{\underline{f}}_-$ at the reflected point must be missing. So again, if a pole of S moves through a positive half-integral $\lambda > 1 + \frac{1}{2}p$, another pole must move through the reflected point. But if a zero of $\underline{f}_-$ moves through a negative half-integer, $\lambda < -1 - \frac{1}{2}p$, then it annihilates the usual pole there and no corresponding zero on the right need occur. In contrast to the situation for integral λ that for half-integral λ depends on the detailed behavior of the potential. It depends on p, and it is modified in an obvious way for potentials that behave near the origin like $r^{-\alpha}$, say.

It is worth summarizing the situation as follows. When a pole of S moves through a positive half-integral value of ℓ, or through a positive integral value with $\ell > \frac{1}{2} + \frac{1}{2}p$, a pole must move at the same energy through the point $-\ell - 1$. When a pole moves through a negative half-integral value of $\ell (\ne -\frac{1}{2})$, or through a negative integral value with $\ell < -\frac{3}{2} - \frac{1}{2}p$, then either a pole moves at the same energy through the positive value $-\ell - 1$, or else its residue must vanish.

We arrive at the question of where the trajectories end up as $E \to \pm\infty$. That can be answered very simply by means of (5-13), which has been shown to hold for each fixed λ not only on the right, but also in the "allowed" region on the left, except when λ has a value where $\underline{f}(\lambda, k)$ has one of its fixed poles. It follows that (5-13) is true uniformly in every closed finite region Γ that excludes those poles.

Hence for every such region Γ in the λ-plane there exists an energy above which it contains no more zeros of $\underline{f}_-$. That implies that a zero of $\underline{f}_-$ can move, as $E \to \infty$ only to infinity, or else to one of the fixed poles of $\underline{f}$. The same holds as $E \to -\infty$.[8]

For a potential of type (4-8), therefore, pole trajectories of S can end up, as $E \to \pm\infty$, only at infinity, or else at negative integral values of $\ell \leq -\frac{3}{2} - \frac{1}{2}p$ (if all derivatives of rV exist at r = 0). And it immediately follows from the discussion below (4-14) that for any potential that is constant in some region $0 \leq r \leq r_0$, all trajectories lead to infinity: a fortiori this is true for square well potentials.[3]

Once a trajectory is known to lead to infinity, nothing general is known about the direction in which it does so. The study of that question is hampered by inadequate information concerning Bessel and Hankel functions of large (complex) order and large (but independent) argument. It is also not known if for a given potential some pole trajectories may lead to infinity and others, to a negative integer[9]; nor, if the two ends, as $E \to +\infty$ and as $E \to -\infty$, of a trajectory must necessarily lead to the same point.

If the potential is of the Yukawa type (3-8) we may readily find explicitly how each trajectory approaches its end point, if it is finite. As $|k| \to \infty$ with Im $k \geq 0$

$$\underline{f}_-(\lambda, k) \sim 1 - i\tfrac{1}{2}\pi e^{-i\pi\lambda}\int_0^\infty dr\ rV(r)H_\lambda^{(2)}(rke^{-i\pi})J_\lambda(kr)$$

In the vicinity of a negative half-integral value of λ, it is J_λ in $H_\lambda^{(2)}$ which dominates the integral; because of the resulting divergence:

$$\underline{f}_- \sim 1 - \frac{e^{-i\pi\lambda}}{2\sin\pi\lambda}\int_0^\infty dr\ rV(r)J_\lambda^2(kr)$$

By using (3-8), we get

$$\underline{f}_- \sim 1 - \frac{e^{-i\pi\lambda}}{2k\sin\pi\lambda}\int d\mu\ \rho(\mu)Q_{\lambda-(1/2)}\left(1 + \frac{\mu^2}{2k^2}\right) \tag{8-2}$$

$Q_{\lambda - (1/2)}$ being the Legendre function of the second kind. From

$$Q_{\lambda-(1/2)}(z) = Q_{-\lambda-(1/2)}(z) - \pi\tan\pi\lambda P_{-\lambda-(1/2)}(z) \tag{8-3}$$

we get for

$$\lambda = -n - \tfrac{1}{2} + \Lambda \qquad \Lambda << 1$$

$$Q_{\lambda-(1/2)}(1) \simeq 1/\Lambda$$

and hence

$$f_- \sim 1 + \frac{i}{2k\Lambda}\int d\mu\ \rho(\mu) = 1 + \frac{i}{2k\Lambda}[rV]_{r=0} \tag{8-4}$$

Thus the zero of $\underline{f}_-$ approaches $\lambda = -n - \frac{1}{2}$ as

$$\Lambda(k) = -(i/2k)[rV]_{r=0} \tag{8-5}$$

For a potential of type (3-8), attractive at the origin, all poles approach their finite end points from above as $E \to +\infty$ and from the right as $E \to -\infty$; for repulsive potentials, from below as $E \to +\infty$, and from the left as $E \to -\infty$.[10]

Notes and References

1. This was explicitly pointed out by Taylor (T2).
2. Examples of branch point singularities of the pole position $\lambda(k)$ are those imaginary values of k at which λ moves into the complex plane, the possibility of which for Re $\lambda < 0$ was discussed in Chapter 7. These are the "anomalous thresholds" mentioned by Lovelace and Masson (L1).
3. See Barut and Calogero (B1).
4. It follows that the concept of a "leading trajectory" is ambiguous. The pole that leads at one energy may not lead at another.
5. See Chapter 2.
6. From the point of view of the S-matrix rather than the Jost function, these points are "indeterminacy points" of a function of two complex variables. Whereas at other points of a surface (when k is complex) of singularity S is infinite, on these points the value of S depends on the direction from which they are approached. This is an example of the simplification that results from discussing the zeros of the Jost function rather than the poles of S.
7. It should be remembered that the residue of a pole of S in the right-hand λ-plane cannot vanish; see Chapter 10.
8. The possible finite trajectory end points are thus seen to be intimately connected with the poles of ϕ, and hence with the precise nature of the potential near r = 0, as is to be physically expected. But it is not correct to say that the integral nature of the trajectory end points is due to the r^{-1} dependence of the potential near the origin, which makes it behave there like a Coulomb potential. Contrary to the concluding remarks of (B6), a finite potential may miss only the first negative integer but may still have all the others as trajectory end points. The fact that the square well leads to no trajectories with finite end points has to do with its constancy near r = 0, not with its boundedness.

9. For Yukawa potentials no trajectories are known at this writing to lead to infinity. It should be noted though that, although many trajectories of the computation in (A2) were found to lead to $\lambda = 0$ from the lower left (see Chapter 12), none were seen to go there from the upper right (see Chapter 9). This may perhaps indicate that the latter end at infinity and not at negative integral ℓ. It has meanwhile been shown analytically in two papers by Azimov, Anselm, and Shekhter, listed in the third part of the bibliography, that for simple Yukawa potentials it is indeed true that those trajectories of 0-type which approach $\lambda = 0$ from the first quadrant, lead to infinity, with Re $\lambda \to \infty$ Im $\lambda \to \infty$, as $E \to +\infty$. I am indebted to Dr. A. Bincer for bringing these papers to my attention.
10. Equation (8-5) cannot be used to exclude the possibility of poles leading to infinity, since it holds only in a finite region in the λ-plane.

Chapter 9

THRESHOLD BEHAVIOR

In this chapter we want to investigate the behavior of the pole trajectories of S as the momentum tends to zero. The threshold value of the energy is of a special nature owing to the fact that $\underline{f}$ there has in general a branch point as a function of k [see (5-10)], containing both $k^{(1/2)+\lambda}$ and $k^{(1/2)-\lambda}$. If it were not for that branch point and the possibility that $\partial \underline{f}_{-}/\partial\lambda = 0$ at $k = 0$, all trajectories would necessarily have to turn into the first quadrant of the λ-plane at right angles to the real axis. For then $\lambda(k)$ would be regular analytic in the vicinity of $k = 0$, and thus it would define an angle preserving mapping. When $\lambda(0) = \frac{1}{2}$, this is indeed the case, and trajectories which happen to arrive at $\ell = 0$ when $E = 0$ do leave at right angles.

The low-energy behavior of the trajectories being intimately connected with the well-known threshold energy dependence of the S-matrix, we shall give the argument directly from that.[1] If the first $(2\ell + 2)$ absolute moments of the potential are finite, the phase shift of angular momentum ℓ goes as

$$\delta_\ell(k) - \delta_\ell(0) = O(k^{2\ell + 1})$$

when $k \to 0$, and so the S-matrix

$$S_\ell = 1 + O(k^{2\ell + 1})$$

Hence we expect that the interpolated unitary S-matrix has a k dependence near $k = 0$ which can be written

$$S(\lambda, k) = \frac{1 - k^{2\lambda} e^{i\pi\lambda} C^*(\lambda)}{1 - k^{2\lambda} e^{-i\pi\lambda} C(\lambda)} \tag{9-1}$$

This will contain the leading powers of k, of course, only if $\lambda < 1$; otherwise $C(\lambda)$ will contain terms such as $k^2, \ldots$, which dominate near $k = 0$.

The function $C(\lambda)$ must, for real λ, be real. That follows immediately upon insertion of (9-1) into (5-17).

The argument for the form (9-1) of S near $k = 0$ can be made rigorous by looking at $\underline{f}(\lambda, k)$. By using the second form of (5-12) we obtain near $k = 0$

$$\underline{f}(\lambda, k) \simeq 1 - \frac{1}{2\lambda}\Big[e^{i\pi\lambda} k^{2\lambda} 2^{-2\lambda} \frac{\Gamma(1-\lambda)}{\Gamma(1+\lambda)} \int_0^\infty dr\, r^{(1/2)+\lambda} V(r)\phi(\lambda, 0; r) - \int_0^\infty dr\, r^{(1/2)-\lambda} V(r)\phi(\lambda, 0; r)\Big]$$

and hence the explicit formula for $C(\lambda)$:

$$C(\lambda) = 2^{-2\lambda} \frac{\Gamma(1-\lambda)}{\Gamma(1+\lambda)} \circ \frac{\int_0^\infty dr\, r^{(1/2)+\lambda} V(r)\phi(\lambda, 0; r)}{2\lambda + \int_0^\infty dr\, r^{(1/2)-\lambda} V(r)\phi(\lambda, 0; r)} \tag{9-2}$$

from which it follows that

$$C(0) = 1 \tag{9-3}$$

This fact, which has an important bearing on the precise nature of the threshold trajectories, is connected with the low-energy behavior of the $\ell = -\frac{1}{2}$ phase shift. Equation (9-3) is equivalent to the statement that

$$\delta_{-1/2}(E) - \delta_{-1/2}(0) \simeq -\pi/|\ln E| \qquad \text{as} \qquad E \to 0+$$

Equation (9-1) implies that the low-energy poles of S in the λ-plane are the solutions to the equation

$$1 - k^{2\lambda} e^{-i\pi\lambda} C(\lambda) = 0 \tag{9-4}$$

It follows that there are two classes of poles of S: those that in the limit as $E \to 0$ tend to $\lambda = 0$ ("0-type"), and those that in that limit tend either to a zero of $C(\lambda)$ in the left half-plane, or to a pole of $C(\lambda)$ in the right half-plane ("C-type").

We first consider the 0-type. Let us write

$$C(\lambda) \equiv e^{\lambda B(\lambda)}$$

so that because of (9-3)

$$B(\lambda) = \lambda^{-1} \ln C(\lambda) \equiv -\ln E_0 + a\lambda + \cdots$$

with real coefficients $\ln E_0$, $a, \ldots$. Furthermore we define

$$A(\lambda) \equiv B(\lambda) + \ln E_0$$

Then (9-4) can be written

$$\exp \lambda[\ln E - i\pi + B] = \exp[\pm 2\pi n i]$$

or

$$\lambda = \frac{\pm 2n\pi}{\pi + iA(\lambda) + i \ln (E/E_0)} \tag{9-5}$$

where n is an integer.

As $E \to 0+$ we get the leading terms in an expansion of λ in inverse powers of $\ln (E/E_0)$ by expanding $A(\lambda)$. The smaller E, the more solutions (9-5) has of the form

$$\lambda^{(n)} \simeq \pm \frac{2n\pi}{\pi - i|\ln E/E_0|}$$

or

$$\lambda^{(n)} \simeq \frac{2n\pi}{|\ln E/E_0|} e^{i\varphi} \qquad n = 1, 2, \ldots << |\ln E/E_0|/2\pi$$

$$\tan \varphi = |\ln E/E_0|/\pi \tag{9-6}$$

independently of the potential.

This shows that there are infinitely many pole trajectories which arrive at the point $\lambda = 0$ as $E \to 0+$, half of them from the lower left and the other half, symmetrically from the upper right. At fixed energy they lie (asymptotically) evenly spaced on a ray from the origin of the λ-plane, and as $E \to 0$ they move along the ray toward $\lambda = 0$, while it is turning counterclockwise. Each pole approaches $\lambda = 0$ along a parabolic arc osculating the imaginary λ-axis, the equation of the nth being ($\lambda \equiv \lambda_i + i\lambda_r$)

$$\lambda_i^{(n)2} = 2n\lambda_r^{(n)} \tag{9-7}$$

Each of the two half-planes, both the left and the right, thus contain infinitely many trajectories that lead to $\lambda = 0$.[2] But it would not be correct to refer to $\lambda = 0$ as an accumulation point of poles of $\overline{S}$. For every fixed energy there is only a finite number of poles near $\lambda = 0$. $\underline{f}_-$ being an analytic function of λ for fixed k, it cannot have a finite accumulation point of zeros. But as the energy decreases toward threshold, more and more poles of S move toward $\lambda = 0$, and infinitely many of them get there in the limit as $E \to 0$.

In fact, we can say more. It follows from (6-10) and (6-15) that for potentials of the Yukawa type (3-8) the number of poles of S in the right half-plane is finite at fixed energy. Consequently, as the energy decreases to zero, more and more poles cross the positive imaginary λ-axis into the right half-plane, then turn and subsequently approach the origin $\lambda = 0$. These right-hand poles thus have no connection whatever with bound states. It seems, therefore, unlikely that they could get close enough to the real axis to cause resonances. However, no such limitation is known at present.

The energy scale of the motion of the poles is provided by E_0, defined by

$$E_0 \equiv \exp\left[-\left.\frac{dC(\lambda)}{d\lambda}\right|_{\lambda = 0}\right]$$

For weak potentials we may replace V by γV and get in the limit as $\gamma \to 0$,

$$E_0 = 4\exp[2\Gamma'(1)]\exp\left[-\frac{2\int_0^\infty dr\, rV(r)\ln r}{\int_0^\infty dr\, rV(r)}\right]\exp\left[\frac{2}{\gamma\int_0^\infty dr\, rV(r)}\right] \times [1 + O(\gamma)] \tag{9-8}$$

Notice that the second term has the dimensionality of an energy. But it is the third term which is of main interest when $\gamma \to 0$. For (on the average) attractive forces the energy scale E_0 approaches zero very strongly as $\gamma \to 0$, and the motion of the poles near $\ell = -\frac{1}{2}$ is extremely rapid. We may say, the weaker the potential, the "thinner" are the trajectories near $\ell = -\frac{1}{2}$.[3]

For (on the average) repulsive potentials, on the other hand, E_0 tends to infinity very rapidly as $\gamma \to 0$, and the poles of type 0 tend to remain near $\ell = -\frac{1}{2}$ until the energy gets rather large. In other words, the weaker the forces, the "thicker" are the trajectories near $\ell = -\frac{1}{2}$ in that case.

The next terms in the expansion of λ in inverse powers of $\ln E/E_0$ are also readily obtained from (9-5). As $E \to 0+$,

$$\lambda_i = \frac{2n\pi}{|\ln E/E_0|}\left[1 - \frac{\pi^2}{|\ln E/E_0|^2} + \cdots\right]$$
$$\lambda_r = \frac{2n\pi^2}{|\ln E/E_0|^2}\left[1 - \frac{2na}{|\ln E/E_0|} + \cdots\right] \qquad (9\text{-}6')$$

The asymmetric bending of the right-hand trajectories toward the imaginary axis and of the left-hand ones, toward the real axis, is clearly visible in the second-order terms for λ, since always $a > 0$, as we shall see shortly. The points at which the right-hand trajectories cross the positive imaginary axis toward the left must be solutions of the equation

$$\text{Im } A(\lambda) = \pi$$

where λ is to be taken purely imaginary. Of course, this equation determines the crossing points only if they occur at small-enough energy. (But this does not necessarily mean $|\ln E/E_0| >> 1$.)

As $E \to 0-$, the equations for the poles become

$$\lambda = \pm \frac{2n\pi i}{A(\lambda) + \ln(-E/E_0)}$$

and hence the leading terms as $E \to 0-$ are

$$\lambda_i \simeq \frac{\pm 2\pi n}{|\ln(-E/E_0)|}$$
$$\lambda_r \simeq \frac{(2\pi n)^2 a}{|\ln(-E/E_0)|^3} \qquad n = 1, 2, \ldots << |\ln(-E/E_0)|/2\pi \qquad (9\text{-}9)$$

Since we know that there can be no complex poles of S on the right, the function $C(\lambda)$ must be such that $a > 0$ always. There are, then, infinitely many negative energy poles that approach $\ell = -\frac{1}{2}$ as $E \to 0-$ from the left half-plane, and they are complex. Of necessity, they therefore occur in complex conjugate pairs. They osculate the imaginary axis even more closely than the positive energy poles, and the more so the larger n.

The fact that the threshold behavior of the S-matrix implies the existence of infinitely many trajectories that lead to $\ell = -\frac{1}{2}$ may be taken as an indication that the S-matrix, for each fixed energy, must have an infinite number of poles. It is not a proof though, since it is conceivable that as the energy decreases more and more poles come from infinity on the left. There is no guaranty that (9-5) has a solution for all n. All we know is that as $E \to 0$, it has more and more solutions, without limit.

If we assume that $\underline{f}_-$ has infinitely many zeros of type 0 at each fixed positive energy, then a convenient representation of all of them in a single factor is given by

$$\Pi(\lambda, E) = \frac{\sin(\frac{1}{2}\lambda|\ln E/E_0|e^{-i\varphi})}{\frac{1}{2}\lambda|\ln E/E_0|e^{-i\varphi}}$$

where

$$\tan\varphi = \frac{1}{\pi}|\ln E/E_0|$$

and $\Pi(0, E) = 1$.

We now turn to the poles of "type C." Let $C(\lambda_0) = 0$ with Re $\lambda_0 < 0$, and write

$$C(\lambda) = (\lambda - \lambda_0)C' + \cdots$$

Then (9-4) becomes for $E > 0$, $R \equiv |\ln E|$

$$(\lambda - \lambda_0)C' \simeq e^{i\pi\lambda_0}e^{\lambda R}$$

Since it is easy to prove that

$$\lim_{R \to \infty} (\lambda - \lambda_0)R = 0$$

it follows that as $E \to 0+$

$$\lambda(E) \simeq \lambda_0 + (1/C')e^{i\pi\lambda_0}E^{-\lambda_0} \tag{9-10}$$

The constant C' may have either sign and λ may approach its threshold value λ_0 from any direction, generally at a finite angle.

As $E \to 0-$, we get similarly

$$\lambda(E) \simeq \lambda_0 + (1/C')(-E)^{-\lambda_0} \tag{9-11}$$

which means that a real λ_0 may be approached from either side, but always along the real axis.

Comparison of (9-10) and (9-11) shows that for every real negative threshold value λ_0 there are only two possible kinds of threshold motions; their dependence upon λ_0 (modulo 2) is exhibited in Table 9-1. It is, however, also possible for λ_0 to be complex. In that event both λ_0 and λ_0^* are threshold pole positions and the poles spiral in toward them, both as $E \to 0+$ and as $E \to 0-$.

The explicit formula (9-2) for $C(\lambda)$ allows us immediately to find some of the left-hand threshold positions for certain kinds of potentials. If the potential is of the type (4-8) then the integral in the numerator of (9-2) converges so long as $\lambda > -p - \frac{3}{2}$, whereas the poles in ϕ cancel out by use of (4-12). The Γ-function in the denominator then makes $C = 0$ at all negative integral values of λ in the region $\lambda > -p - \frac{3}{2}$.

What happens when the potential is made weaker and weaker? S then tends to unity, but the approach is highly nonuniform both in k and λ. We may multiply $V(r)$ by a parameter γ and then let it tend to zero. It is clear from (9-2) that the left-hand zero-energy pole positions in the limit of vanishing potential strength are the zeros of the function

$$C_0(\lambda) = \int_0^\infty dr\, r^{1 + 2\lambda} V(r)/\Gamma(\lambda + 1)$$

If $C_0(\lambda)$ has no left-hand zeros (as is the case for a simple Yukawa potential) then all the left-hand zeros of $C(\lambda)$ must move to infinity as $\gamma \to 0$. Together with the high-energy limit discussion in Chapter 8, we can then understand the pole structure of S in the limit of very weak forces. For large positive or negative energy, down to an energy of the order of the potential strength, the poles remain close to their fixed end-point positions, the negative integral ℓ-values (if the potential is of that kind). Only when the energy gets quite small, do the poles suddenly move very rapidly to their far-away zero-energy positions, the zeros of $C(\lambda)$ and $\lambda = 0$. We may say that as the potential strength shrinks to zero, the heads of the trajectories get small-

Table 9-1

Direction in Which a Left-Hand Pole Leaves its Real Threshold Position λ_0 for Positive Energy, Depending on its Negative Energy Approach.

	If $\lambda > \lambda_0$ for $E < 0$	If $\lambda < \lambda_0$ for $E < 0$
$-\frac{1}{2} < \lambda_0 < 0$	Upper right	Lower left
$-1 < \lambda_0 < -\frac{1}{2}$	Upper left	Lower right
$-\frac{3}{2} < \lambda_0 < -1$	Lower left	Upper right
$-2 < \lambda_0 < -\frac{3}{2}$	Lower right	Upper left

er, and their tails, thinner.

From the fact that for specific potentials the zero-energy pole positions move to infinity as $\gamma \to 0$, while the infinite-energy pole positions remain fixed, it does not, however, follow that each trajectory gets longer and longer. When two trajectories cross or touch one another, as $\gamma \to 0$, it is possible for them to change roles, as indicated schematically in Figure 9-1. Thus they may "exchange tails." A zero-energy pole position may by this mechanism be handed down to trajectories of more and more distant infinite-energy pole positions as the potential strength decreases. This remarkable phenomenon has been seen explicitly in numerical computations for simple Yukawa potentials.[4]

Suppose now that $0 < \lambda_0 < 1$ and that

$$C(\lambda) = B(\lambda - \lambda_0)^{-1} + \cdots$$

Then (9-4) becomes

$$\lambda(E) \simeq \lambda_0 + Be^{-i\pi\lambda_0}E^{\lambda_0} \tag{9-12}$$

as $E \to 0+$. In the region Re $\lambda_0 > 0$, however, it is more instructive to return to the consideration of the Jost function.

We want to see how (8-1) goes as $k \to 0$. Because of (3-15) it is best to use the function $\bar{f}$ of (3-16) for the evaluation of the expectation value of r^{-2}. The diagonal matrix element

$$\int_0^\infty dr\, r^{-2}|\bar{f}|^2$$

is then finite in the limit as $k \to 0$, and different from zero ($F_- = 0$).

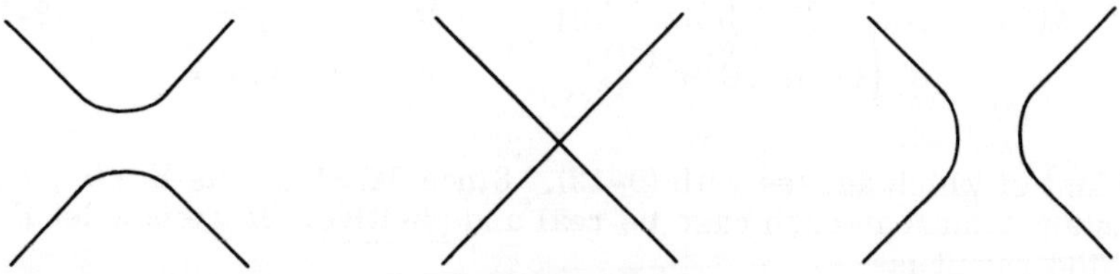

Figure 9-1

The "exchange of tails" of trajectories in the λ-plane as the potential strength decreases, represented schematically. For an actual case, see Figure 12-7.

The normalization integral is

$$\int_0^\infty dr|\bar{f}|^2 = \int_0^R dr|\bar{f}|^2 + \int_R^\infty dr|\bar{f}|^2$$

The first term is finite in the limit as $k \to 0$; in the second we change variables, $x = kr$:

$$\int_R^\infty dr|\bar{f}|^2 = k^{2\lambda - 2}\int_{Rk}^\infty dx\,|f(\lambda, k; x/k)|^2$$

As $k \to 0$, if $\lambda \geq 1$, the dominant contribution to the integral comes from the lower limit, and it is $O(k^{2 - 2\lambda})$ if $\lambda > 1$; $O(\ln k)$ if $\lambda = 1$; if $\lambda < 1$ the integral remains finite as $k \to 0$. Consequently,

$$\int_0^\infty dr|\bar{f}|^2 = \begin{cases} O(1) & \text{if} \quad \lambda_0 > 1 \\ O(\ln k) & \text{if} \quad \lambda_0 = 1 \\ O(k^{2\lambda_0 - 2}) & \text{if} \quad \lambda_0 < 1 \end{cases}$$

and as a result, when $\lambda(0) > 0$, as $E \to 0-$,

$$\frac{d\lambda}{dE} = \begin{cases} O(1) & \text{if} \quad \lambda > 1 \; (\ell > \frac{1}{2}) \\ O(\ln E) & \text{if} \quad \lambda = 1 \; (\ell = \frac{1}{2}) \\ O(E^{\lambda - 1}) & \text{if} \quad \lambda < 1 \; (\ell < \frac{1}{2}) \end{cases} \tag{9-13}$$

It is important to notice that the rate at which a zero of F_- approaches its threshold value λ_0 is <u>infinite</u> when $0 < \lambda_0 \leq 1$.

We conclude that $\lambda(E)$ has the following asymptotic form near $E = 0-$:

$$\lambda(E) - \lambda_0 = \begin{cases} aE & \text{if} \quad \lambda_0 > 1 \\ aE[1 - \ln(Ee^{-i\pi})] & \text{if} \quad \lambda_0 = 1 \\ (1/\lambda_0)aE^{\lambda_0}e^{-i\pi(\lambda_0 - 1)} & \text{if} \quad 0 < \lambda_0 < 1 \end{cases} \tag{9-14}$$

the last of which agrees with (9-12). Since $\partial\lambda/\partial E \geq 0$ as $E \to 0-$, the constant a must in each case be real and <u>positive</u>. If we now let $E \to 0+$, the result is

$$\frac{d\,\mathrm{Re}\,\lambda}{dE} = \begin{cases} a & \text{if} \quad \lambda_0 > 1 \\ -a\ln E & \text{if} \quad \lambda_0 = 1 \\ aE^{\lambda_0 - 1}\cos\pi(\lambda_0 - 1) & \text{if} \quad 0 < \lambda_0 < 1 \end{cases} \tag{9-15}$$

or, if we denote the position of the Regge pole by $\ell = \alpha(E)$, as $E \to 0+$,

$$\frac{d \operatorname{Re} \alpha}{dE} = \begin{cases} a & \text{if} \quad \alpha_0 > \frac{1}{2} \\ -a \ln E & \text{if} \quad \alpha_0 = \frac{1}{2} \\ aE^{\alpha_0 - (1/2)} \cos \pi(\alpha_0 - \frac{1}{2}) & \text{if} \quad -\frac{1}{2} < \alpha_0 < \frac{1}{2} \end{cases} \qquad (9\text{-}15')$$

A plot of Re α against E in the vicinity of E = 0, therefore, looks like Figure 9-2.

In order to obtain the behavior of the imaginary part of $\lambda(E)$ near threshold we use (7-5) together with (5-1) when $F_- = 0$:

$$2 \operatorname{Re} \lambda \operatorname{Im} \lambda \int_0^\infty dr\, r^{-2} |f|^2 = k \qquad (9\text{-}16)$$

$\bar{f}$ of (3-16) being finite as $k \to 0$ and the integral existing because $F_- = 0$, it is easily seen that as $k \to 0+$

$$\int_0^\infty dr\, r^{-2} |f|^2 = O(k^{1 - 2\lambda})$$

and, therefore, by (9-16), as $E \to 0$,

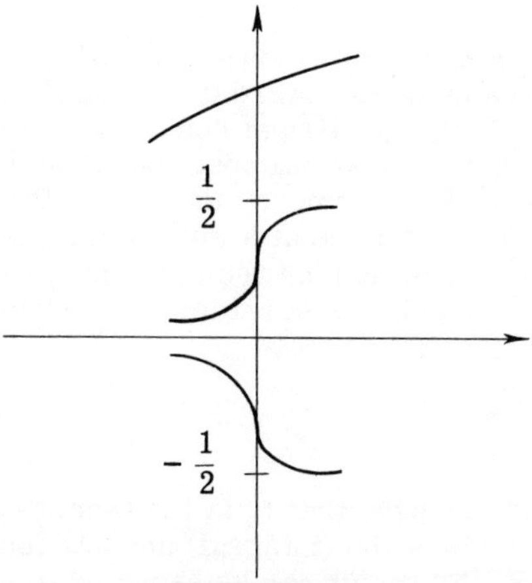

Figure 9-2
Threshold behavior of C-type Regge poles in the right half-plane, plotted schematically Re α versus energy.

$$1/d\,\mathrm{Im}\,\lambda/dE = O(E^{1-\lambda_0}) \tag{9-17}$$

Combination of (9-15) and (9-17) gives us the angle at which a pole trajectory leaves the real axis at threshold. Defining

$$\cot\gamma \equiv \frac{\partial \mathrm{Re}\,\lambda/\partial k}{\partial \mathrm{Im}\,\lambda/\partial k} = \frac{\partial\, \mathrm{Re}\,\alpha/\partial E}{\partial\, \mathrm{Im}\,\alpha/\partial E}$$

we get as $E \to 0+$

$$\cot\gamma = \begin{cases} O(E^{1-\lambda_0}) \to \infty & \text{if} \quad \lambda_0 > 1\ (\alpha_0 > \frac{1}{2}) \\ O(\ln E) \to \infty & \text{if} \quad \lambda_0 = 1\ (\alpha_0 = \frac{1}{2}) \\ O(1) & \text{if} \quad 0 < \lambda_0 < 1\ (-\frac{1}{2} < \alpha_0 < \frac{1}{2}) \end{cases} \tag{9-18}$$

The results (9-15) and (9-18)[5] together imply that a pole trajectory in the complex plane leaves its threshold value α_0 toward the right if $\alpha_0 > 0$ and toward the left if $-\frac{1}{2} < \alpha_0 < 0$. If $-\frac{1}{2} < \alpha_0 < \frac{1}{2}$, the trajectory makes a generally nonzero angle with the real axis; if $\alpha_0 = 0$, it leaves at right angles; if $\alpha_0 > \frac{1}{2}$; it osculates the real axis, and it does so the more closely the larger α_0. Its equation for $E \simeq 0+$ is

$$\mathrm{Im}\,(\lambda - \lambda_0) = c\ \mathrm{Re}\,(\lambda - \lambda_0)^{\lambda_0}$$

These statements have well-known physical consequences. Since the trajectory leaves in the backward direction if $\alpha_0 < 0$, but in the forward direction if $\alpha_0 > 0$, an "almost bound" s-state causes no low-energy resonance, whereas an "almost bound" state of higher angular momentum does. Furthermore, the higher the angular momentum, the sharper the resonance at a given energy. Equation (9-18) leads to a well-known relation between the energy at which a low-energy resonance of angular momentum $\ell \geq 1$ occurs, and its width:

$$\Gamma = O(E^{\ell_0 + (1/2)}) \tag{9-19}$$

It should be noticed, though, that ℓ_0 is the (nonintegral) threshold angular momentum, and not the (integral) angular momentum of the resonance. However, the result can be expected to be applicable only when $\ell_0 \simeq \ell$.

Notes and References

1. The fact that infinitely many trajectories reach $\lambda = 0$ as $E \rightarrow 0$ was shown independently by Gribov and Pomeranchuk (G15) and by Desai and Newton (D4). The argument given here follows essentially (D5).
2. For some numerical examples in the case of square well potentials, see Figures 12-11 to 12-13.
3. The curves of (A2), shown in Chapter 12, show how "thin" the trajectories are near $\lambda = 0$. Poles get near $\lambda = 0$ for extremely small energies only.
4. See Ahmadzadeh et al. (A2), whose relevant curve is reproduced in Figure 12-7.
5. Equations (9-15) and (9-18) were derived first independently by Barut and Zwanziger (B17) and by Newton (N1).

Chapter 10

THE RESIDUES

According to (5-14) the residue β of the S-matrix[1] at a pole $\lambda_0(k)$ determined by $\underline{f}_-(\lambda_0, k) = 0$ is given by

$$\beta(k) = \frac{\underline{f}_+(\lambda, k)}{\partial \underline{f}_-(\lambda, k)/\partial\lambda}\bigg|_{\lambda = \lambda_0} = \exp[i\pi(\lambda - \tfrac{1}{2})]\frac{F_+}{\partial F_-/\partial\lambda}\bigg|_{\lambda = \lambda_0} \tag{10-1}$$

It will be useful to write this in another way.

Since at the point where $F_- = 0$, (5-1) tells us that

$$\phi = \tfrac{1}{2}ik^{-1}F_+f_- \tag{10-2}$$

it follows from (7-4) that

$$\frac{\partial F_-}{\partial\lambda}\bigg|_{\lambda = \lambda_0} = \frac{\lambda_0}{ik}F_+\int_0^\infty dr\, r^{-2}f_-^2 \tag{10-3}$$

and, therefore,

$$\beta(k) = \frac{e^{i\pi\lambda_0}k/\lambda_0}{\int_0^\infty dr\, r^{-2}f_-^2} \tag{10-4}$$

We can now see immediately the analytic structure of $\beta(k)$ as a function of k.

As was discussed at the beginning of Chapter 8, the pole position

$\lambda_0(k)$ is an analytic function of k in the upper half of the k-plane, regular there wherever it is finite, except possibly for isolated points[2]; and it is certainly finite so long as it lies in the right half-plane. Thus (10-2) tells us that $F_+(\lambda_0, k)$ is an analytic function of k for Im $k \geq 0$, except where λ_0 has a singularity. It follows that so long as λ_0 lies in the right half-plane, the residue β is an analytic function of the energy E, regular on the first sheet, except possibly at points where the pole is not simple,[3] i.e., where $\partial F_-/\partial\lambda = 0$. For negative energies and Re $\lambda_0 > 0$ the pole is always simple and the residue regular. Furthermore, in that case always

$$e^{-i\pi\lambda_0}\beta(k) > 0.$$

Specifically, the residue of a negative energy pole on the right cannot vanish. When the pole lies in the left half-plane the residue may also fail to be regular when the pole has moved to infinity. The point k = 0 is always exceptional. It should be noticed that, in spite of the first appearance of (10-1), β has no left-hand cut on the first sheet of the E-surface.[4]

At a point where a pole and a zero of S cross one another, the residue of the pole vanishes. In other words, at such a point both F_+ and F_- vanish. In general this cannot happen, because it would imply by (5-1) that $\phi = 0$, and hence it would contradict the boundary condition (4-1). But it can happen at specific points in the left half-plane, as was discussed in Chapter 8. Almost always, in fact, when a pole of S moves through a negative integral value of λ, or through a negative half-integral value of $\lambda \leq -1 - \frac{1}{2}p$ [for potentials of type (4-8)], the residue β vanishes. The only exceptions occur when, at the same energy, another pole moves through the reflected point in the right half-plane. Specifically, the residue must vanish whenever a positive energy pole crosses the real axis on the left, and whenever a pole on the left passes through a negative integer or half-integer ($\leq -1 - \frac{1}{2}p$) at the reflected value of which the potential is too weakly attractive to support a bound state.

At threshold the residue vanishes. How it does we can see from (10-4). If $\bar{f}$ of (3-16) is used in the denominator integral, it is finite and generally nonzero as $k \to 0$. Therefore, in general,

$$\beta(k) = O(k^{2\ell_0 + 1}) \qquad \text{as} \qquad k \to 0 \tag{10-5}$$

with possible exceptions. But this holds only when at threshold, $\ell_0 > -\frac{1}{2}$. For the "0-type" poles at threshold we obtain from (9-1)

$$\beta(k) = -2\pi i\lambda(k)/\left|\ln |E|\right| \tag{10-6}$$

and, hence, by (9-7) as $E \to 0+$

$$\beta_n \simeq -i\frac{4n\pi^2}{|\ln E|^2} e^{i\varphi} \tag{10-7}$$

$$\tan\varphi = \pi^{-1}|\ln E|$$

whereas by (9-9), as $E \to 0-$,

$$\mathrm{Re}\,\beta_n \simeq \frac{4n\pi^2}{|\ln(-E)|^2} \qquad \mathrm{Im}\,\beta_n \simeq \frac{4n^2\pi^3(A^2 - 2B)}{|\ln(-E)|^4} \tag{10-8}$$

The real and imaginary parts of the residues thus have specific signs depending only on the quadrant from which the pole approaches the origin.

For the "C-type" poles in the left half of the λ-plane we get from (9-1) and (9-10), as $E \to 0+$

$$\beta \simeq 2i(1/C')e^{2\pi\lambda_0 i} \sin \pi\lambda_0 E^{-\lambda_0} \tag{10-9}$$

where $C' = dC/d\lambda$ at λ_0, determined by $C(\lambda_0) = 0$, whereas, as $E \to 0-$,

$$\beta \simeq 2i(1/C')e^{i\pi\lambda_0} \sin \pi\lambda_0(-E)^{-\lambda_0} \tag{10-10}$$

So in this region too the residue generally vanishes at threshold, as $|E|^{|\lambda_0|}$, the same way as on the right, except that when the threshold happens to lie on a negative integral value of λ, the residue vanishes more rapidly.

The symmetry relation (5-11) which enforces poles of S on the left whenever right-hand poles pass through integers or half-integers, appears to lead to no useful symmetry for the residues. Equation (5-21), specifically, breaks down.[5]

The high-energy behavior of a residue, as the corresponding pole approaches a negative half-integral value of λ, is easily obtained explicitly for potentials of the Yukawa type (3-8). By (10-1) and (8-4) we have

$$\beta_n(k) \simeq -\tfrac{1}{2}ik^{-1}[rV]_{r=0} \tag{10-11}$$

The residue is positive or negative imaginary, depending on the sign of the potential at the origin, and it tends to zero with increasing k.

The behavior of the residues of faraway poles in the λ-plane can also be estimated, although in a more heuristic manner. If the potential decreases sufficiently rapidly at infinity, f approached f_0 as $|\lambda| \to \infty$ (see the discussion in Chapter 6). Since the faraway zeros of $\underline{f}_-$ usually lie toward Re $\lambda \to -\infty$, we are interested in the behavior of β in that direction. Then

$$f^2(\lambda, -k; r) \simeq \tfrac{1}{2}\pi i k r e^{-i\pi\lambda}[H_\lambda^{(2)}(-kr)]^2$$

$$\simeq -i(\tfrac{1}{2}kr)^{2\lambda}(kr/\lambda)\exp[-i\pi\lambda + 2\lambda - 2\lambda\ln(-\lambda)]$$

which we insert in (10-4). In spite of the fact that this asymptotic value cannot be used for the whole integral, which converges only because $\underline{f}_- = 0$ and hence f_- is proportional to ϕ, we expect that as Re $\lambda \to -\infty$

$$\ln \int_0^\infty dr\, r^{-2} f_-^2 \propto -2\lambda \ln(-\lambda)$$

and, therefore,

$$\ln \beta = O(2\lambda \ln(-\lambda)) \tag{10-12}$$

If the conditions required for this reasoning to be correct are met, the residues of the faraway poles of S are, therefore, extremely small. There may well be exceptions to this behavior, though. Apart from the fact that the reasoning may break down because of the nonuniform approach of f to f_0, there may be cancellations in the denominator integral in (10-4) which may make the result larger.

Notes and References

1. The β used here is the residue of the S-matrix; in many papers β is instead the residue of the partial wave amplitude. The two, therefore, differ by a factor of 2ik.
2. See footnote 2 of Chapter 8 for a remark concerning branch points.
3. Of course, the definition of the residue of a double pole is not (10-1) but

$$\beta = \left.\frac{2\underline{f}_+}{\partial^2 \underline{f}_-/\partial\lambda^2}\right|_{\lambda=\lambda_0}$$

4. See (T2).
5. A remark to the contrary in (N1) is incorrect.

Chapter 11

REPRESENTATIONS OF THE S-MATRIX

In order to represent the S-matrix in terms of its poles in the angular momentum plane, the asymptotic distribution of these poles far away in the λ-plane must be investigated. Without a knowledge of that distribution the convergence of the ensuing infinite product or series cannot be established. The most convenient way of studying this problem is to find the asymptotic distribution of zeros of the entire analytic function g introduced in (6-18).[1] Since for a large relevant class of potentials $\underline{f}$ has only a finite number of zeros in the right-hand half on the λ-plane, the faraway zeros of g on the left are zeros of $\underline{f}(\lambda, k)$, and those on the right are zeros of $\underline{f}(-\lambda, k)$. The cosine eliminates the poles of both $\underline{f}$'s.

The conditions on the potential necessary for the following discussion are not completely clear. Apart from the assumption that all derivatives of rV at $r = 0$ should be finite, so that the entire left half-plane is accessible and the poles of $\underline{f}$ are eliminated by the cosine in (6-18), we postulate that the potential decreases asymptotically sufficiently rapidly for the heuristic arguments of Chapter 6, which establish the growth rate of g, as $\text{Re}\,\lambda \to \infty$, to be correct. Even though it may well be that in many cases the details of those arguments may break down, that, specifically, $\underline{f}$ may not approach its Born approximation as $|\lambda| \to \infty$, the result (6-22) is probably correct for a large class of forces. It is, after all, not really necessary that $\underline{f}$ approaches its Born approximation for such a result to hold. All that is needed is that the higher-order terms behave no worse than the first. It should also be noticed that the divergence of the first Born approximation, in the limit of large $|\lambda|$, is no evidence against the relative smallness of the higher-order terms. If the potential has a finite range, the arguments of Chapter 6 are surely correct, and in that case the second Born approximation to $\underline{f}$ is, indeed, small compared to the first, even though the latter diverges as $|\lambda| \to \infty$.

The main tools for obtaining the asymptotic distribution of zeros of g are the two theorems by Jensen and Carleman.[2] The first gives us an integrated, average spacing of the magnitudes of the zeros of an entire function from a knowledge of the average rate of growth of the function in all directions. It states that if n(r) is the number of zeros of the function g(z) inside a circle of radius r about the origin, and

$$N(r) \equiv \int_0^r dt\, t^{-1} n(t)$$

then

$$N(r) = \frac{1}{2\pi} \int_0^{2\pi} d\theta\, \ln|g(re^{i\theta})/g(0)|$$

Clearly, N(r) is an average number of zeros in a circle of radius r.

Carleman's theorem allows us to find the distribution of zeros in specific directions from a knowledge of the growth rate in specific directions. It states that if $z_n = r_n e^{i\theta_n}$ is the nth zero of g(z), then

$$\sum_{r_n \leq R} \left(\frac{1}{r_n} - \frac{r_n}{R^2}\right) \sin\theta_n = \frac{1}{\pi R} \int_0^{\pi} d\theta \sin\theta \ln|g(Re^{i\theta})| + \frac{1}{2\pi} \int_0^{R} dx\, (x^{-2} - R^{-2}) \ln|g(x)g(-x)| + \tfrac{1}{2} \operatorname{Im} g'(0)$$

Suppose first that the potential is a simple Yukawa. It was shown in Chapter 6 that then $g(\lambda)$ grows exponentially in all directions, and hence by Jensen's theorem, N(r) grows linearly with r. That implies that asymptotically the magnitudes of the zeros λ_n of g are, on the average, evenly spaced:

$$|\lambda_n| \propto n \tag{11-1}$$

Next we apply Carleman's theorem to the function $g(i\lambda)$. Since for imaginary λ, g also grows exponentially, we get

$$\sum_{|\lambda_n| \leq R} |\mathrm{Re}\, \lambda_n| |\lambda_n|^{-2} \propto \ln R \tag{11-2}$$

The same theorem applied to $g(\lambda)$ yields

$$\sum_{|\lambda_n| \leq R} |\mathrm{Im}\,\lambda_n| |\lambda_n|^{-2} \propto C \ln R \tag{11-3}$$

where $C \to 0$ as $k \to \infty$, because in (6-19), $\Lambda \to 1$. The three results, (11-1) to (11-3), show that both the real and the imaginary parts of the zeros are, on the average, asymptotically evenly spaced, and that, as the energy increases, they tend to remain closer to the real axis. We already know that in the limit as $k \to \infty$, they (or, at least infinitely many of them) move to the real axis, and they are there exactly evenly spaced. However, the approach to the negative integers may be nonuniform. The larger n, the higher the energy may have to be in order for the zero to get close to $\ell = -n$.

We now consider the case of a general superposition of Yukawa potentials (3-8) with all moments of $\rho(\mu)$ finite. It then follows from (6-21) and Jensen's theorem that

$$N(r) \propto r \ln r$$

and, therefore,

$$n(r) \propto r \ln r$$

This implies that the average density of the magnitudes of zeros grows logarithmically, the average spacing between the magnitudes of successive zeros decreases as $1/\ln n$, and

$$|\lambda_n| \propto n/\ln n \tag{11-4}$$

Along the imaginary axis, g still grows exponentially. Carleman's theorem applied to $g(i\lambda)$, therefore, tells us that

$$\sum_{|\lambda_n| \leq R} |\mathrm{Re}\,\lambda_n| |\lambda_n|^{-2} \propto \ln R \tag{11-5}$$

and, therefore,

$$|\mathrm{Re}\,\lambda_n| \propto n/(\ln n)^2 \tag{11-6}$$

while

$$|\mathrm{Im}\,\lambda_n| \propto n/\ln n \tag{11-7}$$

Thus, while the projections of the zeros on the real axis get more and more closely spaced, they diffuse more and more away from the real axis and toward the imaginary axis:

$$|\tan \arg \lambda_n| \propto \ln n \tag{11-8}$$

As the energy increases the diffusion away from the real axis gets less and less rapid.

In the case of the square well we saw in Chapter 6 that the growth rate is the same as in the case of the superposition of Yukawa potentials. So the resulting distribution of zeros is also that described by (11-5) to (11-8). These results are probably of rather general validity.

It follows both from (11-1) and from (11-4) that

$$\sum |\lambda_n|^{-\alpha} < \infty$$

for all $\alpha > 1$. Thus the genus[3] of the set of zeros of $\underline{f}$ in the λ-plane is $p = 1$. Furthermore, $\underline{\bar{f}}$[see above (6-18)] is in all the cases discussed, an entire function of order $\rho = 1$. It can, therefore, be written in a simple way as a product of its zeros. Hadamard's restricted form of the Weierstrass factorization[4] is applicable:

$$\underline{\bar{f}}_-(\lambda, k) = \underline{\bar{f}}_-(0, k)e^{a\lambda}\prod_1^\infty\left(1 - \frac{\lambda}{\lambda_n}\right)e^{\lambda/\lambda_n} \tag{11-9}$$

and the product converges. We assume for simplicity that $\underline{\bar{f}}_-(0, k) \neq 0$. The exponential factor, it should be noticed, is essential for the convergence of the product. Both a and the λ_n in (11-9) are, of course, functions of k.

From (11-9) we immediately get for the S-matrix,

$$S(\lambda, k) = S(0, k) \exp\left\{\lambda[a(-k) - a(k)]\right\}$$
$$\times \prod_1^\infty \frac{\lambda_n(k)}{\lambda_n(-k)} \frac{\lambda - \lambda_n(-k)}{\lambda - \lambda_n(k)} \exp\left\{\lambda[\lambda_n^{-1}(-k) - \lambda_n^{-1}(k)]\right\} \tag{11-10}$$

where $-k = ke^{-i\pi}$. For real k, i.e., $E > 0$, we get from (5-4''),

$$S(\lambda, k) = S(0, k) \exp[-2i\lambda \operatorname{Im} a(k)]\prod_1^\infty \frac{\lambda_n}{\lambda_n^*}\frac{\lambda - \lambda_n^*}{\lambda - \lambda_n}$$
$$\times \exp\left[-2i\lambda \operatorname{Im} \lambda_n^{-1}\right] \tag{11-11}$$

which explicitly exhibits the unitarity.

Another representation of the S-matrix in terms of its poles in the λ-plane uses an infinite series of partial fractions. If the residues of the faraway poles tend to zero as rapidly as was heuristically demonstrated in Chapter 10, then the simplest kind of Mittag-Leffler expansion[5] of the S-matrix is possible:

$$S(\lambda, k) = \mathcal{E}(\lambda, k) + \sum_{1}^{\infty} \frac{\beta_n(k)}{\lambda - \lambda_n(k)} \tag{11-12}$$

where $\mathcal{E}(\lambda, k)$ is, for each fixed k, an entire function of λ. If (10-12) holds, the series converges very rapidly. For large $|\lambda|$, $\mathcal{E}$ will generally dominate. But $\mathcal{E}$ can be expected to be rather smooth and all the rapid variations of S for finite λ should be contained in the series.

Whether (11-10) or (11-12) is more useful, depends on the application. Clearly, (11-10) contains fewer parameters, since in (11-12) there is an entire function $\mathcal{E}$, as well as the residues. In addition, (11-12) does not explicitly show the unitarity. The symmetry relation (5-11), of course, implies additional restrictions on the parameters in (11-10) and (11-12), but they are very difficult to disentangle.

A less explicit representation of the S-matrix in terms of functions without right-hand cut and without the kinematic left-hand cut can be obtained as follows.

The function

$$R(\lambda, k) \equiv k^{2\lambda} e^{-i\pi\lambda} \frac{S(\lambda, k) - e^{2\pi\lambda i}}{S(\lambda, k) - 1} \tag{11-13}$$

is readily shown by the circuit relation (5-17) to satisfy the simple equation[6]

$$R(\lambda, ke^{in\pi}) = R(\lambda, k) \qquad n = \pm 1, \pm 2, \ldots \tag{11-14}$$

This means that R is not only single valued when k goes around the origin, but it is an <u>even</u> function of k.[7] Thus if the potential is of the Yukawa type (3-8), <u>R is for all fixed λ an analytic function of E, regular in the whole E-plane cut from $-\frac{1}{4}\mu_0^2$ to $-\infty$</u>, except for poles that occur where S = 1. The function R has neither the right-hand, nor the kinematical left-hand cut. It follows, furthermore, from (11-14) and (5-16) that

$$R^*(\lambda^*, k^*) = R(\lambda, k) \tag{11-15}$$

The meromorphic function R can now be written as a ratio of two functions A and B, both holomorphic in the E-plane with the dynamical left-hand cut only[8]:

$$R(\lambda, k) = A(\lambda, E)/B(\lambda, E) \tag{11-16}$$

where in addition

$$\begin{aligned} A^*(\lambda^*, E^*) &= A(\lambda, E) \\ B^*(\lambda^*, E^*) &= B(\lambda, E) \end{aligned} \tag{11-17}$$

By inserting (11-16) into (11-13) and solving for S, we obtain the representation[9,10]

$$S(\lambda, k) = \frac{A(\lambda, E) - k^{2\lambda} e^{i\pi\lambda} B(\lambda, E)}{A(\lambda, E) - k^{2\lambda} e^{-i\pi\lambda} B(\lambda, E)} \tag{11-18}$$

Notes and References

1. The discussion below follows Desai and Newton (D4).
2. See Boas (B25), p. 2.
3. See Boas (B25).
4. See Boas (B25), p. 22.
5. See Caratheodory (C27), p. 215.
6. R was introduced by Bottino et al. (B7).
7. R is a generalization of Wigner's R-function.
8. This is proved by Chan (C8).
9. This representation is due to Chan (C8).
10. It is shown in (C8) that a generalization of (11-18) holds also in the many-channel case, where it is considerably more powerful.

Chapter 12

EXAMPLES

In this chapter we want to look at some simple examples of special potentials for which many of the points discussed before in general are explicitly known from numerical calculation.

The simplest known potential for which the S-matrix can be explicitly written down for all angular momenta and all energies, is the Coulomb potential. Unfortunately it represents a rather degenerate case. Because of its slow decrease at infinity, it does not possess a finite first and second absolute moment, nor is it even absolutely integrable, and as a result it does not satisfy the minimal criteria generally assumed here, and the behavior of its S-matrix (the very definition of which has to be modified in a well-known way) reflects this fact.

If the strength of the Coulomb potential[1] is C, and we write $\eta \equiv C/2k$, then the regular solution of (3-1) can be written down in terms of confluent hypergeometric functions, such as near the end of Chapter 4. The resulting S-matrix is

$$S = \Gamma(\tfrac{1}{2} + \lambda + i\eta)/\Gamma(\tfrac{1}{2} + \lambda - i\eta)$$

Each negative integral ℓ-value is the "starting point" of a trajectory at $E = -\infty$. As E increases from $-\infty$, each pole, determined by

$$\tfrac{1}{2} + \lambda + i\eta = -N \qquad N = 0, 1, 2, \ldots$$

moves, in the repulsive instance, toward the left, and in the attractive case, to the right. If a pole occurs at $\lambda = -\frac{1}{2}m$, $m - N = 1, 2, \ldots$, then $\frac{1}{2} + \lambda - i\eta = 1 + N - m$ is also a nonpositive integer, and the residue vanishes because a zero and a pole of S coincide. If it occurs at $\lambda = -\frac{1}{2}m$, $m = 1, 2, \ldots \leq N$, which can happen only in the attractive case, then the residue does not vanish, but instead there is another pole at $\lambda = \frac{1}{2}m$ at the same energy. Whenever a pole occurs at $\lambda = \frac{1}{2}m$, then $\frac{1}{2} - \lambda + i\eta = -N - m$ is a negative integer too, and there is a pole also at $\lambda = -\frac{1}{2}m$.

As the energy increases to zero, each trajectory moves along the real axis, to $+\infty$ in the attractive case, to $-\infty$, in the repulsive. In the attractive case, then, each trajectory passes through all positive integral ℓ and causes, thus, a bound state in each ℓ. This is the essential feature due to the long Coulomb tail.

At E = 0, each trajectory describes a quarter-circle at infinity, and, as E increases from zero, the poles move along straight vertical lines toward their destinations at $E = +\infty$, which are the negative integral ℓ. In the attractive case, they all come down from above, and in the repulsive case, they move up from below.

In the Coulomb case, therefore, as can be expected, the trajectories behave according to the general, "normal" prescription as $|E| \to \infty$, but they are pathologically "open-ended" near E = 0. The "0-type" trajectories near $\ell = -\frac{1}{2}$ as $E \to 0$ are missing in this instance.

In the case of the simple Yukawa potential, a number of pole trajectories have been numerically computed. Figure 12-1 shows the leading trajectory in the ℓ-plane for a number of attractive Yukawa

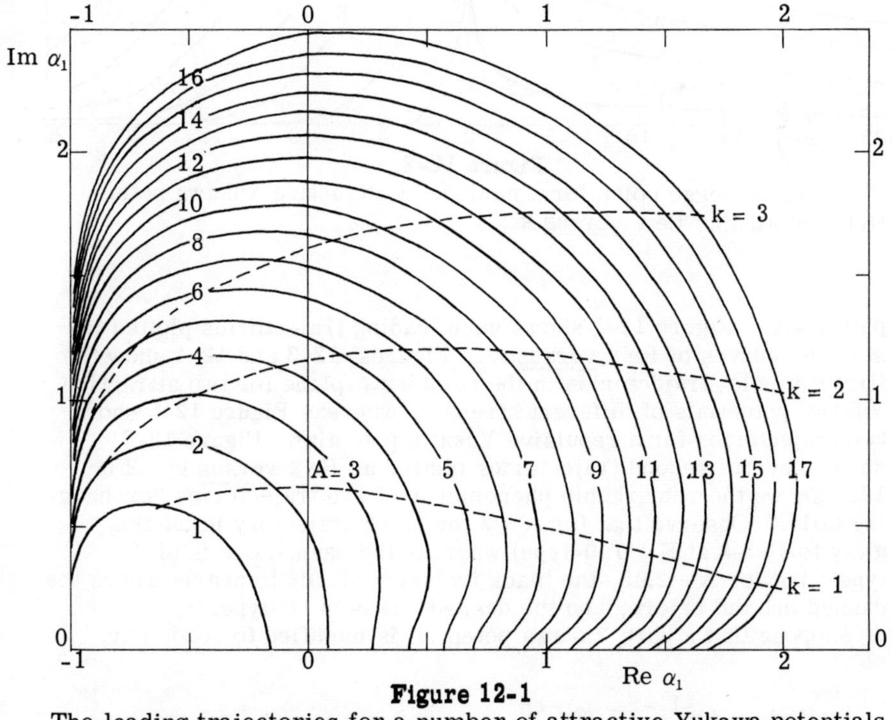

Figure 12-1

The leading trajectories for a number of attractive Yukawa potentials of varying strength A, plotted in the complex $\ell = \alpha$ plane. The units are such that the range of the Yukawa potential is unity.

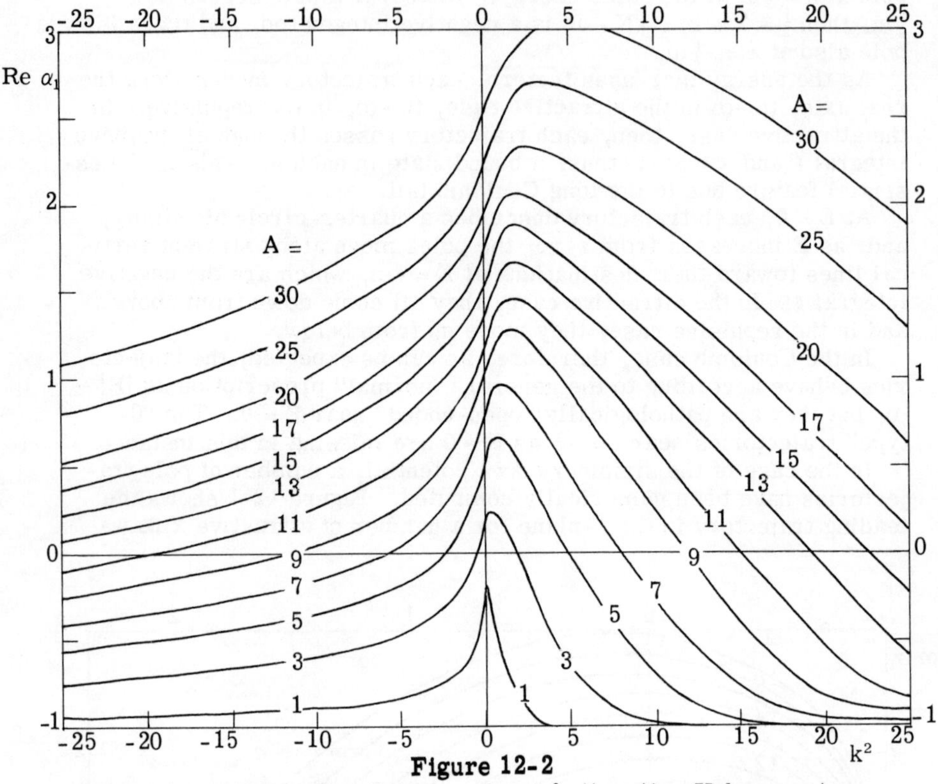

Figure 12-2

The leading Regge poles for a number of attractive Yukawa potentials, plotted as Re ℓ versus k^2.

potentials.[2] Figure 12-2 shows such leading trajectories plotted instead as curves of Re ℓ versus k^2. Figures[3] 12-3 and 12-4 show the first six pole trajectories in the complex ℓ-plane for two attractive Yukawa potentials of different strength, whereas Figure 12-5 shows two trajectories for a repulsive Yukawa potential. Figure 12-6 shows several second trajectories plotted as Re ℓ versus k^2. Figure 12-7 shows the remarkable phenomenon of two trajectories "exchanging tails." Observe that for A = 2 the black trajectory is leading away to $\ell = -\frac{1}{2}$ at E = 0 (0-type) whereas the dashed one is of "C-type"; but for A = 2.05, the black trajectory leads to nearly where the dashed one did before, and the dashed one is of "0-type."[4]

Suppose that a pure Yukawa potential is modified to read, say,

$$V(r) = -Ar^{-1}e^{-r} - \beta^2 e^{-r\mu}$$

For all A $\neq$ 0 the leading trajectory must approach $\ell = -1$ as $E \to \pm\infty$;

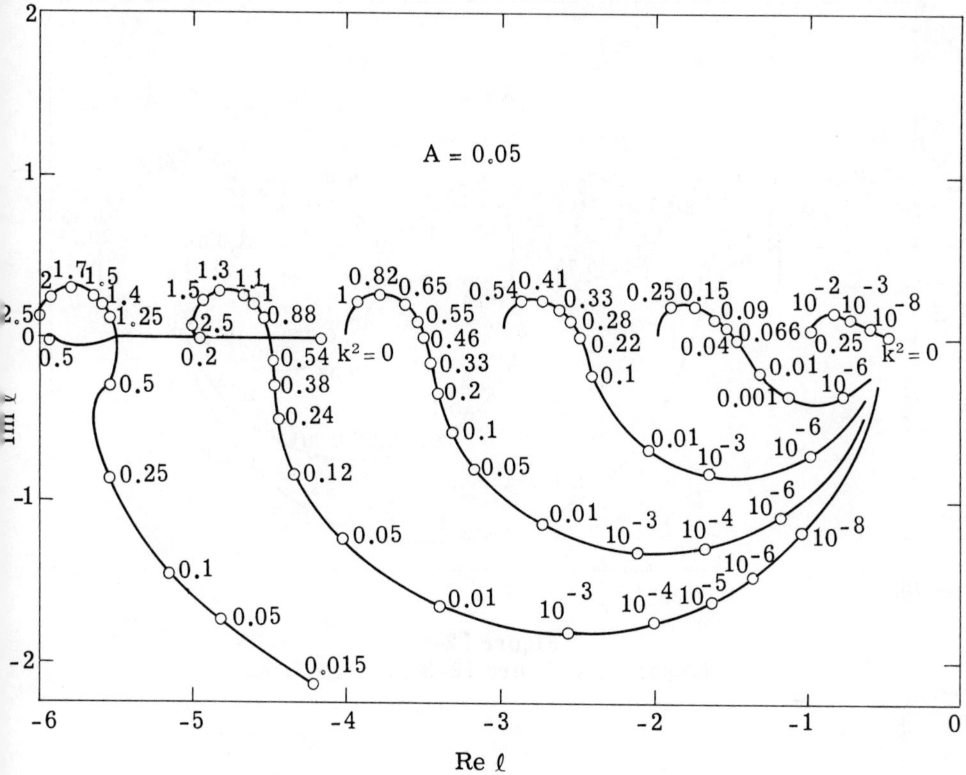

Figure 12-3
A number of trajectories in the complex ℓ-plane for an attractive Yukawa potential of strength A = 0.05. The numbers next to the curves are the values of k^2. The units are the same as in Figure 12-1.

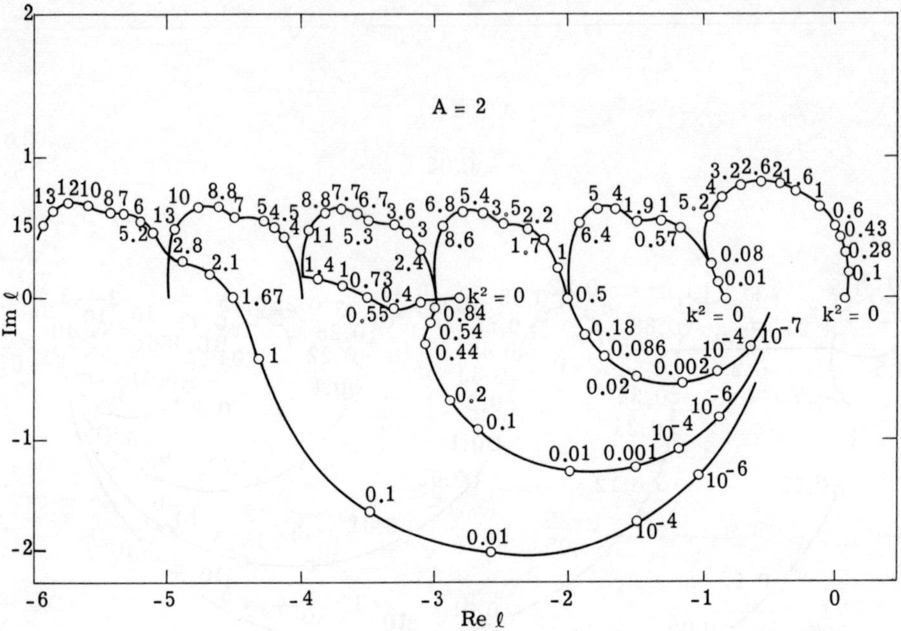

Figure 12-4

The same as Figure 12-3 but for A = 2.

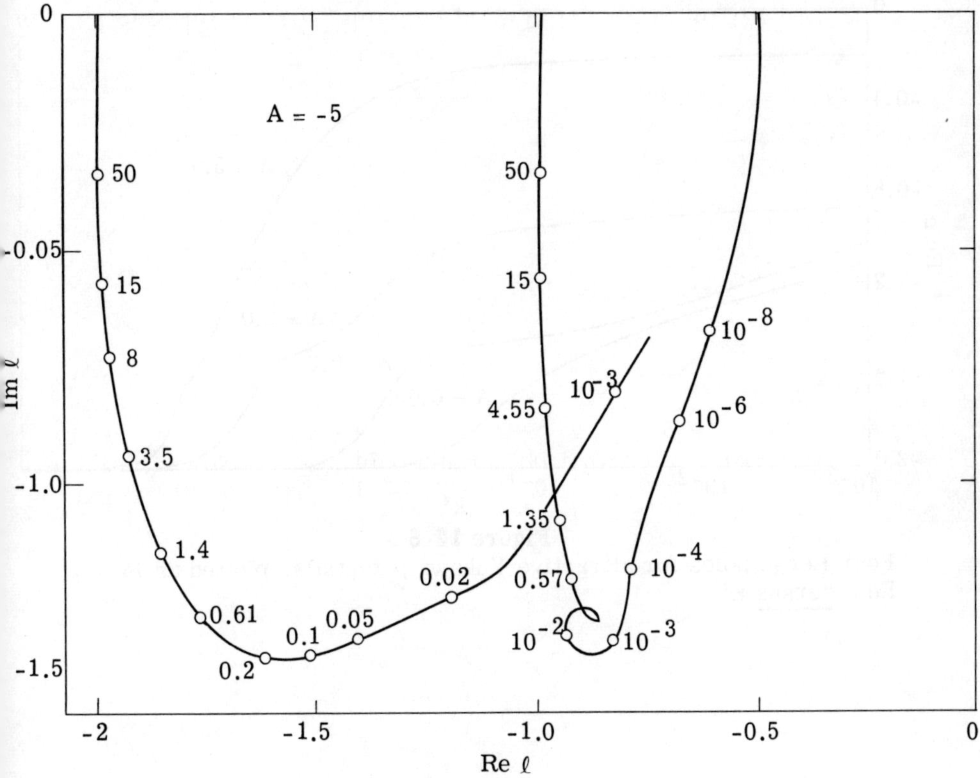

Figure 12-5

Two trajectories in the complex ℓ-plane for a repulsive Yukawa potential of strength A = -5.

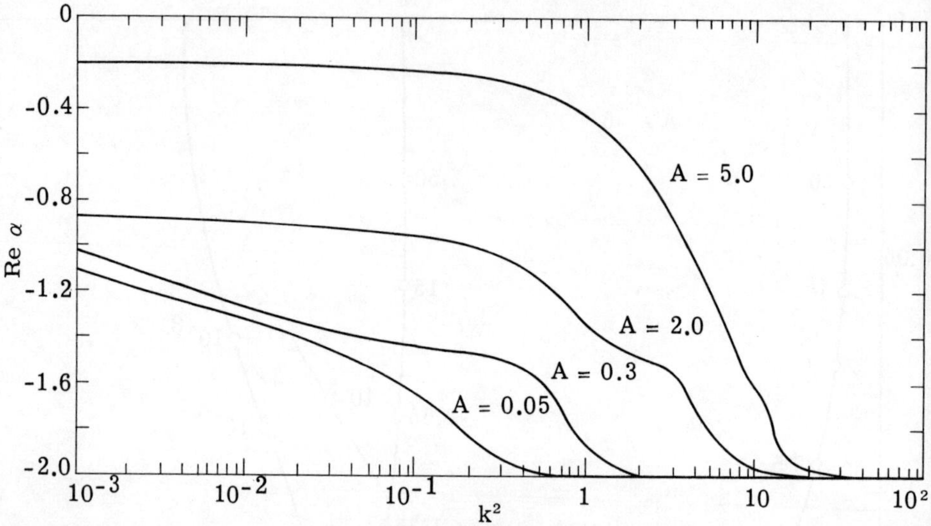

Figure 12-6

Four Regge poles for attractive Yukawa potentials, plotted as Re ℓ = Re α versus k^2.

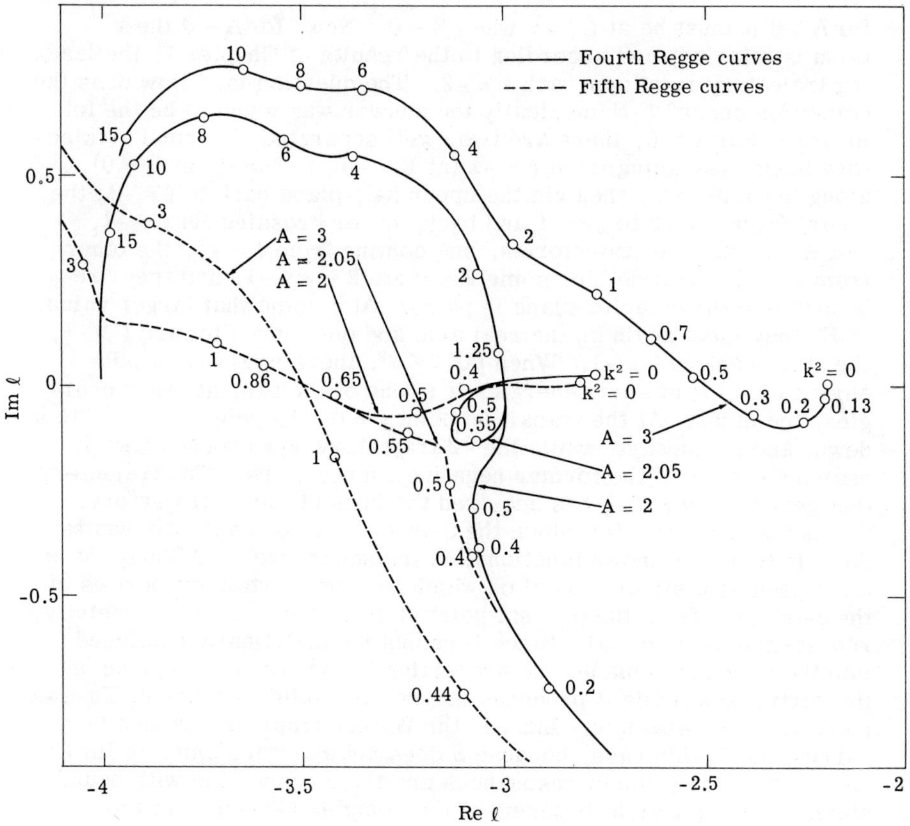

Figure 12-7

Parts of the fourth and fifth trajectories in the complex ℓ-plane, showing their change as the potential strength varies. This figure shows the pheonomenon of "tail switching" of trajectories.

for $A > 0$ it must be at $\ell > -\frac{1}{2}$ when $E = 0$. Now, for $A = 0$ the r^{-1} term is missing, and according to the results of Chapter 4, the leading trajectory must approach $\ell = -2$. The question is, "How does the transition occur?" Numerically the answer was found to be the following.[5] For $A > 0$, there are two, well separated, "normal" trajectory loops, one going from $\ell = -1$ (at $E = -\infty$) to $\ell > -\frac{1}{2}$ (at $E = 0$) along the real axis, then via the upper half-plane back to $\ell = -1$; the other, from $\ell = -2$ to $\ell < -1$ and back, never crossing $\mathrm{Re}\,\ell = -1$. For $A < 0$, the two trajectories, one coming from $\ell = -1$, the other from $\ell = -2$, "collide" for some $E < 0$ at $-2 < \ell < -1$, and they "rebound" into the complex plane in pairs. At a somewhat larger value of E, they meet again on the real axis and one moves toward $\ell > -\frac{1}{2}$, the other back to $\ell = -1$. When $|A| << \beta^2$, there is always a pole close to $\ell = -1$; at some energies it is one of the two, at other energies, the other. At the transition point $A = 0$, the pole at $\ell = -1$ "lies down" and disappears, while the -2 trajectory now crosses $\ell = -1$ near the energy of the former negative energy loops. The trajectory that gets beyond $\ell = -\frac{1}{2}$ has acquired the tails of the -2 trajectory.

Another potential for which the S-matrix can be explicitly written down in terms of known functions, is the square well. Although it is often used as a simple model on which to study certain properties of the S-matrix, from the present point of view it is not a very usefully representative potential. Since it cannot be analytically continued into the complex r-plane, the properties in the complex ℓ-plane of the partial amplitude it produces are not as useful as those of Yukawa potentials, for example. Indeed, the Watson transform cannot be carried out in this case, because S does not approach unity as $\mathrm{Im}\,\ell \to \pm\infty$. The description of resonances and their connection with bound states is still possible in terms of the complex ℓ-plane, but the asymptotic behavior (2-8') as the momentum transfer tends to infinity, no longer holds.

If the square well[6] has a depth D^2 and a width R, then the Jost function is given by

$$\underline{f} = -\tfrac{1}{2}\pi i(k/\kappa)^{\lambda} R[J_\lambda H_\lambda^{(2)\prime} k - J_\lambda' H_\lambda^{(2)} \kappa] \tag{12-1}$$

J_λ being evaluated at κR, and $H_\lambda^{(2)}$, at kR, where

$$\kappa^2 = k^2 + D^2$$

At k = 0 this reduces to

$$\underline{f}(\lambda, 0) = -(\tfrac{1}{2}V)^{1-\lambda}\Gamma(\lambda)J_{\lambda-1}(V) \qquad \text{for} \qquad \text{Re}\,\lambda > 0$$

$$\lim_{k \to 0} (D/k)^{2\lambda}\underline{f} = (\tfrac{1}{2}V)^{1+\lambda}\Gamma(-\lambda)e^{i\pi\lambda}J_{\lambda+1}(V) \qquad \text{for} \qquad \text{Re}\,\lambda < 0$$

where V = RD. Thus the C-type poles of S for E = 0 are given by the solutions of

$$\begin{aligned} J_{\lambda-1}(V) &= 0 \qquad \text{for} \qquad \text{Re}\,\lambda > 0 \\ J_{\lambda+1}(V) &= 0 \qquad \text{for} \qquad \text{Re}\,\lambda < 0 \end{aligned} \tag{12-2}$$

There are infinitely many solutions of (12-2) along the negative real λ-axis, approaching asymptotically the negative integers, both as Re $\lambda \to -\infty$ for fixed V, and as $V \to 0$ in a fixed region in the λ-plane. In addition there are solutions for complex values of λ when the potential is repulsive, i.e., when V is purely imaginary, as can be seen from Figure 12-8.[7]

Figure 12-8 shows some C-type E = 0 pole positions for attractive (a) and repulsive square wells (b). Figure 12-9 shows some pole positions for attractive square wells, as functions of the energy, and Figure 12-10 shows some trajectories in the complex ℓ-plane, compared to a typical Yukawa trajectory. It should be noticed that the trajectories do not turn over; in fact, they don't even turn up.

Figures 12-11 to 12-13[8] exhibit a number of 0-type positive-energy trajectories for square well potentials plotted in the complex ℓ-plane. Figure 12-11 shows several trajectories of the same attractive potential, whereas Figure 12-12 shows how the trajectories of $n = \pm 1$ change when the potential strength is altered, both for attractive and repulsive cases. Figure 12-13 again shows the trajectory changes for repulsive potentials, as the strength varies. Notice that, for the square well, F has fixed poles only at the negative half-integral values of $\ell\,(< -\tfrac{1}{2})$, and hence these are the only possible crossing points. The $n = -1$ trajectory changes crossing points at some value of the potential strength between $V^2 = 9.6$ and $V^2 = 20$.

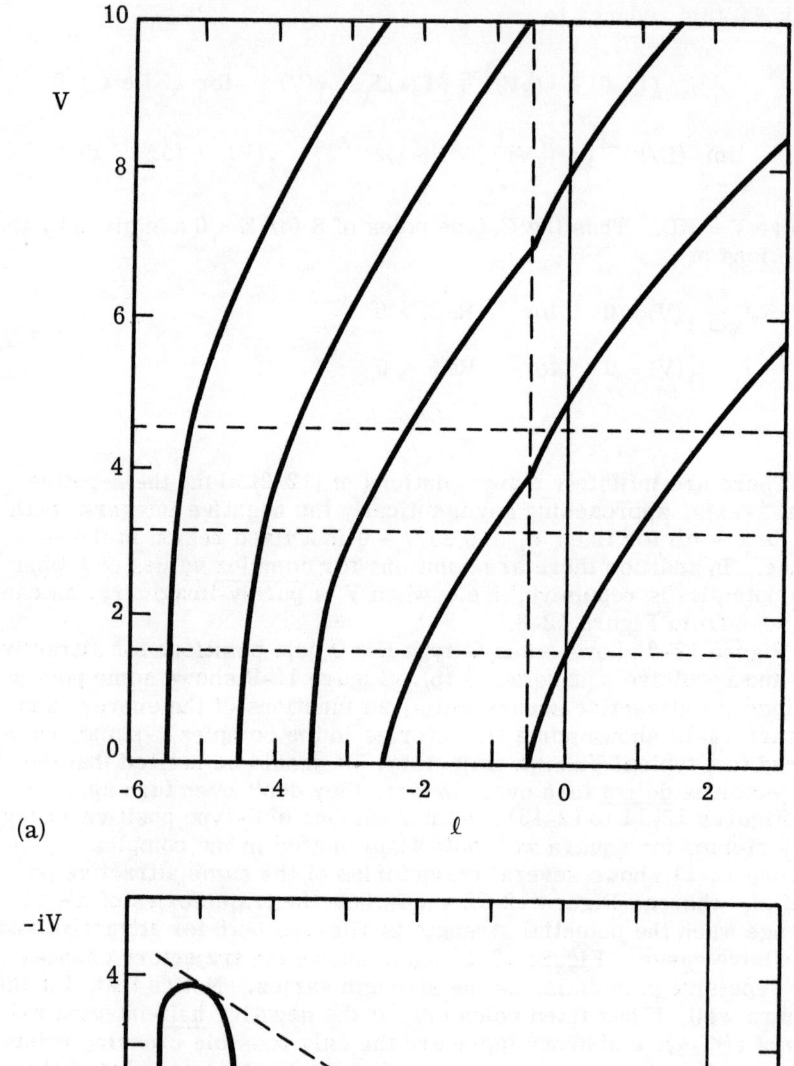

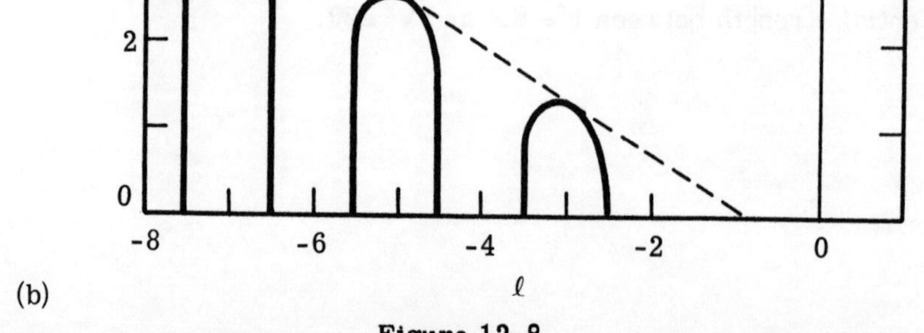

Figure 12-8

Regge pole positions at zero energy for square well potentials, plotted as a function of the potential strength. (a) attractive potentials, (b) repulsive potentials. The loops in (b) show that two zero-energy pole positions collide and "bounce off" into the complex plane.

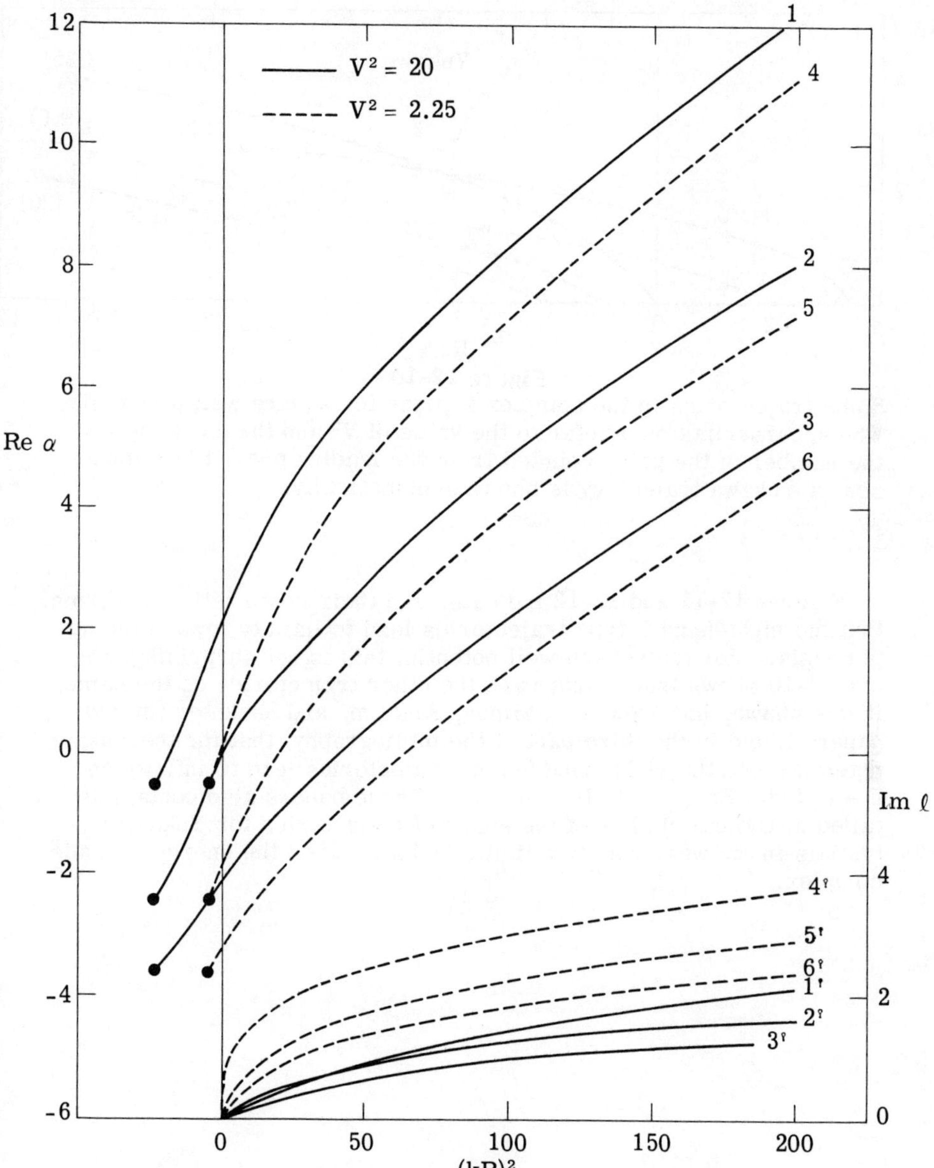

Figure 12-9
Pole positions as a function of $(kR)^2$ for square well potentials. The curves labeled without primes show the real part of $\ell = \alpha$, those with primes, the corresponding imaginary parts.

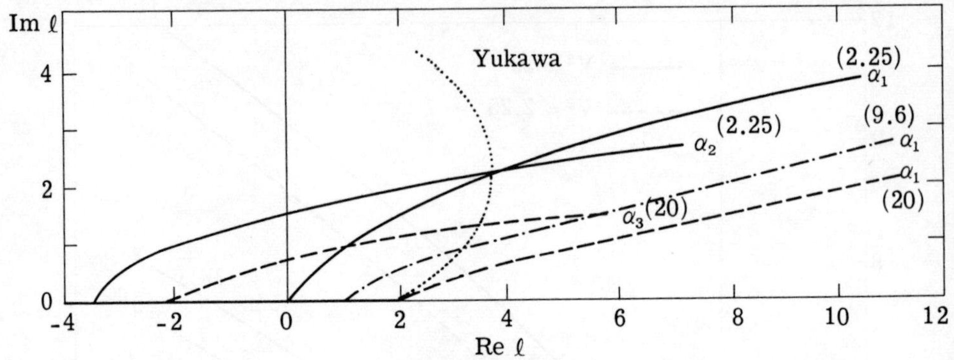

Figure 12-10

Some trajectories in the complex ℓ-plane for square well potentials. The superscripts on α refer to the value of V^2 and the subscripts, to the number of the pole, counted from the leading one. For comparison, a Yukawa trajectory is shown schematically.

Figures 12-11 and 12-12 indicate, and their continuation confirms, that the right-hand 0-type trajectories lead to infinity toward the upper right. For the square well potential this is not surprising; Figure 12-10 shows that in that case the other trajectories do the same. It was shown, however, by Azimov, Anselm, and Shekhter (in two papers listed in the third part of the bibliography) that for the Yukawa potential too, the right-hand 0-type trajectories lead to infinity as $E \to \infty$ (with Re $\lambda \to -\infty$, Im $\lambda \to +\infty$). These papers also contain detailed analytical studies of the shape of trajectories for Yukawa potentials in the weak coupling limit, and also when the energy is made complex.

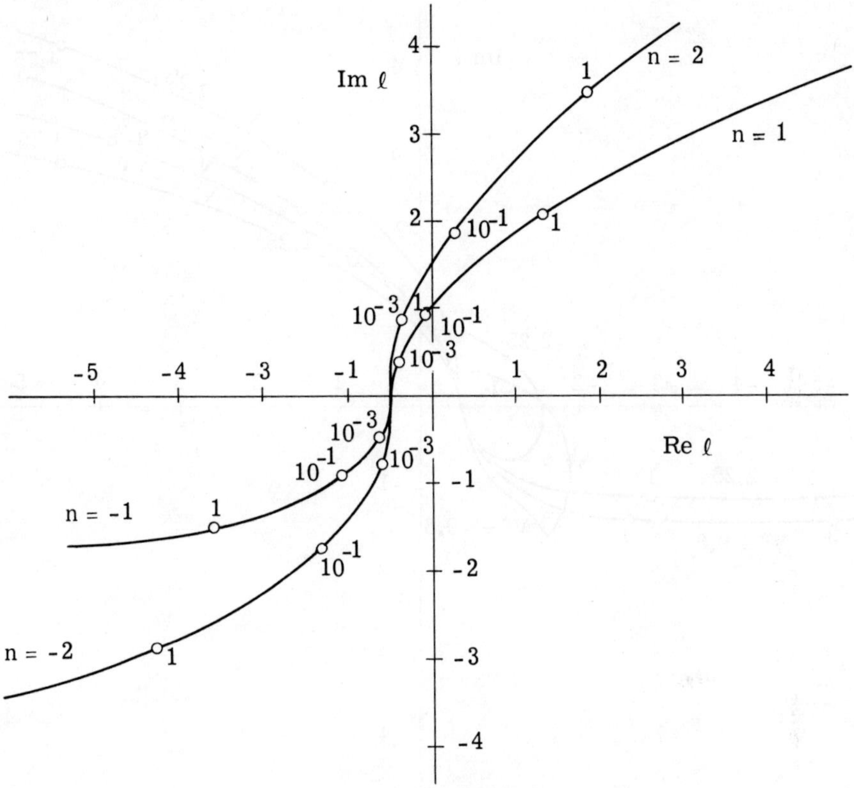

Figure 12-11
This shows four positive-energy trajectories of 0-type for an attractive square well potential of $V^2 = 20$, plotted in the complex ℓ-plane. The numbers adjacent to the little circles represent values of kR.

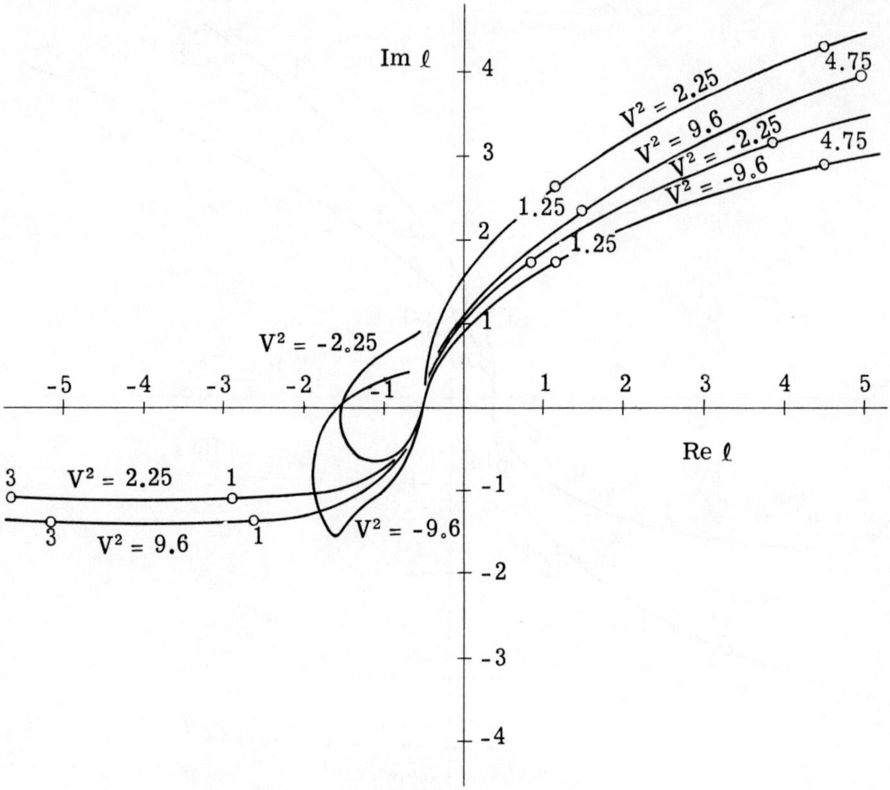

Figure 12-12

This shows four positive-energy trajectories of 0-type in the complex ℓ-plane for $n = 1$, and four for $n = -1$, for various strengths of the square well potential. The numbers adjacent to the little circles represent values of kR.

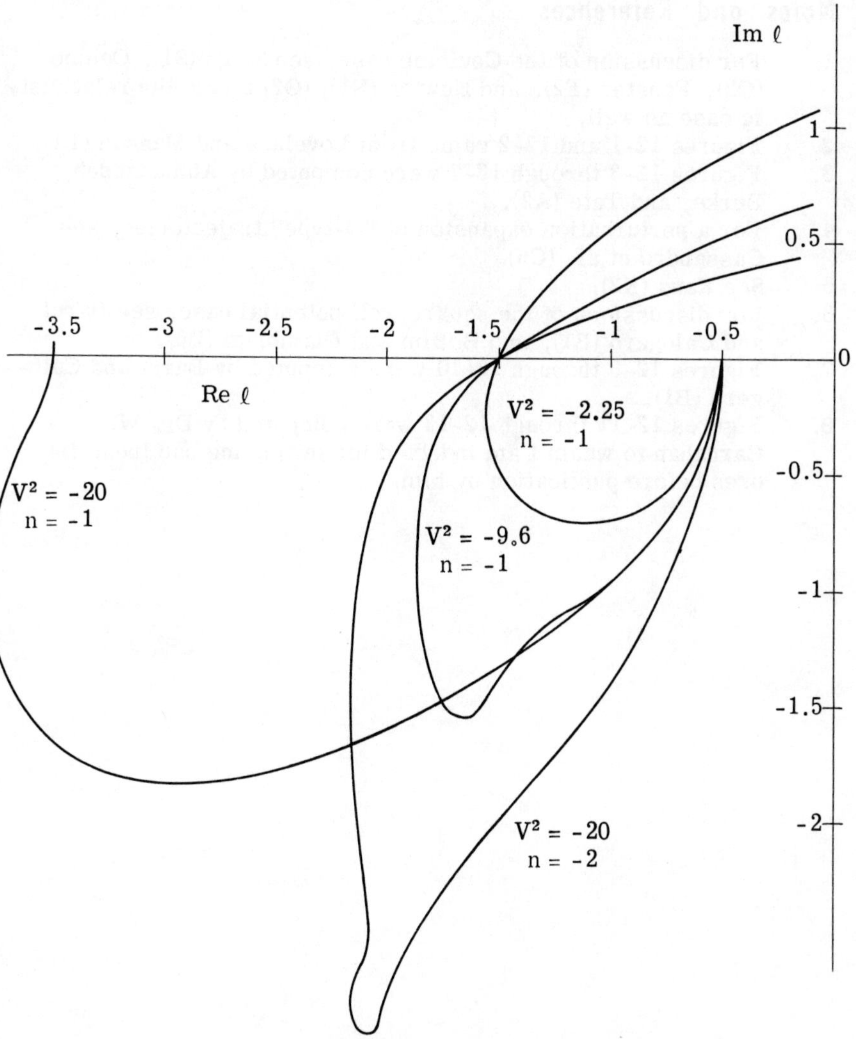

Figure 12-13

This shows four positive-energy trajectories of 0-type in the complex ℓ-plane for various repulsive square well potentials, n = -1 n = -2.

Notes and References

1. For discussion of the Coulomb case, see Singh (S1), Oehme (O2), Fenster (F2), and Newton (N1); (O2) treats the relativistic case as well.
2. Figures 12-1 and 12-2 came from Lovelace and Masson (L1).
3. Figures 12-3 through 12-7 were computed by Ahmadzadeh, Burke, and Tate (A2).
4. For a perturbation expansion of "C-type" trajectories, see Cassandro et al. (C6).
5. See Kaus (K2).
6. For discussions of the square well potential case, see Barut and Calogero (B1), and Bollini and Giambiagi (B6).
7. Figures 12-8 through 12-10 were computed by Barut and Calogero (B1).
8. Figures 12-11 through 12-13 were computed by Dr. W. Carnahan to whom I am indebted for letting me use these figures before publication by him.

Chapter 13

EXCHANGE POTENTIALS

If the interaction between two particles includes not only ordinary forces, but exchange forces as well, then the Schrödinger equation in the center-of-mass coordinate system reads

$$-\nabla^2\psi(\mathbf{r}) + V_D(r)\psi(\mathbf{r}) + V_E(r)\psi(-\mathbf{r}) = E\psi(\mathbf{r})$$

V_D being the direct potential, and V_E, the exchange potential. The radial Schrödinger equations, therefore, are

$$-\psi_\ell'' + \ell(\ell+1)r^{-2}\psi_\ell + [V_D + (-)^\ell V_E]\psi_\ell = k^2\psi_\ell \qquad (13\text{-}1)$$

In attempting to continue (13-1) into the complex ℓ-plane we are faced with the problem of how to handle the $(-)^\ell$. There are two alternatives. The first is to continue $(-)^\ell$ to complex ℓ by writing it as $e^{i\pi\ell}$ or $e^{-i\pi\ell}$. We should presumably choose $e^{i\pi\ell}$ in order to avoid the exponential strengthening of the potential as we go into the first quadrant of the ℓ-plane, where the trajectories are. But we then get that strengthening in the lower half of the ℓ-plane where it may prevent S from approaching unity, and thus it may preclude the Watson transform there. What is more, the complex factor will destroy the unitarity of the S-matrix for real ℓ, except at the integral values. Negative energy poles would no longer be constrained to lie on the real ℓ-axis, except at the integers. For all these reasons this way of handling the factor $(-)^\ell$ is inadvisable.

The second alternative for handling the $(-)^\ell$ is to write two sets of Schrödinger equations, one for the odd values of ℓ:

$$-\psi_\ell'' + \ell(\ell + 1)r^{-2}\psi_\ell + V_o\psi_\ell = k^2\psi_\ell \tag{13-2o}$$

and another for the even values

$$-\psi_\ell'' + \ell(\ell + 1)r^{-2}\psi_\ell + V_e\psi_\ell = k^2\psi_\ell \tag{13-2e}$$

where

$$V_o = V_D - V_E$$
$$V_e = V_D + V_E$$

We then have two entirely independent problems of analytic continuation which can each be handled exactly as before. Each will lead to its own S-matrix and to its own pole trajectories. The only difference is that in the problem that uses V_o, the odd integral ℓ-values only are physical; the even ones are of no physical interest. And in the problem that uses V_e, the even integral ℓ-values are physical, whereas the odd ones are without physical significance.

For example, if a negative energy pole of S_o passes through an odd integral value of ℓ, there is a physical bound state. But if it passes through an even integral ℓ, there is no bound state. Or if a positive energy pole of S_e passes an even integral ℓ close to the real axis, it causes a physically observable resonance; but if it passes an odd integer, no physically observable phenomenon occurs.

The two equations, (13-2o) and (13-2e), continued as was (3-1), produce two sets of pole trajectories which are said to differ by their "signature."[1] The significance of the signature, then, is to determine which points on the real ℓ-axis are physical. For pole trajectories of even signature, the even ℓ are physical; for pole trajectories of odd signature the odd ℓ are physical. The special case of a direct potential only is, therefore, distinguished by the fact that the trajectories of odd and even signatures coincide.

The scattering amplitude for particles interacting via an exchange potential is conveniently split into odd and even parts, $A = A_e + A_o$, where

$$A_e(k, z) = (4ik)^{-1}\sum_\ell (2\ell + 1)(S_\ell - 1)[P_\ell(z) + P_\ell(-z)] \tag{13-3e}$$

$$A_o(k, z) = (4ik)^{-1}\sum_\ell (2\ell + 1)(S_\ell - 1)[P_\ell(z) - P_\ell(-z)] \tag{13-3o}$$

Each of these can be treated via the Watson transform as in Chapter 2. The amplitude A_e then contains $S_e(\lambda, k)$ only, and A_o, $S_o(\lambda, k)$. Since S_o and S_e have generally different poles, the asymptotic behavior, with $|z| \to \infty$, of A_o and A_e will generally be different and thus they will require different numbers of subtractions in a momentum transfer dispersion relation.

Notes and References

1. See Frautschi et al. (F5) and Gell-Mann (G3).

Chapter 14

TRAJECTORIES IN THE k-PLANE

We have so far considered the singularities of $S(\lambda, k)$ in the complex λ-plane when k is either real or purely imaginary. This led to pole positions $\lambda(k)$ which move as functions of the energy, describing trajectories in the complex λ-plane. An alternative procedure is to search for the poles in the k-plane, or on the E-surface at fixed real λ. We then get pole positions $k(\lambda)$ which move as functions of the angular momentum and thus describe trajectories in the complex k-plane.

The two procedures lead, of course, to the same physical results. They are merely two different mathematical devices to describe or analyze the same phenomena. In the first language, for example, we describe a resonance as caused by a pole in the ℓ-plane which at the resonance energy passes an integer close to the real axis. As we change the energy the pole moves away from the integer and the partial cross section decreases. In the second language, we describe the same phenomenon as caused by a pole in the energy plane, which for a specific integral ℓ-value gets close to the real energy axis. When we change the angular momentum the pole moves away from the real axis. The energy dependence of the cross section comes from the fact that the resonance energy is nearest to the pole; as we move away from the pole, the cross section drops. Both descriptions are equally valid and the question of whether the resonance is really caused by a fixed or a moving pole is meaningless.[1]

If for now we adopt the attitude of looking for poles of S in the k-plane (or on the E-surface) with fixed angular momentum, we are still looking for solutions of the equation

$$F_-(\lambda, k) = 0$$

(with suitable restrictions so as to rule out poles of F_+ as discussed in Chapter 7). We obtain solutions $k(\lambda)$ which are analytic functions of λ, regular wherever F_- is regular and where $\partial F_-/\partial k \neq 0$. With appropriate assumptions on the potential previously discussed, regularity is obtained in the whole λ-plane, with the exception of certain isolated points.

The first set of exceptional points are the fixed poles of $\underline{f}_-$, at negative half-integral values of λ, or for specifically different potentials, at other specific points in the left half of the λ-plane. These being the points to which $\lambda(k)$ tends as $|k| \to \infty$, $k(\lambda)$ tends to infinity as λ approaches them. But they need not necessarily be simple poles. The only other points of singularity of $k(\lambda)$ are those at which the zero of F_- is not simple (as a function of k).

We are, however, not so much interested in $k(\lambda)$ for arbitrary complex λ, but analogously to the previous discussion, we want to keep λ real. The function $k(\lambda)$ then defines a trajectory of a zero of F_-, or of a pole of S, in the complex k-plane.[2]

For real positive λ and complex k we easily find, just as we did (7-1), that

$$-2i \,\mathrm{Im}\, k^2 \int_0^\infty dr\,|\phi|^2 = \lim_{r \to \infty} W(\phi^*, \phi) \tag{14-1}$$

Assuming now that $F_- = 0$, ϕ is a multiple of f_-, and hence if Im $k > 0$ the right-hand side vanishes. Since the integral cannot vanish, it follows that Re $k = 0$. For real positive λ all zeros of F_- in the upper half-plane must lie on the imaginary axis. When λ has a half-integral value, such a zero "causes" a bound state. Furthermore, the zeros of F_- for positive λ and positive imaginary k must be simple. This follows from the analog of (7-4),

$$\frac{\partial F_-}{\partial k} = 2kc \int_0^\infty dr\, \phi^2 \tag{14-2}$$

when $F_- = 0$. Equation (8-1) shows that as λ increases, the zero moves <u>downward</u> along the positive imaginary k-axis. For negative λ, all these statements break down. But if F_- has a zero in the first quadrant of the k-plane, then it must also have one, for the same λ, at the reflected point in the second quadrant, and vice versa. This follows from (5-4).

For each positive λ there is a finite upper bound to the value of $-ik$ at which a zero of F_- can occur [because of (5-13)], and hence the number of zeros in the upper half-plane is finite.[3] But as λ decreases to $-\infty$, more and more zeros will usually cross into the upper half-plane, and their number there may increase without bounds. As λ approaches one of the fixed poles of F, a trajectory may approach infinity and disappear from the upper half-plane.

For positive λ, F_- can have no zeros on the real k-axis; otherwise, according to (5-4), F_+ would be zero too and hence by (5-1) ϕ would vanish, contradicting the boundary condition (4-1). That statement holds also for negative λ, except at the fixed poles of F, i.e., the negative integral values of λ, and at the negative half-integers $\lambda \leq -1 - \frac{1}{2}p$ for potentials of the form (4-8). [There we must consider f_- and the symmetry relation (5-11).] At those privileged values of λ (or others, for other kinds of potential) a zero of F_- may cross the real k-axis and enter or leave the upper half-plane.

In the lower half of the k-plane zeros of F_- may occur anywhere, but they must occur in pairs symmetric across the imaginary axis. As λ approaches one of the fixed poles of F, a trajectory may enter or leave the lower half-plane, either by crossing the real axis or by going to infinity (or coming from there).

We may readily derive a simple limitation on the position of zeros of F_- in the k-plane. The technique is the same used in Chapter 7 to derive (7-8) and (7-9), but we now have λ real and k complex. The result is the analog of (7-10), namely that for some x

$$\lambda^2 x^{-2} \cos \alpha - \text{Re } k^2 \cos (2\varphi - \alpha) - \text{Im } k^2 \sin (2\varphi - \alpha) + \cos \alpha \text{ Re } V_\varphi + \sin \alpha \text{ Im } V_\varphi < 0$$

provided that the potential is "analytic," and $0 \leq \alpha \leq \frac{1}{2}\pi$. Assuming again (7-11), we derive

$$|\text{Re } k| < M\lambda^{-1} \tag{14-3}$$

in perfect analogy with the proof of (7-13). All zeros of F_- in the upper half of the k-plane must satisfy this inequality. It follows that, as $\lambda \to \infty$, the zeros of F_- are more and more concentrated near the imaginary k-axis, and each trajectory approaches it.[4]

The inequality (14-3) shows that the trajectories in the k-plane too, turn around. The physical effect of (14-3) is the same as that of (7-13). Both inequalities provide the same limitation on the energy and angular momentum of resonances.

From the point of view of S, we may describe the trajectories as follows. At $\lambda = 0$ we have a finite number of poles on the negative axis of the physical sheet. As λ increases each of these moves toward the right and disappears through the right-hand cut. After a pole has moved onto the second sheet, it usually collides with another and both "bounce" off in complex conjugate pairs, with that in the lower half-plane, if on the right, "near" the upper rim of the cut, and that in the upper half-plane "near" the lower rim. As λ tends to infinity, all the poles on the second sheet approach the negative real axis.

As λ decreases toward $-\infty$, more and more poles enter the physical sheet at the threshold branch point, and they need not remain on the negative real axis. Two poles may collide and bounce off symmetrically into the complex plane (physical sheet). At specific privileged negative values of λ (e.g., the negative integers and half-integers) poles may cross in pairs through the cut, at <u>positive</u> E, and thus either enter or leave the physical sheet. At the same values of λ, pole trajectories on either sheet may lead to infinity.

The threshold behavior of the trajectories can be obtained from that in the λ-plane. For the threshold value $\ell_0 > \frac{1}{2}$, (9-14) and (9-17) yield the equation

$$E \simeq c(\ell - \ell_0) \exp\left[\pm ia(\ell - \ell_0)^{\ell_0 - (1/2)}\right] \tag{14-4}$$

as $\ell \to \ell_0+$, or

$$\text{Im } E \simeq b(\text{Re } E)^{\ell_0 + (1/2)} \tag{14-4'}$$

For $-\frac{1}{2} < \ell_0 < \frac{1}{2}$ we get from (9-14)

$$E \simeq -c(\lambda - \lambda_0)^{1/\lambda_0} e^{-i\pi/\lambda_0} \tag{14-5}$$

with $c > 0$.

Equation (14-4) shows that when a pole crosses the threshold at $\ell_0 > \frac{1}{2}$ it does so in the forward direction at zero angle with the real axis, and it osculates the right-hand cut more and more closely, the higher the threshold angular momentum. From (14-5) it is evident that when $-\frac{1}{2} < \ell_0 < \frac{1}{2}$, the trajectory makes a nonzero angle with the real E-axis; if $\frac{1}{6} < \ell_0 < \frac{1}{2}$, then it leaves in the forward direction; if $0 \leq \ell_0 < \frac{1}{6}$, it leaves in the backward direction; and if $\ell_0 < 0$, then it does not appear on the second sheet but instead it goes on one of the infinitely many other sheets reached through the "kinematic left-hand cut." The closer to $-\frac{1}{2}$ the threshold value is, the further away is the sheet on which the pole appears above threshold, i.e., the more often it would have to wind around the threshold before appearing on the second sheet.

Equation (14-4') immediately gives us the relation between width and resonance energy for a low-energy resonance of angular momentum $\ell \geq 1$

$$\Gamma = O\left(E_r^{\ell_0 + (1/2)}\right)$$

where $\ell_0 \simeq \ell$ is the angular momentum value at which the pole crosses the threshold. This is, of course, in agreement with (9-19).

It is apparent from the foregoing discussion that many of the nice physical results of the method of complex angular momentum are obtainable also by making the angular momentum merely continuous but real, and letting the energy be complex. The same connection between bound states and resonances of different angular momenta is obtained. What is missing is, of course, the Watson transform and its consequences.

It is not clear, incidentally, if two "resonances" that lie on the same trajectory in the ℓ-plane must necessarily lie on the same trajectory in the energy plane. But that question is of little practical consequence.

We now arrive at the problem of correspondence between points on a trajectory in the ℓ-plane (ℓ-trajectory) and points on a trajectory in the k-plane (E-trajectory). That correspondence is largely a matter of convention. In the first case we look for a solution of $F_- = 0$ demanding that k be real, but allowing λ to be complex. In the second, we look for a zero of F_- demanding λ to be real but allowing k to be complex. We may construct a mapping of points on an ℓ-trajectory Λ onto points on an E-trajectory Γ as follows. We descend on a straight line from a point A on Λ to the real λ-axis. The solution $k(\lambda)$ of $F_-(\lambda, k) = 0$ defines a mapping of the λ-plane to the k-plane, which produces an image of that straight line in the k-plane, starting at the real k-axis, and ending at a point A' in the k-plane, the image of the projection of A on the real λ-axis. A' is taken as "corresponding" to A.

It must be clearly recognized that this correspondence is entirely conventional. One could, for example, instead follow a curve in the λ-plane from A to the real axis whose image in the k-plane is a straight line, or one could use other forms of projection.

If A lies on a part of an ℓ-trajectory that moves toward the right with increasing energy, then the image of its projection starts to go into the lower half of the k-plane: The real part of

$$\delta\lambda = -\left(\frac{\partial F_-}{\partial k}\Big/\frac{\partial F_-}{\partial \lambda}\right)\delta k$$

is positive for positive δk; hence the imaginary part of

$$\delta k = -\left(\frac{\partial F_-}{\partial \lambda}\Big/\frac{\partial F_-}{\partial k}\right)\delta\lambda$$

at the same point is negative for negative imaginary $\delta\lambda$. Since the image of the projection line from A to the real axis cannot cross the real k-axis, the point A' lies in the lower half of the k-plane. By the same token, the image of the projection of a point B that lies on a part of an ℓ-trajectory which moves toward the left with increasing energy, starts by going into the upper half of the k-plane. As we descend, then, down the projection line of a point such as B in Figure 14-1, we go into the upper half of the k-plane, and when we reach A

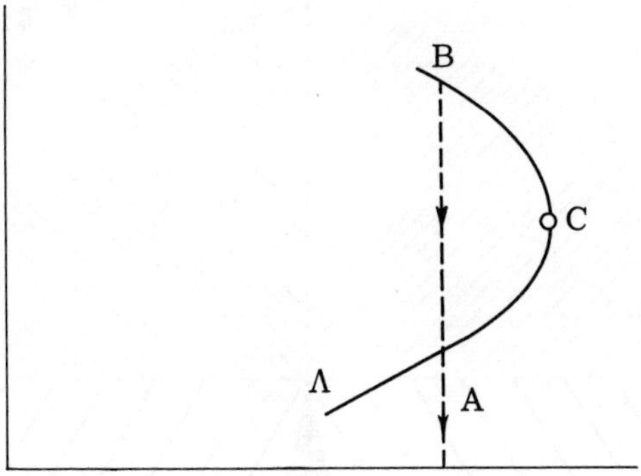

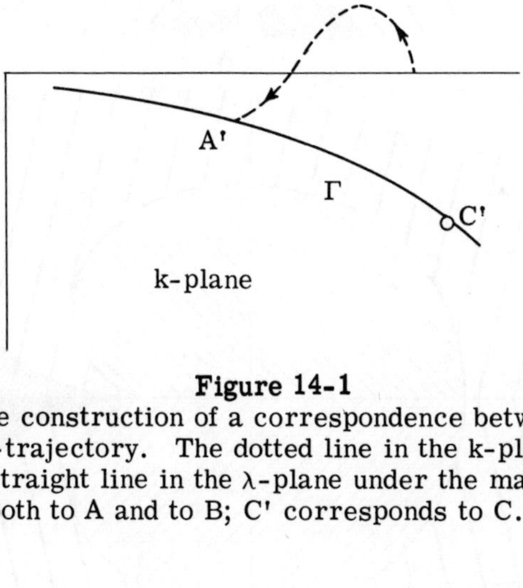

Figure 14-1
This shows the construction of a correspondence between an ℓ-trajectory and an E-trajectory. The dotted line in the k-plane is the image of the dotted straight line in the λ-plane under the mapping $k(\lambda)$. A' corresponds both to A and to B; C' corresponds to C.

we must be back on the real k-axis, being on the same ℓ-trajectory that defines the mapping. As we descend further, we simply repeat the projection from A. Consequently, the point B' that "corresponds" to B is identical to the point A' that "corresponds" to A. This means that the leftward moving "return part" of the ℓ-trajectory has no separate correspondence in the E-trajectory.

Now if we draw the entire E-trajectory, then it is clear that the points on it that correspond to points on the ℓ-trajectory are all to the left of C', the point corresponding to the turning point C of the ℓ-trajectory. The points beyond C' on the E-trajectory have no correspondence on any ℓ-trajectory. This is simply because no curves

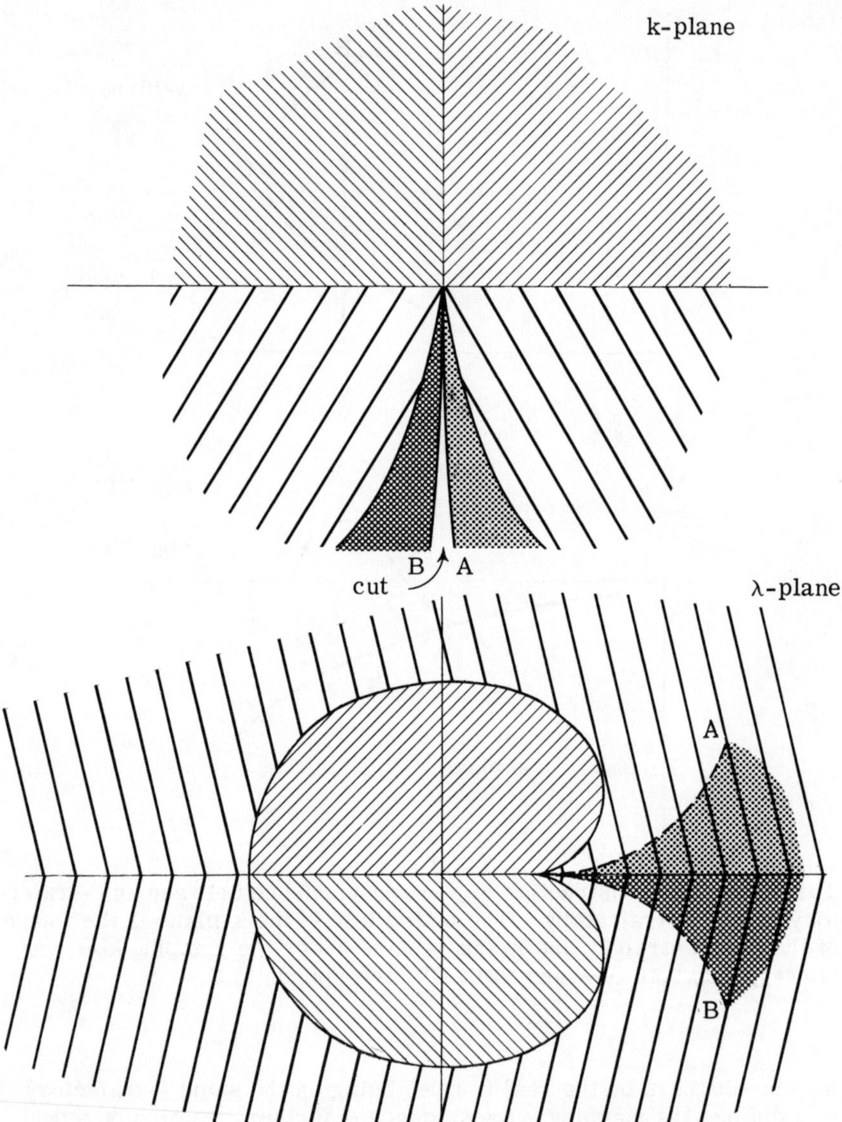

Figure 14-2
A schematic representation of the mapping $\lambda(k)$. The region between the two dotted curves in the λ-plane is covered twice.

from beyond C' whose images are straight verticals in the ℓ-plane ever reach the real k-axis.

Such lack of correspondence will happen no matter how the correspondence is defined, even though its exact nature depends on the convention. It is evident that the consideration of ℓ-trajectories is not equivalent to the consideration of E-trajectories. There are always pieces of trajectories that have no counterpart. The return part of an ℓ-trajectory is needed to account, in this picture, for the downward passage of a phase shift through $\frac{1}{2}\pi$. In the other language no analog is needed since a single pole in the k-plane accounts for both the upward and the downward trend of the phase shift.

Some further remarks on the mapping problem. Each zero of F_- defines a map of the k-plane onto the λ-plane, the image of the positive real k-axis being the positive energy part of the ℓ-trajectory; that of the negative real axis, its reflection in the lower half of the λ-plane. The image of the positive real λ-axis beyond the threshold point is the k-trajectory. Regions are mapped as shown in Figure 14-2. Because of the branch point of $\lambda(k)$ at $k = 0$, there is a region of double coverage in the λ-plane, reached again by that between the E-trajectory and its reflection across the negative imaginary k-axis.[5]

Notes and References

1. This is not to be confused with the (relativistic) question of whether there are fixed (i. e., energy independent) poles in the j-plane, corresponding to "elementary particles."
2. For a discussion of the more general case in which both λ and k are complex, see Bottino and Longoni (B8).
3. The point $k = 0$ requires special consideration; see, for example, (N8)
4. This was shown first by Bottino and Longoni (B8).
5. If $\lambda(k)$ has branch points at $k \neq 0$, as discussed in footnote 2 of Chapter 8, the mapping is, of course, more complicated.

Chapter 15

THE UNIQUENESS PROBLEM

In spite of the usefulness of the introduction of continuous, and complex, values of the angular momentum, the physically meaningful content of scattering theory is, of course, already contained in the partial amplitudes, or the S-matrix, at integral (or half-integral) values of the angular momentum. "Physically," the angular momentum is still quantized and a knowledge of S at integral values of ℓ is still entirely sufficient to determine the scattering amplitude and all its properties.

From a purely mathematical point of view, the introduction of the Watson transform poses a problem which at first sight appears quite difficult. There are, after all, infinitely many ways of interpolating the S-matrix (as well as the other functions involved, such as the Legendre polynomials) between its physically given values at integral ℓ. For example, any given interpolation S may be replaced by

$$S' = S + f \sin \pi\ell$$

where f can be any arbitrary function of ℓ which is finite at the integers. How do we pick the "right" interpolation, and what does "right" mean?[1]

One of the procedures which at first glance seems most tempting to follow is clearly "wrong." The partial wave amplitudes a_ℓ may be simply obtained from the scattering amplitude

$$A(\theta) = \sum_\ell (2\ell + 1) a_\ell P_\ell(\cos \theta) \qquad (15\text{-}1)$$

by the familiar integral

$$a_\ell = \tfrac{1}{2}\int_{-1}^{1} d\cos\theta\, A(\theta) P_\ell(\cos\theta)$$

We may now interpolate the Legendre polynomials in the standard manner and define a_ℓ for nonintegral values of ℓ by this integral. That this procedure, although mathematically possible, is not useful follows at once from the fact that among other things, the a_ℓ so defined cannot contain any poles. The integral extends over a finite range and the integrand is bounded. We would then never see the Regge poles, and the point of the Watson transform would be lost.

This example shows that the definition of the right interpolation depends on its usefulness in the Watson transform. In the foregoing chapters we have always followed one specific procedure, which might be called the "dynamical" one. That is, the interpolation was made via the Schrödinger equation. The radial Schrödinger equation was interpolated in an obvious manner, and that led in a most natural way to an interpolation of the wave functions and hence of the S-matrix. Only in this way do we obtain simple physical interpretations, such as connections between bound states and resonances. In addition, this method allowed us, at least for certain classes of potentials, to prove certain important properties of the interpolated S-matrix which are needed for carrying out the Watson transform and its concomitant changes of the contour of integration.

There are various reasons why it is important to know how and in what sense the interpolation of the partial wave amplitude can be made unique. For one thing, there are physically interesting cases where a simple, well defined underlying dynamical scheme which would allow the natural introduction of complex angular momenta does not exist or is unknown. High-energy physics of strongly interacting particles is a case in point. For another, there may be cases in which the dynamical scheme yields an interpolation which has undesirable properties from the point of view of the Watson transform. It will be seen in Chapter 18, for example, that in the case of more than two particles, cuts may occur in the angular momentum plane, and that it is extremely difficult to prove the asymptotic properties of the S-matrix needed in order to perform the Watson transform. The question then arises if there is not another interpolation with better properties, which would still allow us to prove the asymptotic behavior (2-8') of the scattering amplitude as the momentum transfer tends to infinity. Any interpolation that serves to prove (2-8') will do, but, if a given interpolation does not prove it, (2-8') is not thereby disproved.

The uniqueness can be answered very simply in the following sense: If there exists one interpolation of the partial wave amplitudes that is analytic everywhere in the right-hand λ-plane except for a finite number of poles and which allows us to carry out the Watson transform (i.e., which allows specifically the change of contour of the integral involved), then that interpolation must be unique.

In order to see that this is so, we assume that there are two such interpolations of the S-matrix, $S^{(1)}$ and $S^{(2)}$. Clearly

$$S^{(3)} \equiv S^{(1)} + \frac{S^{(1)} - S^{(2)}}{\ell - \ell_0}$$

is then also an "allowed" interpolation, and we may choose ℓ_0 as we like (with Im $\ell_0 \neq 0$). But if Re ℓ_0 is chosen larger than the real parts of all the poles of $S^{(1)}$ and $S^{(2)}$, then insertion of $S^{(3)}$ in (2-2) yields an asymptotic behavior of the amplitude, as the magnitude of the momentum transfer tends to infinity, which is different from (2-8'). Hence such a procedure must be impossible.

A somewhat more direct argument is based on a theorem by Carlson[2]: If f(z) is regular in Re $z > 0$ and it is $O(e^{k|z|})$ there as $|z| \to \infty$, with $k < \pi$, and if $f(z) = 0$ for $z = 0, 1, 2, \ldots$, then $f(z) \equiv 0$. From this it follows immediately that any two interpolations of the S-matrix which at infinity behave sufficiently well so as to allow the Watson transform, and which have only a finite number of poles in Re $\lambda \geq 0$, must be identical. We need only apply Carlson's theorem to their difference multiplied by a polynomial that vanishes at the poles of each interpolation.

Let us assume, now, that the amplitude A(z), $z = \cos\theta$, is known to vanish asymptotically at least like $|z|^{-1/2}$ as $|z| \to \infty$. It is then subject to the "dispersion relation"

$$A(z) = \frac{1}{2\pi i} \int_{z_0}^{\infty} \frac{dz' \, \Delta(z')}{z' - z} \tag{15-2}$$

where $\Delta(z)$ is the discontinuity of A(z) across the cut from $z = z_0 > 1$ to $z = \infty$. The partial wave amplitudes are obtainable from (15-1) by the integral[3]

$$a_\ell = \frac{1}{2\pi i} \int_C dz \, A(z) \, Q_\ell(z) \tag{15-3}$$

Q_ℓ being the Legendre function of the second kind, and the contour C going around the two points -1 and +1 in the positive sense. Insertion of (15-2) and inversion of the order of integrations, yields

$$a_\ell = \frac{1}{2\pi i} \int_{z_0}^{\infty} dz \, \Delta(z) \, Q_\ell(z) \tag{15-4}$$

In this formula we may now allow ℓ to be nonintegral, using the standard interpolation of the Legendre functions. It defines the "correct" interpolation of the partial wave amplitude, or of the S-matrix[4]:

$$S(\lambda, k) = 1 + \frac{k}{\pi} \int_{z_0}^{\infty} dz\, \Delta(k, z)\, Q_{\lambda - (1/2)}(z) \tag{15-5}$$

That (15-5) defines the "right" interpolation follows from the fact that

$$Q_{\lambda - (1/2)}(z) = O\left(z^{-\lambda - (1/2)}\right) \quad \text{as} \quad |z| \to \infty \tag{15-6}$$

The integral, therefore, converges absolutely for all Re $\lambda > 0$. The function S defined by (15-5) has no singularities for Re $\lambda > 0$. What is more, as $|\lambda| \to \infty$ in the right half-plane, S vanishes because of the behavior of the Legendre function. Hence the Watson transform can be carried out, and the uniqueness theorem tells us that (15-5) is <u>the</u> correct interpolation in this special case.

The argument leading to (15-5) may readily be extended to the case in which A(z) is asymptotically of order $|z|^{\delta}$. The momentum transfer (or cos θ), dispersion relation (15-2), must then be replaced by one with n subtractions, where $n > \delta$, but the result is still (15-5). However, since now

$$\Delta = O(|z|^{\delta}) \tag{15-7}$$

the integral in (15-5) converges absolutely only for Re $\lambda > \delta + \frac{1}{2}$. In that region the thus interpolated S-matrix, therefore, has no singularities. That (15-5) yields the right interpolation of the a_{ℓ} (for $\ell > \delta + \frac{1}{2}$) follows again from the uniqueness theorem.

We may verify explicitly that (15-5) has the correct pole structure. If the amplitude contains a typical (leading) Regge pole term with $\delta =$ Re α,

$$A_P(z) = i\pi k^{-1}(\alpha + \tfrac{1}{2})\beta P_{\alpha}(-z) \csc \pi\alpha \tag{15-8}$$

then the corresponding contribution to Δ is

$$\Delta_P(z) = 2\pi k^{-1}(\alpha + \tfrac{1}{2})\beta P_{\alpha}(z) \tag{15-9}$$

because the discontinuity of the Legendre functions is[5]

$$\Delta P_{\lambda - (1/2)}(-z) = 2i \cos \pi\lambda \, P_{\lambda - (1/2)}(z)$$

Insertion of (15-9) in (15-5) yields the following contribution to the S-matrix:

$$S = (2\alpha + 1)\beta \int_i^\infty dz \, Q_{\lambda - (1/2)}(z) P_\alpha(z) + \cdots$$

$$= \beta(\lambda - \alpha - \tfrac{1}{2})^{-1} + \cdots \qquad (15\text{-}10)$$

since[6]

$$\int_i^\infty dz \, Q_\nu(z) P_{\nu'}(z) = (\nu - \nu')^{-1}(\nu + \nu' + 1)^{-1} \qquad (15\text{-}11)$$

In other words, the appearance of a term such as (15-8) in the amplitude yields precisely a pole term at the right position and with the right residue in the S-matrix defined by (15-5).

This shows that (15-5) defines the "correct" interpolation even when there are Regge poles present. It should be noted, though, that the integral explicitly defines S only to the right of its leading pole. In the region to the left of the leading pole, S can be obtained from (15-5) only by either successively subtracting terms such as (15-8) from Δ, or else by analytic continuation.[7] What is more, there is no guaranty that the function analytically continued from (15-5), with Re $\lambda > \delta + \frac{1}{2}$, toward Re $\lambda \leq \delta + \frac{1}{2}$ coincides at $\lambda = \ell + \frac{1}{2}$, $\ell = 0, 1 \ldots \leq \delta + \frac{1}{2}$, with the partial wave amplitudes (15-3).[8] Indeed, in general the interpolation will not agree with the partial wave amplitudes for $\ell \leq \delta + \frac{1}{2}$, because (15-5) contains no reference whatever to the additional parameters in the subtracted dispersion relation. For example, if $A(z) = O(1)$ as $|z| \to \infty$, we may write

$$A(z) = A(z_1) + \frac{1}{2\pi i}\int_{z_0}^\infty dz' \, \Delta(z') \frac{z - z_1}{(z' - z)(z' - z_1)}$$

Insertion in (15-3) again gives (15-4) and (15-5), and all reference to $A(z_1)$ has disappeared. Yet we cannot determine $A(z)$ uniquely from $\Delta(z)$ without a knowledge of $A(z_1)$. We conclude therefore that the existence of a "good" interpolation of a given set of partial wave amplitudes (in the sense that it has no singularities beyond a finite point, and it is unique by virtue of Carlson's theorem) implies a much stronger correlation between the members of the set than does the existence of a momentum transfer dispersion relation for the amplitude obtained from them.

This point may be examined further by supposing that of a given set of partial wave amplitudes which is known to allow both a momentum transfer dispersion relation and a "good" interpolation, a single member, say a_L, is changed by Δa_L. The concomitant change in the amplitude is

$$\Delta A(z) = \Delta a_L P_L(z) \tag{15-12}$$

which asymptotically, as $|z| \to \infty$, is $O(|z|^L)$. The new amplitude, therefore, still obeys a momentum transfer dispersion relation with a finite number of subtractions, but it does not possess a good interpolation of its set of partial wave amplitudes. The interpolation calculated by means of (15-5) or (15-4) is the same as that for the old amplitude because (15-12) does not contribute to the discontinuity function Δ. We may construct a new interpolation by adding

$$\Delta a_\ell = (-)^L \Delta a_L \frac{\sin \pi \ell}{\ell - L}$$

to the old, but that is not a "good" one in the sense of Carlson's theorem, since it is $O(\ell^{-1} e^{\pi |\mathrm{Im}\, \ell|})$ as $\mathrm{Im}\, \ell \to \pm\infty$. The Watson transform cannot be carried out for it (when z is complex). We therefore have before us an amplitude that satisfies a momentum transfer dispersion relation with a finite number of subtractions, but for which this fact is not demonstrable by means of the Watson transform.

If the given amplitude is known to be produced by a local potential of the Yukawa type (3-8), such a situation cannot arise. We may then construct the interpolation "dynamically," i.e., via the Schrödinger equation.[9] Such an interpolation is necessarily unique in the Carlson sense, it agrees with each given partial wave amplitude, and it allows a Watson transform. In that case the alteration of a single partial wave amplitude will in general destroy, not the correlation to a local potential, but the Yukawa nature of the latter and, consequently, the Watson transform. Nevertheless, a cos θ dispersion relation with a finite number of subtractions remains valid.

Notes and References

1. For discussions of the uniqueness problem see Regge (R1), Regge and Viano (R4), Prosperi (P3), Squires (S2), Cheng and Nunez-Lagos (C15), and Martin (M2).
2. See Titchmarsh (T4), p. 186.
3. See Whittaker and Watson (W6), p. 322.
4. This interpolation is due to Froissart (unpublished) and Gribov (G8). For its extension to the case of particles with spin, see Calogero, Charap, and Squires (C3).
5. From Bateman Project (B22), Vol. 1, p. 140, Eq. (10).

6. See Bateman Project (B22), Vol. 1, p. 170, Eq. (4).
7. For a procedure to reach that region explicitly, see Mandelstam (M5).
8. I am indebted to M. Froissart for a clarifying discussion on this point.
9. Strictly speaking, that interpolation of the radial Schrödinger equation is, of course, not a priori uniquely determined either. In the problem of two particles without spin, the "right interpolation" is obvious; for particles with spin, or in problems of several channels, it is less so, but it still does not give rise to serious ambiguities; in the three (or more) particle problem there are many equally "reasonable" procedures and it is not clear which, if any, is to be preferred.

Chapter 16

TWO PARTICLES OF SPIN-1/2

We now want to extend the results of the previous chapters to the case in which the two particles each have an intrinsic angular momentum of $\frac{1}{2}\hbar$.[1,2] In addition to its interest as a physically relevant problem by itself, this case serves as an important model for the understanding of the more general many-channel problem[3] and as a stepping stone for the approach to the three-body problem.

The force between the two particles is now assumed to be derived from the most general local spherically symmetric potential possible between two particles of spin $\frac{1}{2}$:

$$V(\mathbf{r}) = V_c(r) + V_\sigma(r)\boldsymbol{\sigma}_1 \cdot \boldsymbol{\sigma}_2 + V_t(r)S_{12}$$

where $\boldsymbol{\sigma}_1$ and $\boldsymbol{\sigma}_2$ are the two spin vectors, S_{12} is the tensor operator

$$S_{12} = 3\boldsymbol{\sigma}_1 \cdot \mathbf{n}\boldsymbol{\sigma}_2 \cdot \mathbf{n} - \boldsymbol{\sigma}_1 \cdot \boldsymbol{\sigma}_2$$

and $\mathbf{n} \equiv \mathbf{r}/r$. Spin-orbit forces will be considered later on in this chapter. The potentials V_c, V_σ, and V_t are assumed to satisfy criteria similar to those assumed previously for V, specifically that they are not too "singular" near $r = 0$.

Partial wave analysis leads to a set of ordinary radial Schrödinger equations for the singlet states and for the triplet states of parity $(-)^j$. These states are treated just as the spin zero case and we need not pay attention to them here. For the triplet state of parity $(-)^{j+1}$, however, there emerges a set of coupled radial Schrödinger equations for $\ell = j \pm 1$, which in matrix notation reads

$$-\psi'' + C(j)r^{-2}\psi + V\psi = k^2\psi \tag{16-1}$$

The centrifugal term contains the diagonal matrix

$$C(j) = \begin{pmatrix} (j-1)j & 0 \\ 0 & (j+1)(j+2) \end{pmatrix} \tag{16-2}$$

and the potential matrix is, with $V_d \equiv V_c + V_\sigma$

$$V^{(j)} = \frac{1}{2j+1}\begin{pmatrix} (2j+1)V_d - 2(j-1)V_t & 6[j(j+1)]^{1/2}V_t \\ 6[j(j+1)]^{1/2}V_t & (2j+1)V_d - 2(j+2)V_t \end{pmatrix} \tag{16-3}$$

An irregular (matrix) solution f(j, k;r) of (16-1)[4] that satisfies the boundary condition (3-2) is defined by an integral equation perfectly analogous to (3-4), where now f_0 is the diagonal matrix whose elements are the f_0 of (3-6), with $\lambda = j - \frac{1}{2}$ and $\lambda = j + \frac{3}{2}$, respectively; and g is the corresponding diagonal matrix of the functions defined by (3-5).

A regular solution is similarly defined by an integral equation, but because of the coupling of angular momenta it is necessary to introduce "counterterms" in it in order to avoid divergences at r = 0[5]:

$$\begin{aligned} \varphi(r) &= \varphi_0(r)\left\{1 + 6[j(j+1)]^{1/2}\int_i^r dr'\, r'^{-1}V_t(r')P\right\} \\ &+ \int_0^r dr'\left\{g(r,r')V^{(j)}(r')\varphi(r') - 6[j(j+1)]^{1/2} \right. \\ &\left. \times r'^{-1}\varphi_0(r)V_t(r')P\right\} \end{aligned} \tag{16-4}$$

where

$$P \equiv \begin{pmatrix} 0 & 0 \\ 1 & 0 \end{pmatrix}$$

and φ_0 is the diagonal matrix

$$\varphi_0(r) \equiv (\tfrac{1}{2}\pi kr)^{1/2}k^{-j}\begin{pmatrix} J_{j-(1/2)}(kr) & 0 \\ 0 & J_{j+(3/2)}(kr) \end{pmatrix} \tag{16-5}$$

The normalization of the regular function adopted here is somewhat different from that in Chapter 4, for reasons of later convenience.

A Jost matrix function is defined in analogy with (5-2) by

$$F = \tilde{f}'\varphi - \tilde{f}\varphi' \tag{16-6}$$

where the transposition, indicated by the tildes, is necessary for the r independence of the matrix.[6] Equation (5-1) then holds again, and we obtain the analog of (5-18) for the S-matrix:

$$S = -e^{i\pi j} F_+ F_-^{-1} \tag{16-7}$$

It follows from

$$\tilde{\varphi}'\varphi - \tilde{\varphi}\varphi' = 0$$

that S is <u>symmetric</u>; furthermore it is readily shown to be unitary for real k and $j \geq 0$.

The over-all analytic properties of f, φ, and F as functions of j and as functions of k, are the same as those of the corresponding functions in the spin zero case. A look at $V^{(j)}$, however, seems to indicate trouble at $j = -\frac{1}{2}$. Since a pole in the potential is effectively iterated infinitely many times, it looks as though there will be an essential singularity in f and φ at $j = -\frac{1}{2}$. This is entirely spurious, though, as is easily seen as follows.

The potential matrix $V^{(j)}$ is diagonalized by the matrix

$$U_j = \begin{pmatrix} (j+1)^{1/2} & j^{1/2} \\ j^{1/2} & -(j+1)^{1/2} \end{pmatrix} \tag{16-8}$$

which satisfies the relation[7]

$$U_j^{-1} = U_j/(2j+1)$$

We have

$$W \equiv U_j V^{(j)} U_j^{-1} = \begin{pmatrix} V_d + 2V_t & 0 \\ 0 & V_d - 4V_t \end{pmatrix} \tag{16-9}$$

Multiplication of the integral equations for f and φ by U_j on the left, yields integral equations for the matrix functions $f_1 \equiv U_j f$ and $\varphi_1 \equiv U_j \varphi$ in which W replaces $V^{(j)}$ and

$$G \equiv U_j g U_j^{-1}$$

replaces g. Now, the recurrence relations of the Bessel functions entail the cancellation of the $2j + 1$ that U_j^{-1} brings into the denominator of G; G thus is regular at $j = -\frac{1}{2}$ (as well as everywhere else). As a result, f_1 and φ_1 contain no singularity there either, and

$$F = \tilde{f}_1' U_j^{-2} \varphi_1 - \tilde{f}_1 U_j^{-2} \varphi_1'$$

$$= (\tilde{f}_1' \varphi_1 - \tilde{f}_1 \varphi_1')/(2j + 1) \tag{16-10}$$

has a simple pole at $j = -\frac{1}{2}$.

Before considering the point $j = -\frac{1}{2}$ further, it is convenient to introduce the functions

$$\overline{f} \equiv U_j f U_j^{-1} = f_1 U_j^{-1} \tag{16-11}$$

and

$$\overline{\varphi} \equiv U_j \varphi U_j^{-1} = \varphi_1 U_j^{-1} \tag{16-12}$$

which satisfy the differential equation

$$-\psi'' + D(j) r^{-2} \psi + W\psi = k^2 \psi \tag{16-13}$$

with

$$D(j) \equiv U_j C(j) U_j^{-1} = \begin{pmatrix} \lambda^2 - \frac{1}{4} & -2(\lambda^2 - \frac{1}{4})^{1/2} \\ -2(\lambda^2 - \frac{1}{4})^{1/2} & \lambda^2 + \frac{7}{4} \end{pmatrix}$$

and $\lambda \equiv j + \frac{1}{2}$. Hence the transformed equation (16-13) is again only a function of λ^2, and since the boundary condition for $\overline{f}$ is independent of λ, $\overline{f}$ is a function only of λ^2 (in contrast to f and f_1).

Similarly we introduce

$$\overline{F} \equiv U_j F U_j^{-1} = \tilde{\overline{f}}' \overline{\varphi} - \tilde{\overline{f}} \overline{\varphi}' \tag{16-14}$$

and

$$\overline{S} \equiv U_j S U_j^{-1} = -e^{i\pi j} \overline{F}_+ \overline{F}_-^{-1} \tag{16-15}$$

which is also unitary and symmetric where S is.

Consider now the point $j = -\frac{1}{2}$, i.e., $\lambda = 0$. The fact that both F_+ and F_- have simple poles there does not imply that that pole cancels in S. In the case of matrices, F^{-1} need not vanish where F has a pole; on the contrary, it is possible for F and F^{-1} both to have poles at the same point. It is, in fact, a matter of simple calculation by means of the (convergent) series for (det F_-) S in powers of the potential strength, to see that S in general does have a pole at $j = -\frac{1}{2}$. We now want to show that, nevertheless, $\overline{S}$ is regular there.[8]

The pole of $\overline{\varphi}$ at $\lambda = 0$ comes from the pole in $\overline{\varphi}_0$, which by use of the recurrence formulas for the Bessel functions is found to read

$$\overline{\varphi}_0 = (2\pi r)^{1/2} k^{1-\lambda}\left[(\lambda/kr)J_\lambda(kr)1 + \tfrac{1}{2}J'_\lambda(kr)\lambda^{-1}A(\lambda)\right] \tag{16-16}$$

with

$$A(\lambda) \equiv \begin{pmatrix} 1 & (4\lambda^2 - 1)^{1/2} \\ (4\lambda^2 - 1)^{1/2} & -1 \end{pmatrix}$$

Thus the residue of $\overline{\varphi}_0$ at $\lambda = 0$ is proportional to the singular matrix

$$A \equiv \begin{pmatrix} 1 & i \\ i & -1 \end{pmatrix} \tag{16-17}$$

and the residue of $\overline{\varphi}$ there is a left multiple of A, and so is that of $\overline{F}$:

$$B(\lambda, k) \equiv \lambda\overline{F}(\lambda, k) = R_0(k) + R_1(k)\lambda + R_2(k)\lambda^2 + \cdots \tag{16-18}$$

where

$$R_0(k) = M(k)A \tag{16-19}$$

The function $\overline{f}$ is regular at $\lambda = 0$, because it solves the differential equation (16-13) with the boundary condition (3-2).

Consider now the determinant of $\overline{F}$. The matrix R_0 being singular, det $\overline{F}$ = det F has at most a simple pole at $\lambda = 0$. We examine the (convergent) series for det F in powers of the potential strength and find that to first order there is no pole, but the constant term at $\lambda = 0$ is in general different from zero, just as it is in the absence of the tensor force. Although we cannot, at this point, rule out a pole of det F at $\lambda = 0$, the constant term at $\lambda = 0$ can vanish at most for specific values of k. Higher-order terms in V cannot alter this state of affairs. It follows that $\overline{F}^{-1}$ has at most a simple pole at $\lambda = 0$ (except possibly for specific values of k), i.e., that B^{-1} has at most a double pole there:

$$B^{-1} = \lambda^{-2} N_{-2} + \lambda^{-1} N_{-1} + N_0 + \cdots \tag{16-20}$$

Next we observe that R_0 annihilates the constant vector

$$a \equiv \begin{pmatrix} 1 \\ i \end{pmatrix}$$

and since

$$\lim_{\lambda \to 0} \frac{\partial}{\partial \lambda}(\lambda \bar{\varphi}_0) a = 0$$

so does R_1:

$$R_0 a = R_1 a = 0 \tag{16-21}$$

But (16-18) and (16-20) imply that

$$N_{-2} R_2 + N_{-1} R_1 + N_0 R_0 = 1$$

right multiplication of which by a shows that

$$N_{-2} \neq 0$$

on account of (16-21). This proves that $\bar{F}^{-1}$ has a simple pole at $\lambda = 0$,

$$\bar{F}^{-1}(\lambda, k) = R_0'(k)\lambda^{-1} + R_1'(k) + \cdots \tag{16-22}$$

whose residue $R_0' = N_{-2}$ can vanish at isolated values of k only.

As an immediate consequence of the fact that both $\bar{F}$ and $\bar{F}^{-1}$ have simple poles at $\lambda = 0$, det F cannot have a pole there.

Now (16-18) and (16-22) imply that

$$R_0(k) R_0'(k) = 0$$

$$R_0(k) R_1'(k) + R_1(k) R_0'(k) = 0$$

Since $A^2 = 0$, it follows from the first equation and (16-19) that

$$R_0'(k) = A M_0'(k) \tag{16-23}$$

and, therefore, from the second equation and (16-21), that

$$R_1'(k) = AM_1'(k) \tag{16-24}$$

Equations (16-15), (16-21), (16-23), and (16-24) prove the important fact that $\overline{S}$ does not have a pole at $j = -\frac{1}{2}$.

The presence of the tensor force also introduces other singularities in the S-matrix. The potential (16-3) contains the factor $[j(j + 1)]^{1/2}$, which causes both f and φ, and hence F and S, to acquire a branch line running from $j = -1$ to $j = 0$. In the region $-1 < j < 0$, the potential matrix $V^{(j)}$ is not Hermitian and as a result S is not unitary in that region, even for real k. Because only the off-diagonal elements of $V^{(j)}$ contain the square roots, only the off-diagonal elements of S contain the branch points, and they are of the square root type. The diagonal elements of S are even functions of the off-diagonal elements of $V^{(j)}$, the off-diagonal ones, odd.

The unitarity

$$S^{\dagger}S = 1$$

for real k and $j \geq 0$, leads by analytic continuation into regions connected with the real k-axis and $j > 0$, to[9]

$$S^{\dagger}(j^*, k^*)S(j, k) = 1 \tag{16-25}$$

For real k and $-1 < j < 0$ this, however, connects S on the upper rim of the cut with $S^{\dagger}$ on the lower, and vice versa. The place of the unitarity relation for real k and $-1 < j < 0$, is taken by

$$S^{\dagger}MS = M \tag{16-25'}$$

where

$$M = \begin{pmatrix} -1 & 0 \\ 0 & 1 \end{pmatrix}$$

As for the poles of S in the angular momentum plane, their behavior is essentially the same as in the spin zero case. The threshold motion is modified only in obvious ways. If the "bound state" at E = 0 contains any admixture of $\ell = j - 1$, then whether the trajectory of the points

$$\det F_- = 0$$

leaves in the forward or in the backward direction is determined by

$\ell = j - 1$, and hence depends on whether at threshold $j > 1$ or $j < 1$. If the admixture of $\ell = j - 1$ is small, of course, the shape of the trajectory will follow that appropriate to $\ell = j - 1$ only at very small energies.

The point $j = 0$ merits special attention. Since $V^{(j)}$ is diagonal there, so are F and the S-matrix. Only one of its two diagonal elements then has physical significance, that for $\ell = 1$. The $\ell = j - 1$ term at $j = 0$ has been referred to by Gell-Mann as the "nonsense term."[10] Now any zero of det F_- passing through $j = 0$ must either pass through the "sense" or through the "nonsense" term, the determinant there being the product of the two. If it passes through the "sense" term it signifies a physical bound state of $j = 0$ and $\ell = 1$; if it passes through the "nonsense" term, it has no physical significance. It is, therefore, possible for a bound state or a sharp resonance to occur at $j = 1$, say, without the necessity of having a bound state at $j = 0$, an impossibility for particles without spin. This phenomenon is well known in nuclear physics.

The residue of the S-matrix at a pole is usually a singular matrix. Although each element can generally be expected to have a pole when det $F_- = 0$, there is typically only one vector (or a multiple of it) which, when multiplied by S, has a pole. (If there are more, the state is called "accidentally degenerate.") This implies that, if we are dealing with an $n \times n$ S-matrix (in the present case, $n = 2$) the residue β annihilates an $n - 1$ dimensional space (its null space). Since S is symmetric it follows that the matrix β can be written[11]

$$\beta_{ij}(k) = a_i(k)a_j(k) \tag{16-26}$$

so that $\beta b = 0$ for all the $n - 1$ linearly independent vectors b orthogonal to a.

The relation of the vector a to the matrix F_- at the point where det $F_- = 0$ is easily seen. Since we assume (in the absence of accidental degeneracy) that the null space of F_- is one-dimensional, its range[12] must be $n - 1$ dimensional and that range must equal the null space of the residue of F_-^{-1}. Hence a is orthogonal to the range of F_-.

Another connection follows from the symmetry of S, which implies that a spans the range of β. Since the range of the residue of F_-^{-1} must equal the null space of F_-, it follows from

$$F_- c = 0$$

and (16-7) that

$$a \propto F_+ c$$

In the context of the conventional treatment of resonances as poles in the complex energy plane, (16-26) is, of course, well known, the a_i being partial widths. In either case it considerably reduces the number of parameters necessary for a resonance description. It can be expected to break down only when two poles of S accidentally coincide. This need not imply a double pole, but in the present instance the degeneracy produced would mean $F_- = 0$ where $\det F_- = 0$.

The symmetry relation (5-7) between the right and the left half of the λ-plane has its analog in the present case. However, we must work with the transformed quantities indicated by bars. Evaluation of the Wronskian

$$\tilde{\bar{\varphi}}(\lambda, k; r)\bar{\varphi}'(-\lambda, k; r) - \tilde{\bar{\varphi}}'(\lambda, k; r)\bar{\varphi}(-\lambda, k; r) = -\sin \pi\lambda \quad (16\text{-}27)$$

yields

$$\tilde{\bar{F}}_+(\lambda)\bar{F}_-(-\lambda) - \tilde{\bar{F}}_-(\lambda)\bar{F}_+(-\lambda) = -2ik \sin \pi\lambda \quad (16\text{-}28)$$

where it should be remembered that $\bar{F}$ has poles at the negative half-integral λ, and at $\lambda = 0$. If we want to eliminate these, we must introduce[13]

$$\bar{\bar{F}} \equiv \bar{F}\lambda/\Gamma(\tfrac{1}{2} + \lambda)$$

and (16-28) reads

$$\tilde{\bar{\bar{F}}}_+(\lambda)\bar{\bar{F}}_-(-\lambda) - \tilde{\bar{\bar{F}}}_-(\lambda)\bar{\bar{F}}_+(-\lambda) = (ik/\pi)\lambda^2 \sin 2\pi\lambda \quad (16\text{-}28')$$

while the corresponding relation for the transformed S-matrix

$$\begin{aligned} e^{-i\pi\lambda}\bar{S}(\lambda, k) - e^{i\pi\lambda}\bar{S}(-\lambda, k) &= -2k \sin \pi\lambda[\bar{F}_-(-\lambda)\tilde{\bar{F}}_-(\lambda)]^{-1} \\ &= -(k/\pi)\lambda^2 \sin 2\pi\lambda[\bar{\bar{F}}_-(-\lambda)\tilde{\bar{\bar{F}}}_-(\lambda)]^{-1} \quad (16\text{-}29) \end{aligned}$$

is the analog of (5-20).

The foregoing symmetry relations have the same consequences as the ones in the spin-zero case. In addition there is the following detail concerning the point $j = 0$ which may have physical significance in the case of the so-called Pomeranchuk, or vacuum trajectory.[14]

Suppose a pole of S goes through $j = 0$, i.e., $\lambda = \frac{1}{2}$. The right-hand side of (16-28') then vanishes and furthermore, both $\bar{\bar{F}}(\lambda)$ and $\bar{\bar{F}}(-\lambda)$ are diagonal. The discussion of Chapter 8 then applies to each of the diagonal elements, and it should be realized from (16-2) that while the upper element of $F(\lambda)$ at $j = 0$ refers to $\ell = -1$, and the lower, to $\ell = +1$, the upper element of $F(-\lambda)$ refers to $\ell = +1$, and the lower, to $j = -1$. Consequently, if the pole goes through the "sense" term, $\ell = +1$, then there must also be a pole, at the same energy, at $\ell = -1$, $j = -1$, and the residue of S cannot vanish. But if the pole goes through the "nonsense" term, $\ell = -1$, then either there is another pole, at the same energy, at $j = -1$, $\ell = +1$, or else the residue of S must vanish.

We must now look at the use of the S-matrix considered in this chapter for the scattering amplitude and the Watson transform. Using the abbreviations

$$\begin{aligned} T^j_{++} + 1 &\equiv \bar{S}^j_{++} = (2j+1)^{-1}\left\{jS^j_{--} + (j+1)S^j_{++} - 2[j(j+1)]^{1/2}S^j_{-+}\right\} \\ T^j_{--} + 1 &\equiv \bar{S}^j_{--} = (2j+1)^{-1}\left\{(j+1)S^j_{--} + jS^j_{++} + 2[j(j+1)]^{1/2}S^j_{-+}\right\} \\ T^j_{+-} &\equiv [j(j+1)]^{1/2}\bar{S}^j_{-+} = j(j+1)(2j+1)^{-1}\left\{S^j_{--} - S^j_{++} - [j(j+1)]^{1/2}S^j_{-+}\right\} \end{aligned} \tag{16-30}$$

for the triplet state of parity $(-)^{j+1}$ (where the subscript "±" on S means "$\ell = j \pm 1$"),

$$T^j_t + 1 \equiv S^j_{j,j} \tag{16-31}$$

for the triplet state of parity $(-)^j$, and

$$T^j_s + 1 \equiv S^j \tag{16-32}$$

for the singlet state, we get for the set of "helicity amplitudes" in the center-of-mass system[15]

$$A_{++,++} = A_{--,--} = (4ik)^{-1} \sum_{j=0}^{\infty} (2j + 1)(T^j_{++} + T^j_s)P_j$$

$$A_{--,-+} = A_{+-,++} = A_{++,-+} = A_{+-,--} = -A_{++,+-} = -A_{-+,--}$$

$$= -A_{-+,++} = -A_{--,+-} = (4ik)^{-1} \sin\theta \sum_{j=1}^{\infty} (2j + 1)T^j_{+-}\pi_j$$

$$A_{+-,+-} = A_{-+,-+} = (4ik)^{-1}\left[\sum_{j=1}^{\infty} (2j + 1)(T^j_{--} + T^j_t)(\pi_j + \tau_j) + T^0_t(\pi_0 + \tau_0)\right] \tag{16-33}$$

$$A_{+-,-+} = A_{-+,+-} = (4ik)^{-1}\left[\sum_{j=1}^{\infty} (2j + 1)(T^j_{--} - T^j_t)(\pi_j - \tau_j) - T^0_t(\pi_0 - \tau_0)\right]$$

$$A_{++,--} = A_{--,++} = (4ik)^{-1}\sum_{j=0}^{\infty} (2j + 1)(T^j_{++} - T^j_s)P_j$$

The first set of indices on A refers to the final state, the second, to the initial; "±" refers to forward or backward spin direction, respectively, for each of the two particles. The angle functions used are Legendre polynomials, P_j, and

$$\pi_j(\cos\theta) \equiv P'_j(\cos\theta)/j(j + 1)$$
$$\tau_j(\cos\theta) \equiv P_j(\cos\theta) - \cos\theta\,\pi_j(\cos\theta) \tag{16-34}$$

The first thing to notice is that the T's contain none of the kinematic branch points at j = 0 and j = -1 which S contains, and since they are expressed in terms of $\overline{S}$, they contain no fixed pole at $j = -\frac{1}{2}$. Hence the terms on the right-hand sides of (16-33) contain no unwanted singularities. Provided that the potentials have the right properties to produce a finite number of Regge poles on the right and to let the T's vanish as $|j| \to \infty$ in all directions on the right (which properties are no different from those required in the spin-zero case), the Watson transform can now be taken just as in Chapter 2. The resulting asymptotic behavior of the amplitudes as $|\cos\theta| \to \infty$ is then the same as before, except for simple, obvious modifications owing to the π and τ. It should be noted, though, that the j = 0 terms in some of the amplitudes are missing, whenever they would refer to the "nonsense" case, $\ell = -1$. Thus, if the integral is to be pushed to Re $j = -\frac{1}{2}$, then these terms must be artificially added and subtracted, leading to the appearance of fixed pole terms at $j = 0$ on the right-hand side of (2-3). These fixed pole terms then have the effect of canceling the pole in the (negative energy) amplitudes which would otherwise be there when a Regge pole goes through the nonsense term at $j = 0$.[16] This cancelation is, of course, necessary, since the original form of the amplitudes, i.e., (16-33) does not contain that pole. In addition, it is possible in the nonsense case that the residue vanishes, as was discussed above, and if it is the leading pole, the asymptotic behavior of the amplitudes, as $|\cos\theta| \to \infty$, will depend on whether it does or not.[14]

Other kinds of amplitudes, with the spin projected on fixed axes, for example, exhibit the same behavior as (16-33). We need not write them down here.[17]

Some further remarks concerning extensions of the results of this section are in order.

The presence of a spin-orbit force, described by

$$V_{LS} = \mathbf{L} \cdot \mathbf{S}\, V_0(r)$$

manifests itself in (16-3) as an additional matrix

$$\Delta V^{(j)} = \begin{pmatrix} j - 1 & 0 \\ 0 & -j - 2 \end{pmatrix} V_0(r) \tag{16-35}$$

and in (16-9) as a j-dependent addition to W:

$$W \to W + \begin{pmatrix} -1 & [j(j+1)]^{1/2} \\ [j(j+1)]^{1/2} & -2 \end{pmatrix} V_0(r) \tag{16-36}$$

Since this contains no pole at $j = -\frac{1}{2}$ and it is a function only of λ^2, our previous results apply again. The only essential effect of the spin-orbit force comes from its increase as $|j| \to \infty$. It may, therefore, have a seriously distorting effect on the faraway trajectories and on the behavior of S as $|j| \to \infty$. It is not clear in that case if the Watson transform can still be taken, nor is it necessarily true that all trajectories turn and disappear toward the left. Even if the Watson transform is possible, this implies that no matter how large the energy, the amplitudes may now increase to infinity with increasing momentum transfer.

The preceding remarks are a fortiori true for more strongly, angular momentum dependent potentials (such as $\mathbf{L} \cdot \mathbf{L}$ forces, for example). Such can exist, of course, also when the particles have spin zero.[18]

As was mentioned at the beginning of this chapter, we may consider the case of two spin-$\frac{1}{2}$ particles as a model for the study of the interaction of particles of an intrinsic angular momentum higher than $\frac{1}{2}$, and of the case in which one or both of the particles have internal degrees of freedom leading to inelastic processes usually described as "many channels."[3] From the present point of view, the complications never come from the difference in kinetic energies in the various channels, but solely from the difference in angular momenta. We then get the generalization of the present kinematic branch points, owing to the normalization factors in Clebsch-Gordan coefficients, at integral values of j. These can be shown to disappear in the amplitudes just as they do here. Similarly, there occur generalizations of the kinematic poles in the potential matrix, also due to normalization factors of Clebsch-Gordan coefficients. Again it should be possible to introduce a transformation that eliminates these from the potential and to show that they do not produce complications in the S-matrix.[19] In other words, all the essentially new points that arise in the many-channel problem have their prototype in the case considered in this chapter, and they can be treated by similar means.

Notes and References

1. For a treatment of the case in which one particle has spin zero and the other, $\frac{1}{2}\hbar$, see Favella and Reineri (F1).
2. This chapter follows Desai and Newton (D3). For more general discussions of the influence of spin, see Calogero et al. (C3), and Calogero and Charap (C5).
3. For treatments of the many-channel problem, see Charap and Squires (C10-12), Favella and Reineri (F1), and Jaffe and Kim (J1).
4. It is very convenient to mean by a "solution" of (16-1), not a column vector, but a square matrix. Each of its columns then solves (16-1), but they differ by their boundary condition; for example, by the angular momentum in which the incoming wave is found asymptotically.
5. See (N7); this complication can be avoided only by assuming that the potential vanishes rapidly at $r = 0$.
6. At this point the symmetry of the potential matrix, corresponding to time reversal invariance, is essential.
7. In order to avoid the introduction of unnecessary square roots, U_j is not made unitary.
8. It is, of course, easy to introduce other Jost matrix functions in place of $\overline{F}$, which do not have a pole at $j = -\frac{1}{2}$. In that case it must be proved that the inverse does not have a fixed pole at $j = -\frac{1}{2}$, which would come from a fixed zero of the determinant. It should be noted that, whereas in the spin zero case the unitarity rules out fixed S-matrix poles, we now do not have unitarity between $j = 0$ and $j = -1$; see (16-25'). Although there exists another generalization of unitarity, namely (16-25), that is not sufficient to rule out fixed poles of the S-matrix or of its trans-

formation. In the case of many channels of various angular momenta, the problem of the point $j = -\frac{1}{2}$ occurs at many other points as well, and in that case it is at this writing an open question whether there are fixed poles or not. In view of their absence in $\bar{S}$ in the present case, one would, of course, expect them to be absent also in the more general case.

9. This may be called "generalized unitarity," but its shortcomings compared to unitarity must not be overlooked; see (C12).
10. See, for example, (G3).
11. The factorization of the residue at an angular momentum pole was first pointed out by Gell-Mann (G1). See also Charap and Squires (C9). The argument here is that of (D3).
12. The range of a matrix M is the space of all vectors a which can be written a = Mb for some b.
13. Notice that, since det $\bar{\bar{F}}$ has no pole at $\lambda = 0$, det $\bar{F}$ has a fixed double zero there.
14. See (N6).
15. The j = 0 terms were not written down separately in (D3).
16. See Berestetsky (B18).
17. See (D3).
18. On the other hand, one may wish to consider spin-orbit forces in which V_0 is ℓ dependent, in order to dampen the strengthening of the force for large $|\ell|$.
19. However, see footnote 8.

Chapter 17

THE THREE-BODY PROBLEM

In this chapter the method of complex angular momenta will be extended to the case of more than two particles. Specifically the three-body problem will be investigated in some detail.[1]

Physically, we are interested in a situation in which initially two particles form a bound system upon which the third impinges, and finally there emerges either again a bound system and the third particle free, or else all three particles are free. The final bound system may consist of the same particles as the initial, either at the same energy level or at an excited state, or else it may consist of the particle initially free and one of those initially bound. It is the possibility of all three particles to emerge freely that distinguishes this problem from the conventional many-channel problem, and which makes it the nearest manageable analog to the relativistic possibility of particle production. It is also precisely this that leads to the essentially new result, namely that there may be not only poles in the angular momentum plane, but also branch points. These will be investigated in Chapter 18.

It must be noted at the outset that there is, in this problem, an ambiguity which did not arise before. In the center-of-mass coordinate system there are two orbital angular momenta, that of two of the particles in their center-of-mass system, and that of the third; call them ℓ_1 and ℓ_2. (We assume for simplicity that none of the particles have spin.) And then there is the total angular momentum j. It is not clear which of these three should be made continuous and complex, and which, if any, should remain integers.

Quite possibly it will eventually be of interest to let all three of these angular momenta be independent complex variables. (See the discussion at the end of Chapter 18.) However, we shall here consider only the simpler problem in which one, at least, of the three remains discrete. If we choose the total angular momentum j as the one that remains an integer, much of interest will be lost. For one thing, j is the one variable that is the same in the elastic and inelastic processes and connects them. By studying the analytic structure of the S-matrix as a function of j, we learn not only properties of the production amplitudes, but at the same time, the repercussions of these properties, via unitarity and angular momentum conservation, in the elastic amplitude. For that reason the analytic continuation should be of j.

If we were to continue the j variable alone, and leave both orbital momenta discrete, we should learn nothing very interesting. Specifically, we should remain ignorant about momentum transfer behavior or angular variables. Instead of studying dynamics, we should simply be continuing Clebsch-Gordan coefficients. Another, more incisive argument comes from the recollection of the reason for the power of the new method, as discussed earlier. The assumption is exploited that the scattering is caused by a local, angular momentum independent potential. If we wish to exploit similarly the assumption that even among three particles there are binary forces only whose potentials are local and angular momentum independent, then it is clearly necessary to continue at least one of the orbital angular momenta associated with an interparticle distance.

The most natural thing then is to continue the total angular momentum variable j and along with it one of the orbital momenta. If the two were independently continuous, there would be too much freedom and the consequences of the three-body properties in the elastic amplitude, via angular momentum conservation and unitarity, would again be lost. The difference between j and one of the orbital angular momenta will, therefore, be assumed to remain an integer. The resulting procedure is in most respects a simple generalization of that of Chapter 16.

There remains in addition the ambiguity of the choice of coordinates and consequently of the angular momentum coupling. In the conventional treatment this is unavoidable. Each choice leads to its own singularities, and they must all be combined to complete the picture. We shall return to this point later.

In order to simplify the procedure without losing anything essential in the process we shall assume at first that one of the three particles is infinitely massive. Subsequently this supposition will be dropped and we shall consider the general case.

The wave function for a scattering or "production" process in which initially particle number 1 comes in with asymptotic momentum k_1 and particle number 2 is bound with energy E_2, angular momentum ℓ_2, z-component of angular momentum m_2, is $\psi(E; \mathbf{k}_1, E_2, \ell_2, m_2; \mathbf{r}_1, \mathbf{r}_2)$ where[2]

$$E = E_2 + (\mathbf{k}_1^2/2\mu_1)$$

is the total energy.

We make an angular momentum expansion. Set[3]

$$Y^M_{j\ell_1\ell_2}(\mathbf{r}_1, \mathbf{r}_2) \equiv \sum_{m_1 m_2} C_{\ell_1\ell_2}(j, M, m_1, m_2) Y^{m_1}_{\ell_1}(\mathbf{r}_1) Y^{m_2}_{\ell_2}(\mathbf{r}_2)$$

$$\mathcal{Y}_j^M(\ell_1, \ell_2, m_2; \mathbf{k}) \equiv \sum_{m_1} C_{\ell_1 \ell_2}(j, M, m_1, m_2) i^{-\ell_1} Y_{\ell_1}^{m_1}(\mathbf{k})$$

Then expand:

$$\psi(E; \mathbf{k}_1, E_2, \ell_2, m_2; \mathbf{r}_1, \mathbf{r}_2) = \sum_{\ell_1' \ell_2' j M} Y_{j\ell_1\ell_2}^{M}(\mathbf{r}_1, \mathbf{r}_2) \mathcal{Y}_j^{M*}(\ell_1', \ell_2', m_2; \mathbf{k}_1)$$
$$\times r_1^{-1} r_2^{-1} \psi_{\ell_1\ell_2, \ell_1'\ell_2'}(j; E, E_2; r_1, r_2) \tag{17-1}$$

$\psi(E; \mathbf{k}_1, E_2, \ell_2, m_2; \mathbf{r}_1, \mathbf{r}_2)$ satisfies the Schrödinger equation

$$\left(-\frac{1}{2\mu_1}\nabla_1^2 - \frac{1}{2\mu_2}\nabla_2^2 + V_1 + V_2 + V_{12} - E\right)$$
$$\times \psi(E; \mathbf{k}_1, E_2, \ell_2, m_2; \mathbf{r}_1, \mathbf{r}_2) = 0 \tag{17-2}$$

where V_1 and V_2 are the potentials between particles 1 and 2 and the "core" particle 3, respectively, and V_{12} is the potential between particles 1 and 2. We multiply this by $Y_{j\ell_1\ell_2}^{M*}(\mathbf{r}_1, \mathbf{r}_2)$ and integrate over Ω_1 and Ω_2. This yields

$$\left[-\frac{1}{2\mu_1}\frac{\partial^2}{\partial r_1^2} - \frac{1}{2\mu_2}\frac{\partial^2}{\partial r_2^2} + \frac{\ell_1(\ell_1+1)}{2\mu_1 r_1^2} + \frac{\ell_2(\ell_2+1)}{2\mu_2 r_2^2} + V_1 + V_2 - E\right]$$
$$\times \psi_{\ell_1\ell_2, \ell_1'\ell_2'}(j; E, E_2; r_1, r_2)$$
$$= -\sum_{\ell_1''\ell_2''} W_{\ell_1\ell_2, \ell_1''\ell_2''}(j; r_1, r_2)\psi_{\ell_1''\ell_2'', \ell_1'\ell_2'}(j; E, E_2; r_1, r_2) \tag{17-3}$$

where

$$W_{\ell_1\ell_2, \ell_1''\ell_2''}(j; r_1, r_2) \equiv \int d\Omega_1\, d\Omega_2\, Y_{j\ell_1\ell_2}^{M*}(\mathbf{r}_1, \mathbf{r}_2)$$
$$\times V_{12} Y_{j\ell_1''\ell_2''}^{M}(\mathbf{r}_1, \mathbf{r}_2) \tag{17-4}$$

In order to simplify the notation we write

$$\ell_1 \equiv j + t$$

Then for fixed $\ell_2 = \ell$, t runs from $-\ell$ to $+\ell$ through integral values. When j is an integer then the Clebsch-Gordan coefficients assure automatically that W vanishes unless, in fact, $\ell_1 \geq |j - \ell|$. The "unphysical" values of ℓ_1 (or of t) are, therefore, uncoupled from the "physical" ones when j is an integer. However, when j is allowed to take on nonintegral values, then this is no longer true. Just as in the spin-$\frac{1}{2}$ case, there is no way of avoiding the coupling to those values of ℓ_1 which, although $j - \ell < \ell_1 < j + \ell$, are such that $\ell_1 < |j - \ell|$; these are the "nonsense" terms.

Let's suppress, then, all matrix indices and write simply $W(j; r_1, r_2)$. This is, first of all, an infinite square matrix in ℓ-space, each element $W_{\ell\ell'}$ of which is, second, a rectangular matrix in t-space, $W_{t\ell, t'\ell'}$, where t runs from $-\ell$ to $+\ell$, and t', from $-\ell'$ to $+\ell'$.

Let L be the diagonal matrix in ℓ-space whose elements are simply ℓ (times the unit matrix in t-space); and let T be the diagonal matrix whose elements are simply t when $-\ell \leq t \leq +\ell$, and zero otherwise. We then write

$$\left[-\frac{1}{2\mu_1}\frac{\partial^2}{\partial r_1^2} - \frac{1}{2\mu_2}\frac{\partial^2}{\partial r_2^2} + \frac{(j + T)(j + T + 1)}{2\mu_1 r_1^2} + \frac{L(L + 1)}{2\mu_2 r_2^2} + V_1 + V_2 - E\right]$$

$$\times \psi(j; E, E_2; r_1, r_2) = -W(j; r_1, r_2)\psi(j; E, E_2; r_1, r_2) \qquad (17\text{-}3')$$

If we choose the phases of the Y_ℓ^m appropriately[4] and the Clebsch-Gordan coefficients real, so that

$$Y_{j\ell_1\ell_2}^{M*} = (-)^{j + M} Y_{j\ell_1\ell_2}^{-M}$$

then the matrix W is not only Hermitian (assuming V_{12} is) but real and hence symmetric (assuming V_{12} is real and hence time-reversal invariant).

We are here interested in the case in which $V_{12} = V_{12}(|\mathbf{r}_1 - \mathbf{r}_2|)$. It therefore conserves parity. That implies that W has matrix elements only between states for which $\ell_1 + \ell_2$ and $\ell_1' + \ell_2'$ differ by an even integer, and hence

$$W_{t\ell, t'\ell'} = 0 \qquad \text{unless} \qquad \ell + t = \ell' + t' + 2n \qquad (17\text{-}5)$$

Consequently, for a given j, (17-3) [or (17-3')] fall apart into two separate sets: For the states of parity $(-)^j$, t takes on the values ℓ, $\ell - 2, \ldots, -\ell$; for the states of parity $(-)^{j+1}$, t takes on the values $\ell - 1, \ell - 3, \ldots, 1 - \ell$. We therefore modify the meaning of the matrix indices accordingly.

The complete set of bound state and scattering wave functions for particle 2 of angular momentum ℓ is introduced next:

$$\left[-\frac{1}{2\mu_2}\frac{d^2}{dr_2^2} + \frac{\ell(\ell+1)}{2\mu_2 r_2^2} + V_2 - E_2\right]\psi_\ell(E_2, r_2) = 0 \tag{17-6}$$

normalized so that

$$\int_0^\infty dr_2\, \psi_\ell^*(E_2, r_2)\psi_\ell(E_2', r_2) = \begin{cases} \delta(E_2 - E_2') & \text{in the continuum} \\ \delta_{E_2, E_2'} & \text{in the discrete spectrum} \end{cases}$$

and

$$\int \psi_\ell(E_2, r_2)\, d\rho_\ell(E_2)\psi_\ell^*(E_2, r_2') = \delta(r_2 - r_2')$$

where

$$\frac{d\rho_\ell}{dE} = \begin{cases} \sum_n \delta\left(E - E_\ell^{(n)}\right) & E \le 0 \\ 1 & E > 0 \end{cases}$$

the $E_\ell^{(n)}$ being the bound state energies of particle 2 (with the core, number 3) of angular momentum ℓ.

The function $\psi_{\ell_1\ell_2, \ell_1'\ell_2'}(j; E, E_2'; r_1, r_2)$ can then be written

$$\psi_{\ell_1\ell_2, \ell_1'\ell_2'}(j; E, E_2'; r_1, r_2) = \int \psi_{\ell_2}(E_2, r_2)\, d\rho_{\ell_2}(E_2) \times \psi_{\ell_1\ell_2E_2, \ell_1'\ell_2'E_2'}(j, E; r_1) \tag{17-7}$$

In our matrix notation ρ and $\psi(E_2, r_2)$ are diagonal matrices in ℓ-space, and multiples of unit matrices in t-space:

$$\psi(j; E, E_2; r_1, r_2) = \int \psi(E_2', r_2)\, d\rho\, (E_2')\psi_{E_2', E_2}(j, E; r_1) \tag{17-7'}$$

The Schrödinger equation becomes

$$\left[-\frac{1}{2\mu_1}\frac{d^2}{dr_1^2} + \frac{(j+T)(j+T+1)}{2\mu_1 r_1^2} + V_1 - E + E_2\right]\psi_{E_2, E_2'}(j, E; r_1) = -\int W(j; E_2, E_2''; r_1)\, d\rho\, (E_2'')\psi_{E_2'', E_2'}(j, E; r_1) \tag{17-8}$$

where

$$W_{\ell_1\ell_2, \ell_1'\ell_2'}(j; E_2, E_2''; r_1)$$

$$\equiv \int_0^\infty dr_2\, \psi^*_{\ell_2}(E_2, r_2) W_{\ell_1\ell_2, \ell_1'\ell_2'}(j; r_1, r_2) \psi_{\ell_2'}(E_2'', r_2) \tag{17-9}$$

We now multiply everything by $2\mu_1$ and use a matrix notation for E_2 also. In this E_2-space there are then (at least one) discrete points with $E_2 \leq 0$, plus a continuum from $E_2 = 0$ to $E_2 = \infty$. W(j, r) is thus a matrix integral operator. Write

$$2\mu_1 E_1 \equiv K_1^2 \equiv 2\mu_1(E - E_2) \times \begin{cases} \delta_{\alpha\beta} & \text{for the discrete part} \\ \delta(E_{2\alpha} - E_{2\beta}) & \text{for the continuous part} \end{cases}$$

and the radial Schrödinger equations become

$$\left[-\frac{d^2}{dr^2} + \frac{(j + T)(j + T + 1)}{r^2} + V(r) - K_1^2\right]\psi(j, E; r)$$
$$= -W(j, r)\psi(j, E; r) \tag{17-10}$$

It may be well to recall at this point the meaning of the two sets of indices (suppressed) on $\psi_{\ell_1\ell_2 E_2, \ell_1'\ell_2' E_2'}(j, E; r)$. The first refers to the angular momenta of the two particles and to the energy of particle 2, as they can be measured in the infinite future; that is, of the outgoing wave. The second set refers to the same quantities in the infinite past; that is, of the incoming wave. The first set refers to wave function components, which are coupled together by the wave equation. The second set refers to the boundary condition, that is, to the way the beam was prepared.

We now proceed to solve the coupled equations (17-10). First the uncoupled equations are solved in which W(j, r) = 0. These, then, are diagonal matrices in ℓ, t and E_2-space. Let the elements of the regular solution $\phi^{(0)}(j, E; r)$ be

$$\phi^{(0)}_{t\ell E_2, t'\ell' E_2'}(j, E; r) = \delta_{tt'}\delta_{\ell\ell'}\delta(E_2 - E_2')\hat{\phi}(j + t, k_1; r) \tag{17-11}$$

where $k_1^2 = 2\mu_1(E - E_2)$ and $\hat{\phi}(s, k; r)$ is the solution of the equation for particles 1 and 3 in the absence of particle 2:

$$\left[-\frac{d^2}{dr^2} + \frac{s(s + 1)}{r^2} + V(r) - k^2\right]\hat{\phi}(s, k; r) = 0 \tag{17-12}$$

which satisfies the boundary condition analogous to (4-1),

$$\lim_{r \to 0} r^{-s-1}\hat{\phi}(s, k; r) = 1 \tag{17-13}$$

Irregular solutions $\hat{f}_\pm(s, k; r)$ of (17-12) are defined by the boundary conditions (3-2). Their Wronskians with $\hat{\phi}$, as in (5-2), we call $\hat{F}_\pm$. Out of $\hat{f}_\pm$ and $\hat{F}_\pm$ we form the diagonal matrices $f_\pm^{(0)}(j, E; r)$ and $F_\pm^{(0)}(j, E)$, respectively, as in (17-11).

The Green's function which satisfies the equation

$$\left[\frac{d^2}{dr^2} - \frac{s(s+1)}{r^2} - V(r) + k^2\right]\hat{\mathcal{G}}\ (s, E; r, r') = \delta(r - r') \tag{17-14}$$

and the boundary condition

$$\hat{\mathcal{G}}(s, E; r, r') = 0 \qquad r \leq r' \tag{17-15}$$

is given by

$$\hat{\mathcal{G}}(s, E; r, r') = \begin{cases} \hat{g}\ (s, E; r, r') & r \geq r' \\ 0 & r \leq r' \end{cases} \tag{17-16}$$

where

$$\begin{aligned} &\hat{g}(s, E; r, r') \\ &= \left[\hat{\phi}(s, k; r)\hat{f}_+(s, k; r') - \hat{\phi}(s, k; r')\hat{f}_+(s, k; r)\right]/\hat{F}_+(s, k) \\ &= \left[\hat{\phi}(s, k; r)\hat{f}_-(s, k; r') - \hat{\phi}(s, k; r')\hat{f}_-(s, k; r)\right]/\hat{F}_-(s, -k) \end{aligned} \tag{17-17}$$

The diagonal matrices formed out of $\hat{\mathcal{G}}$ and $\hat{g}$ according to (17-11) are called $\mathcal{G}^{(0)}$ and $g^{(0)}$.

We now define a regular solution of (17-10) by the integral equation

$$\begin{aligned} \phi(j, E; r) = \phi^{(0)}(j, E; r) + \int_0^r dr'\ g^{(0)}(j, E; r, r') \\ \times W(j, r')\phi(j, E; r') \end{aligned} \tag{17-18}$$

Owing to the fact that $\hat{g}(\ell_1, E_2; r, r')$ contains irregular solutions and hence at $r' \to 0$ goes as $r'^{-\ell_1}$, while $\phi_{\ell_1' \ldots}$ goes as $r'^{1+\ell_1'}$, the same problem arises that arose in Chapter 16. The integral diverges and, therefore, the integral equation breaks down, unless

$$W_{\ell_1\ldots,\ell_1'\ldots}(r)r^{1-|\ell_1-\ell_1'|}$$

is integrable at r = 0. It will be shown in Appendix C that if V_{12} is a reasonable superposition of Yukawa potentials then, in fact,

$$W_{\ell_1\ldots,\ell_1'\ldots}(r) = O(r^{|\ell_1-\ell_1'|}) \quad \text{as} \quad r \to 0 \tag{17-19}$$

This is quite probably true under much more general conditions. In any case, the integral equation (17-18) can be assumed not to contain any convergence difficulties at r = 0, and no "counterterms" are needed.

The functions $f_\pm$ are solutions of the integral equations

$$f_\pm(j,E;r) = f_\pm^{(0)}(j,E;r) - \int_r^\infty dr'\, g^{(0)}(j,E;r,r') \times W(j,r')f_\pm(j,E;r') \tag{17-20}$$

and a generalized Jost function is defined by (16-6).

The function $\phi(j,E;r)$ may be expressed in terms of $f_+(j,E;r)$ and $f_-(j,E;r)$ by means of $F_\pm$ in analogy with (5-1)

$$\phi(j,E;r) = \tfrac{1}{2}i\Big[f_-(j,E;r)K_1^{-1}F_+(j,E) - f_+(j,E;r)K_1^{-1}F_-(j,E)\Big] \tag{17-21}$$

From this it follows that (for integral values of j) the modified scattering matrix is given by the analog of (5-18)[5]

$$S'(j,E) = e^{i\pi(j+T)}K_1^{-1}F_+F_-^{-1}K_1 \tag{17-22}$$

The integral representation

$$F_\pm(j,E) = F_\pm^{(0)}(j,E) + \int_0^\infty dr\, f_\pm^{(0)}(j,E;r)W(j,r)\phi(j,E;r) \tag{17-23}$$

is derived analogously to (5-12). Furthermore, insertion of

(17-21) in

$$\tilde{\phi}'\phi - \tilde{\phi}\phi' = 0$$

yields

$$\tilde{F}_- K_1^{-1} F_+ = \tilde{F}_+ K_1^{-1} F_- \qquad (17\text{-}24)$$

and, therefore,

$$e^{-i\pi T} S \equiv e^{i\pi j} K_1^{-1/2} F_+ F_-^{-1} K_1^{1/2}$$

$$= e^{-i\pi T} K_1^{1/2} S' K_1^{-1/2} \qquad (17\text{-}25)$$

is symmetric. S is the scattering matrix proper. The scattering and reaction amplitudes are obtained from it without insertion of velocity ratios.[6]

When j is made a continuous variable and moved away from integral values in the way previously discussed, then (17-19) still holds, with $\ell_1 - \ell_1' = t - t'$. However, the integrand in (17-18) contains terms of order

$$r'^{\,1 + t + t' + |t - t'| + 2j}$$

which, since t runs down to $-\ell$, diverge for each j when ℓ is sufficiently large. Thus for each nonintegral value of j, almost all of the integrals in the series of successive approximations to (17-18) must be defined by analytic continuation from a region where they absolutely converge. If we assume that all the derivatives of all the elements of rW exist at r = 0, this will produce no difficulties and can be done as demonstrated in Chapter 4. The only result will be simple poles at (in general) all the integral and half-integral values of j. Since at integral values of j the nonsense part of ϕ splits off and the sense part is finite, the residues of ϕ there must be matrices confined to the nonsense part.

Similar remarks apply, mutatis mutandis, to the integral representation (17-23). The function ϕ having been defined by the necessary analytic continuations in (17-18), almost all terms in the (suppressed) ℓ-summations in (17-23) must, for nonintegral j, be obtained by analytic continuation from a region in the j-plane where they converge absolutely. This produces no singularities other than simple poles at integral and half-integral j. At integral j, the projections of the residues onto the sense part of F are zero.

We now want to consider the unitarity and the analog of the kinematic branch points at $j = 0$ and $j = -1$ in the spin-$\frac{1}{2}$ case.

In order that the potential matrix W be an analytic function of j, the complex conjugation in (17-4) must be allowed to act only on the φ dependence in the spherical harmonics, but not on the functions of j, which are all real for integral values of j. Insertion of the explicit form of the spherical harmonics and of the Clebsch-Gordan coefficients in (17-4) shows that W contains square roots. The resulting singularities in the j-plane are the kinematic branch points. Isolating the radicals we find that[7]

$$W_{t\ell, t'\ell'}(j; r_1, r_2) = N_{t\ell}(j)\overline{W}_{t\ell, t'\ell'}(j; r_1, r_2)/N_{t'\ell'}(j) \qquad (17\text{-}26)$$

with

$$N_{t\ell}(j) = \left[\frac{(2j + t + 1 + \ell) \cdots (2j + t + 1 - \ell)}{2j + 2t + 1}\right]^{1/2}$$

and $\overline{W}$ is free of branch points.

In our matrix notation we have

$$\overline{W} = N^{-1}WN \qquad (17\text{-}27)$$

where N is diagonal. Hence by (17-18)

$$\overline{\phi} \equiv N^{-1}\phi N \qquad (17\text{-}28)$$

is free of kinematic branch points, and so are

$$\overline{f}_{\pm} \equiv N^{-1}f_{\pm}N \qquad (17\text{-}29)$$

and consequently also

$$\overline{F}_{\pm} \equiv N^{-1}F_{\pm}N \qquad (17\text{-}30)$$

By (17-22), therefore,

$$\overline{S}' \equiv N^{-1}S'N \qquad (17\text{-}31)$$

is free of the fixed kinematic branch points at integral values of j which are due solely to the Clebsch-Gordan coefficients and to the spherical harmonics' normalization factors. The matrix S' itself, however, contains them.

Now for real j and E it follows from the differential equation (17-12) and the boundary condition (17-13) that $\phi^{(0)}(j, E; r)$ is real; similarly, from (17-12) and (3-2), that

$$f_+^{(0)*}(j, E; r) = f_-^{(0)}(j, E; r)\theta_+ + f_+^{(0)}(j, E; r)\theta_- \tag{17-32}$$

We have written θ_+ for the projection on the open channel part; that is, θ_+ is the diagonal matrix $\theta(E_1)$ where

$$\theta(x) = \begin{cases} 1 & \text{if} \quad x > 0 \\ 0 & \text{if} \quad x < 0 \end{cases}$$

and

$$\theta_- \equiv \theta(-E_1) = 1 - \theta_+$$

Because of the kinematic branch points, the reality of $\phi^{(0)}$ and the equation (17-32) for $f^{(0)}$ cannot be directly transformed into relations for ϕ and f. But it does follow that for real j and E, $\overline{\phi}(j, E; r)$ is real and

$$\overline{f}_+^*(j, E; r) = \overline{f}_-(j, E; r)\theta_+ + \overline{f}_+(j, E; r)\theta_- \tag{17-33}$$

and, therefore,

$$\overline{F}_+^*(j, E) = \theta_+\overline{F}_-(j, E) + \theta_-\overline{F}_+(j, E) \tag{17-34}$$

In order to investigate the unitarity of the S-matrix we define a matrix function I(j, E) so that

$$\theta_- F_- I = 0 \tag{17-35}$$

and as a result

$$\phi^{(R)} \equiv \phi I$$

contains no exponentially increasing terms as $r \to \infty$. In that limit, then,

$$2i\phi^{(R)} \sim e^{iK_1 r} K_1^{-1} F_+ I - e^{-iK_1 r} K_1^{-1} F_- I$$

and so the part of the S-matrix which refers to open channels only can be written

$$S'^{(+)} = e^{i\pi(j + T)} K_1^{-1} (F_+ I)^{(+)} (F_- I)^{(+) - 1} K_1 \tag{17-36}$$

where the superscript "(+)" stands for "open channel part":

$$M^{(+)} \equiv \theta_+ M \theta_+$$

Equation (17-35) does not define I uniquely, but it may be explicitly represented, for example, by

$$I = [\theta_- F_- + \theta_+ F_-^{(0)}]^{-1} \tag{17-37}$$

Then we have for

$$\bar{I} \equiv N^{-1} I N$$

by (17-34)

$$\bar{I}^* = [\theta_- \bar{F}_- + \theta_+ F_-^{(0)}]^{-1} F_-^{(0)* - 1} F_-^{(0)}$$

$$= \bar{I} F_-^{(0)* - 1} F_-^{(0)}$$

As a result, again by (17-34),

$$\bar{S}'^{(+)*} = e^{-i\pi(j + T)} K_1^{-1} (\bar{F}_- \bar{I})^{(+)} (\bar{F}_+ \bar{I})^{(+) - 1} K_1 \tag{17-38}$$

Since this holds for $\bar{S}$ whereas the symmetry holds by (17-25) for $e^{-i\pi T} S$, we do not get unitarity for general values of j. Use of (17-34) in (17-24) shows that

$$\tilde{F}_- K_1^{-1} \theta_+ F_+ = \tilde{F}_+ K_1^{-1} \theta_+ F_-$$

and, therefore, by (17-38)

$$N^*S^{(+)\dagger}N^{*-1} = NS^{(+)-1}N^{-1}$$

or in other words,

$$S^{(+)\dagger}MS^{(+)} = M \tag{17-39}$$

where M is the diagonal matrix function of j,

$$M \equiv NN^{*-1}$$

Equation (17-39) means that for general values of j the unitarity relation is modified. The terms belonging to "unphysical" values of ℓ_1 must be handled differently. The matrix M(j) automatically assigns them a minus sign. For integral values of j the "sense" and the "nonsense" parts of $S^{(+)}$ are uncoupled. The "sense" part alone is then unitary, whereas the "nonsense" part is physically of no interest. For nonintegral values of j, however, the sense and nonsense parts are always coupled, and as a result there is no unitarity for either.

It can be shown in detail that, just as in the spin-$\frac{1}{2}$ case, the partial wave amplitudes contain compensating factors of N so that they are free of the kinematic branch points. The latter, therefore, are no obstacle in carrying out the Watson transform.[8]

In addition to the kinematic branch points, there are fixed poles in S which are the analog of the pole at $j = -\frac{1}{2}$ in the spin-$\frac{1}{2}$ case. These can presumably be eliminated just as they could in Chapter 16. We shall not go into this in detail since we have seen the prototype there.[9]

Notes and References

1. This chapter follows (N2); see also Kazes (K4) and Drummond (D6).
2. μ_1 and μ_2 are the masses of particles 1 and 2, respectively.
3. The notation for the Clebsch-Gordan coefficients is the same as in Blatt and Weisskopf (B24), for example.
4. See, for example (N8).
5. The factor $\exp(i\pi T)$ can also be written

$$(-)^T = \exp(i\pi T) = \begin{cases} (-)^L & \text{for parity } (-)^j \\ -(-)^L & \text{for parity } (-)^{j+1} \end{cases}$$

6. The factors $K^{1/2}$ take care of the phase space, or the ratio of final-to-initial velocities.
7. See Charap and Squires (C10).
8. See Charap and Squires (C10-12).
9. See footnote 8 of Chapter 16.

Chapter 18

THE THREE-BODY PROBLEM *(Continued)*: THE DYNAMICAL BRANCH POINTS

We now want to investigate what kinds of singularities occur in the three-body S-matrix. To start with, we still assume that one of the particles is infinitely massive and we use the formalism and the results of Chapter 17.

In order to obtain the S-matrix we must, in view of (17-22), form the inverse of the matrix integral operator F_-. Let us write (17-23) schematically[1]

$$F(\alpha; x, x') = g(\alpha, x)\bar{\delta}(x - x') - M(x, x') \tag{18-1}$$

where in the present instance, $F = F_-$, $\alpha = j$, and $x = E_2$. By $\bar{\delta}(x - x')$ we mean a Dirac δ-function for $x, x' > 0$, a Kronecker δ if $x, x' < 0$, and zero otherwise. The functions g and M are matrices, and $M(x, x')$ does not contain any δ-function contributions. We are to construct the inverse $G(\alpha; x, x')$ of the (matrix) integral operator $F(\alpha; x, x')$, where the x integrations are Stieltjes integrals according to (17-7'), for example; discrete for $x < 0$ and continuous for $x > 0$.

Considered as a function of α, the inverse G of F has branch points defined by the equations

$$\det g(\alpha, 0) = 0 \qquad \det g(\alpha, \infty) = 0 \tag{18-2}$$

which are connected by cuts whose positions are most simply defined by the equations

$$\det g(\alpha, x) = 0 \qquad 0 \leq x < \infty \tag{18-3}$$

but which, of course, can be shifted to other positions.

In order to show that (18-2) defines branch points we may use the

Fredholm method to construct the inverse G of F. First we form the inverse of the integral operator $(1 - g^{-1}M)$, the inverse g^{-1} causing no difficulty since it is diagonal in the continuous indices. Then, calling $g^{-1}M \equiv R$, we have[2]

$$N^{(L)} \equiv (1 - g^{-1}M)^{-1} = B/\Delta \tag{18-4}$$

where

$$B = 1 + \sum_{1}^{\infty} B^{(n)} \tag{18-5}$$

$$B^{(1)} = R \qquad B^{(n+1)} = RB^{(n)} - n^{-1} R \operatorname{Tr} B^{(n)} \tag{18-6}$$

$$\Delta = 1 - \sum_{1}^{\infty} n^{-1} \operatorname{Tr} B^{(n)} \tag{18-7}$$

Here Tr stands for the trace over all discrete and continuous indices.

Consider, as a prototype, the second term in Δ:

$$\operatorname{Tr} R = \int_{-\infty}^{\infty} d\rho\,(x) \operatorname{tr} [g^{-1}(\alpha, x) M(x, x)] \tag{18-8}$$

where tr stands for the trace over the discrete matrix indices. Considered as a function of α, the integral in (18-8), whose continuous part runs from zero to infinity, has a branch cut along (18-3), connecting branch points at (18-2) which are "end-point singularities" of the integrand. This indicates, but does not prove, that (18-2) defines branch points of G.

However, we may easily compute the discontinuity across the cut along (18-3), as follows. When α lies on (18-3), we expand g^{-1} about its pole

$$g^{-1}(\alpha, x) = [x - x_0(\alpha)]^{-1} R(\alpha) + \cdots \tag{18-9}$$

Except in case of degeneracy, the residue R is factorable (see Chapter 16):

$$R_{ij} = R_i^{(L)} R_j^{(R)} \tag{18-10}$$

When α is shifted at right angles to (18-3), x_0 changes by a purely imaginary amount

$$x_0(\alpha) \to x_0(\alpha) \pm i\epsilon$$

provided that

$$\frac{dx_0(\alpha)}{d\alpha} = -\frac{\partial \det g/\partial\alpha}{\partial \det g/\partial x} \neq 0$$

The difference between the values of g^{-1} on the two sides of (18-3) is, therefore,

$$\Delta g^{-1} = 2\pi i\, \delta(x - x_0)R$$

We now use the integral equations

$$N^{(L)} = 1 + N^{(L)}g^{-1}M \qquad N^{(R)} = 1 + Mg^{-1}N^{(R)}$$

for $N^{(L)}$ of (18-4) and

$$N^{(R)} = (1 - Mg^{-1})^{-1}$$

to calculate the discontinuity of $G = N^{(L)}g^{-1}$. Some simple algebra yields the "generalized unitarity"

$$\Delta G = N_+^{(L)}\, \Delta g^{-1}\, N_-^{(R)} = N_-^{(L)}\, \Delta g^{-1}\, N_+^{(R)} \tag{18-11}$$

where the subscripts "+" and "-" indicate the values above and below the cut, respectively. Written out explicitly, (18-11) means that

$$\Delta G(\alpha; x, x')_{ij}$$

$$= 2\pi i\left[\sum_k N_\pm^{(L)}(\alpha; x, x_0)_{ik} R_k^{(L)}(\alpha)\right]\left[\sum_\ell R_\ell^{(R)}(\alpha) N_\mp^{(R)}(\alpha; x_0, x')_{\ell j}\right] \tag{18-11'}$$

This shows, first of all, provided that the zero of det g on (18-3) is simple, both as a function of α and as a function of x, the end-point singularities produced by the vanishing of det g are always branch points, even though their precise nature depends on the remaining integrand near the end point. In addition (18-11) generalizes the factorization of the residue at a pole.

G has not only cuts, as a function of α, but also poles. Some of these manifest themselves as δ-functions in (18-11) and are explicitly visible in the first three terms of the alternative form of (18-11)

$$\Delta G = \Delta g^{-1} + G_{\pm} M \Delta g^{-1} + \Delta g^{-1} M G_{\mp} + G_{\pm} M \Delta g^{-1} M G_{\mp} \qquad (18\text{-}11'')$$

The poles there visible depend on x and x'. In addition, G has x and x' independent poles at those values of α where the Fredholm determinant of F vanishes.

The implications of the foregoing general considerations for the case at hand are easy to see. Since g is $F_-^{(0)}$, which is diagonal also in the discrete angular momentum indices, the branch cuts (18-3) are those defined by[3]

$$\hat{F}_-(j + t,\ k_1) = 0 \qquad (18\text{-}12)$$

This curve is precisely the trajectory of the Regge pole of particle 1 in interaction with particle 3, without the presence of particle 2. Since $k_1^2 = 2\mu_1(E - E_2)$ and the continuum integration over E_2 starts at $E_2 = 0$, the branch points (18-2) in the j-plane at which the cut (18-12) starts (and which, in contrast to the cut, contains no element of arbitrariness) is at the position of the two-body Regge pole for a two-body energy E_1 equal to the total energy E. The branch point, therefore, moves as a function of E and traces out the two-body pole trajectory.

Equation (18-12) shows at the same time that each two-body pole produces not only one branch point image, but infinitely many. Since t takes on the integral values from $-\ell$ to $+\ell$, there are for each ℓ, $2\ell + 1$ cuts shifted horizontally by integers, the right-most being given by

$$\hat{F}_-(j - \ell, k_1) = 0$$

Furthermore, each ℓ appears in the sum. Consequently, F_-^{-1} contains infinitely many cuts. Each two-body Regge pole trajectory appears as a cut infinitely many times repeated, shifted horizontally by integral values, both to the left and to the right.

While one end of each branch cut is energy dependent, the other end is fixed. It corresponds to $E_1 = \infty$ and thus, if rV_1 has all finite derivatives at $r = 0$, it must be either at infinity or else at an integer. In other words, at the integral values of j there are, in general, not only the kinematic branch points discussed in Chapter 17, but in addition dynamical ones, and each of these is connected by a cut to a dynamical, energy-dependent branch point. The most directly given positions of these connecting cuts are the displaced images of the two-body pole trajectories, but they may for convenience be distorted. If the cuts are in their "natural" positions, then (18-11) or (18-11') gives the discontinuities across them.

In order to establish the nature of the branch point at (18-12) we must examine the integrand, say in (18-8), near $E_2 = 0$. From (17-9) and the fact that[4]

$$\psi_{\ell}(E_2, r) = O\left(k_2^{\ell + (1/2)}\right) \quad \text{as} \quad k_2 \to 0$$

we get

$$W_{t\ell, t'\ell'}(j, E_2, E_2'; r) = O\left(k_2^{\ell + (1/2)}\right) \quad \text{as} \quad k_2 \to 0$$

The E_2-integral in (18-8) is, therefore, by (17-18) and (17-23)

$$\int_0^\infty \frac{dE_2\, E_2^{\ell + (1/2)}}{\ell_1 - \ell_{10}(k_1)} \cdots \simeq \int_0^\infty \frac{dE_2\, E_2^{\ell + (1/2)}}{\ell_1 - \ell_{10}(k) - cE_2} \cdots$$

$\ell_{10}(k_1)$ being a solution of (18-12), and $k^2 = 2\mu_1 E$. Because of the factor $E_2^{1/2}$ this integral is readily seen to have a branch point of the square root type as a function of ℓ_1 at $\ell_1 = \ell_{10}(k)$. Thus the branch points in the j-plane are of the same nature as those in the E-plane at inelastic thresholds, which are well known to be of the square root type. The present arguments, of course, are applicable to both; α in (18-1) could be taken to be the energy instead of the angular momentum.

We have found, then, in the instance of an infinitely massive particle 3, if the orbital angular momenta introduced are those of particles 1 and 2 about 3 and if we continue j analytically taking ℓ_1 along but keeping ℓ_2 (and $j-\ell_1$) integral, that the S-matrix has infinitely many dynamical, energy-dependent branch points in the complex j-plane; these being images of the Regge poles of the system of particle 1 interacting with 3. The poles of system (2, 3) do not produce branch point images in the same way, because ℓ_2 is not taken into the complex plane along with j. The fact that the bound states (and their "Reggeization") of the (2, 3) system do not produce dynamical branch points in the j-plane when the continuation takes ℓ_1 along, can be seen most directly from the fact that the corresponding branch points in the E-plane are independent of j. These occur, of course, just at the thresholds of the various channels introduced by removing the coordinates of particle 2, and they come from the expression of k_1 in (17-11) for $f^{(0)}$, in terms of E and E_2. All elements of S, even after the analytic continuation in j, will contain these fixed threshold branch points. Now, j-independent singularities in the E-plane cannot correspond to E-dependent singularities in the j-plane.[5] The branch points in the E-plane at the thresholds due to the bound states of the (1, 3) system, on the other hand, do depend on j now; they are determined by (18-12) after setting $\alpha = k_1$. The reason why they occur for each physical, i.e., integral j at the same value of E, is that there are infinitely many of them, spaced one unit of j apart, so that if there is one at $E = E_s$ for $j = j_0$, then there is also one at $E = E_s$ for $j = j_0 \pm 1$.

We could have obtained things the other way around by removing the coordinates of particle 1 instead of those of 2, as in (17-6); V in (17-10) would then be V_2. That would have been appropriate to taking ℓ_2 along with j into the complex plane,[6] setting $\ell_2 = j + t$. In that event the Regge poles of the (2, 3) system would cause branch points, but those of the (1, 3) system would not.

The attentive reader will ask himself at this juncture: What about the bound states and Regge poles of the (1, 2) system? They will not cause cuts in either of the above two procedures, just as the corresponding thresholds do not cause singularities in the E-plane if coordinates and energies are introduced as above; that is, so long as the energy of one of the two moving particles is held fixed, and that of the other follows E (since $E_1 + E_2 = E$). In order for these branch points to occur, the S-matrix (or the amplitude) must be expressed as a function of the center-of-mass energy of particles 1 and 2, and of their energy in the center-of-mass system. If the latter is held fixed, and the former consequently follows E, then there will be branch points in the E-plane at the thresholds due to the bound states and the "ionization" of the (1, 2) system.

Correspondingly we may introduce the coordinates **R** of the center of mass of particles 1 and 2, and **r** of their mutual distance; then, angular momenta canonically conjugate to the rotation of these, L and ℓ. If we now remove R as in and below (17-6), the ψ_ℓ will be <u>free</u> solutions[7] since there is no potential that depends only on **R**. The place of potential V_1 in (17-8) is taken by V_{12}, and W is formed from $V_1 + V_2$. One may now set $\ell = j + t$ and let j become complex, taking ℓ along. The previous argument then shows that the S-matrix <u>so parametrized</u> has infinitely many branch point images of the Regge poles <u>of the (1, 2)</u> system in the complex j-plane. The bound states and their Reggeization, of the (1, 3) and (2, 3) systems will cause no branch points in this way of parametrizing the S-matrix. The singularities depend entirely upon the manner in which variables are introduced in order to exhibit the scattering operator explicitly as a matrix.

There is, however, another way of proceeding after the introduction of the coordinates R and r and of their angular momenta, L and ℓ. We may remove all reference to r, instead of to R. The place of V_2 in (17-6) is then taken by V_{12}, and W is still formed from $V_1 + V_2$. In other words, the channels are now defined by the bound states of the (1, 2) system, and these cause <u>fixed</u> threshold singularities in the E-plane. The place of (17-8) is taken by an equation with $V_1 = 0$, and W contains no diagonal part, i.e., no term proportional to a δ-function in the partial energies. That is because there is no potential which is a function of **R** only. If we now take j into the complex plane, taking L along with it by defining $L = j + t$, the S-matrix has <u>no dynamical branch points</u>. The unit matrix takes the place of $F^{(0)}$ <u>in (17-23)</u>, and in addition to the fixed, kinematical branch points, F^{-1} will contain only poles.[8]

There is, as we see, an important difference between continuing j into the complex plane taking ℓ along while L remains integral, and taking L along while ℓ remains integral. The fundamental reason for that difference is that ℓ is associated with a coordinate that belongs to a possibly isolated system, while L is conjugate to the rotation of a coordinate that does not. No matter how far particle 3 is from the center of mass of the (1, 2) system, the interaction of the latter remains. If we take the angular momentum corresponding to the coordinates describing the isolated interaction of the (1, 2) system, into the complex plane along with j, then its Regge poles cause branch points. But if we keep it integral and instead take the other angular momentum along with j, then no branch points appear.[9]

Looking back now at our first treatment of the three-body problem with infinitely massive particle 3, in which we used directly the coordinates of particles 1 and of 2, we realize that the result of obtaining branch points no matter which ℓ was taken along with j (although different ones), was an accident which disappears as soon as all three particles have finite mass. The discussion introducing coordinates **R** and **r** can immediately be generalized to that case. No matter how we label the particles, we get dynamical cuts in the j-plane if the angular momentum taken along with j is the one corresponding to an interparticle distance. If, instead, we keep that one fixed and take the one along that does not belong to an interparticle distance, then no cuts appear.

It will add to the physical insight to discuss the matter in a somewhat different language which allows for an easier generalization.

Owing to unitarity the open channel part of the S-matrix can be written in terms of the Hermitian $\mathcal{K}$-matrix in the well-known way[10]

$$S^{(+)} = (1 + i\mathcal{K})(1 - i\mathcal{K})^{-1} \tag{18-13}$$

The $\mathcal{K}$-matrix will contain a part that is diagonal in the partial energy. In the language of diagrams (either Feynman, or generated by the generalized unitarity relation) this part is due to the unconnected graphs as in Figure 18-1, and, therefore, it is nothing but a multiple

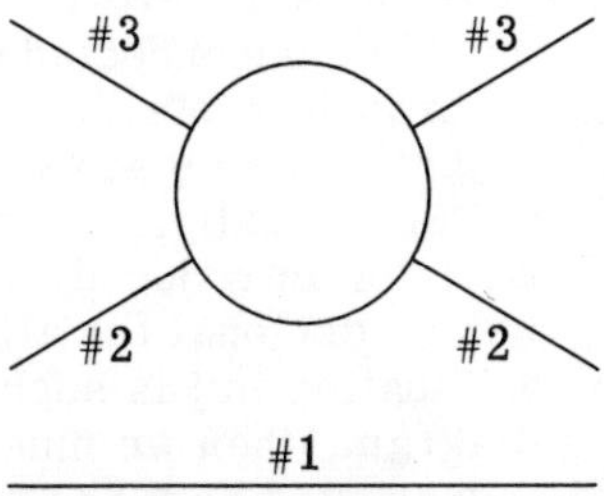

Figure 18-1

A disconnected diagram for three-particle to three-particle processes (the "six-point function").

of the two-body $\mathcal{K}$-matrix. Accordingly we write

$$\mathcal{K} = \mathcal{K}_D + \mathcal{K}' \tag{18-14}$$

where $\mathcal{K}'$ contains no diagonal part (i.e., it is due to connected diagrams only). Then

$$(1 - i\mathcal{K})^{-1} = \left[(1 - i\mathcal{K}_D) - i\mathcal{K}'\right]^{-1}$$

and the arguments following (18-1) are applicable, with $g = 1 - i\mathcal{K}_D$ and $M = i\mathcal{K}'$. Furthermore, (18-2) and (18-3) then again describe the position of the two-particle to two-particle Regge pole, and the results are the same as described previously.

But notice that in order for (18-2) to cause dynamical branch points, it is necessary that the angular momentum of the two-particle system described by $\mathcal{K}_D$ be taken into the complex plane along with j. If it is, the two-particle poles will cause branch points in S. However, if we keep that ℓ fixed and instead take along the other ℓ, which refers to particle 1 relative to the center of mass of particles 2 and 3, and which in $\mathcal{K}_D$ appears only as a Kronecker δ, then no cuts are produced.

In every conventional parametrization of the three-particle S-matrix we have an option of taking one or the other of the two orbital angular momenta along with j, keeping the other fixed. A given parametrization will make the $\mathcal{K}$-matrix diagonal for certain disconnected diagrams, say, such as Figure 18-1. If we take along the angular momentum of the unconnected parts, the Regge poles of the latter cause branch points in S. Moreover, they must each cause infinitely many branch points, shifted by unity relative to one another, because otherwise we could not have threshold branch points in the E-plane whose position is the same for each physical j. But if the angular momentum of the unconnected part is kept fixed and the other is taken along, no branch points appear. The $\mathcal{K}$-matrix parametrized so as to be diagonal for the disconnected diagrams of Figure 18-1, will in general not be diagonal for those of Figure 18-2. In this parametrization then the Regge poles of the unconnected parts of Figure 18-2 (a) and (b) will never cause branch points.

There are, of course, other possible ways of parametrizing the S-matrix (and the $\mathcal{K}$-matrix). Specifically, one may want to avoid the asymmetry between the particles introduced in the conventional method.[11] The $\mathcal{K}$-matrix may then be diagonal for all disconnected diagrams. If the analytic continuation in j is such as to continue the unconnected part of such a diagram, then we must get branch points wherever that continued unconnected part has a pole. But if the continuation is such that the $\mathcal{K}$-matrices of the unconnected parts are kept fixed, then no cuts will appear in the j-plane.

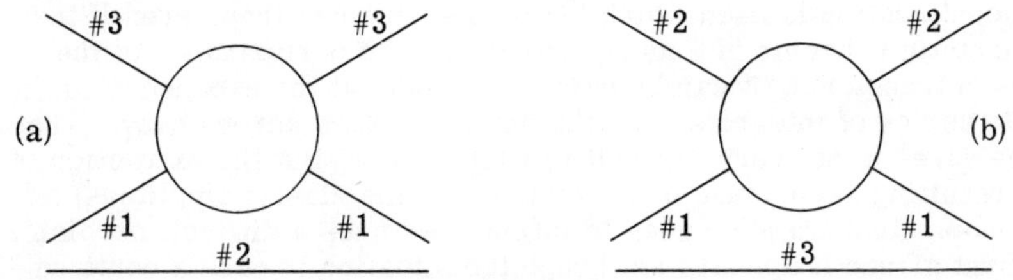

Figure 18-2
Other disconnected diagrams for three-particle to three-particle processes.

It is easy to generalize the foregoing arguments to more than three particles. The "danger" always comes from those disconnected graphs that produce (partially) diagonal pieces of $\mathcal{K}$. We shall always get cuts in the j-plane if the analytic continuation is defined so as to take the angular momentum of the unconnected parts of such diagrams into the complex plane along with j. The branch points and poles of the latter produce branch points in the whole S-matrix. But if the continuation is such that the (partially) diagonal pieces of $\mathcal{K}$ corresponding to unconnected parts remain fixed, then no branch points appear. Those disconnected diagrams which do not make S diagonal in a continuous parameter (such as a partial energy) produce no branch points.

The most important question in the present context is, of course, whether the Watson transform of the amplitudes (elastic or inelastic) can be carried out in the three- (or more) body problem. The answer is, at this writing, quite unknown. There are two separate problems involved which have to be solved before this question can be answered, and they both seem considerably more difficult than those discussed in this book.

The first problem is that of the asymptotic behavior of the S-matrix for large $|j|$. That is complicated not only by the additional integrations and (infinite) matrix multiplications involved, but primarily by the fact that each j is coupled to infinitely many values of ℓ, both to the left, and to the right of it. The left-hand ℓ-plane in the two-body problem acquires additional importance because of this. All the "strange" goings-on in the left-hand plane, which in the two-body problem alone could perhaps be dismissed as of entirely academic interest, now come fully into view, since the right-hand j-plane in the three-body problem is directly coupled to infinitely many, shifted, left-hand ℓ-planes of the two-body problem. It is, therefore, impossible, for example, to determine whether S approaches unity anywhere in the vertical j-direction without answering that question first <u>everywhere</u> in the left half-plane in the two-body problem.

The second problem arises from the possible presence of infinitely many cuts in the j-plane, instead of only a finite number of poles.

If a continuation is used which leads to such cuts, then, even if the asymptotic behavior of S as $|j| \to \infty$ allows the performance of the Watson transform, it can be carried out only at the expense of an infinite series of integrals over the discontinuities across cuts. That, to be sure, is not very difficult to write down. But the extraction of the resulting asymptotic behavior (say, of the elastic amplitude) as the momentum transfer goes to infinity becomes a difficult problem. At first glance it appears as though the situation in such a continuation is hopeless so far as a finite power behavior is concerned. Since there is no right-hand bound to the singularities, it looks as though no equation such as (2-8) can exist. Possibly, however, such an impression is misleading. The original form of the two-body scattering amplitude in terms of an infinite series (2-1) also appears to preclude a behavior such as (2-8) at first sight; but the Watson transform changes all that. Analogously, it may be necessary and possible to carry out a second Watson transform on the infinite series of terms that arises in the three-body problem after the first has been performed. That would, then, necessarily involve making the second angular momentum also independently complex. This program would obviously not be easy to tackle.

It is clear for all these reasons that other things being equal, a continuation in j which avoids the infinity of branch points is to be much preferred. The question is, however, if other things are equal. That will primarily depend on the asymptotic behavior of S for large complex j. If the meromorphic continuation is unique in the sense of the Carlson theorem (see Chapter 15) then it is, of course, <u>the</u> one to be used. In the absence of a proof of this, we cannot tell whether the continuation which leads to cuts may not be preferable. In contrast to the situation in the two-body problem, there is no unique "dynamical" continuation in the more than two-particle case (even neglecting the more trivial ambiguities that arise in the continuation of the Schrödinger equation) dictated solely by the equations of motion. The S-matrix interpolation in that case can be made unique at best by a Carlson criterion. Another possibility is, of course, that none of the discussed dynamical continuations in the three- (or more) body problem allow a proof of a momentum transfer dispersion relation with a finite number of subtractions via the Watson transform, and yet such a dispersion relation may nevertheless be true. Then the "right" continuation would differ from all the dynamical ones. Such a situation would, from a physical point of view, be most unpalatable.

Notes and References

1. The argument here follows (N2) and (N3).
2. See (N9).
3. Branch cuts in the angular momentum plane were first argued to exist by Amati et al. (A4), but their argument, based on summing a partial set of diagrams in the relativistic theory,

was not conclusive. The first demonstration of their existence in a special nonrelativistic model is due to Drummond (D6). The general proof for the nonrelativistic three-body problem was first given in (N2).

4. See, for example (N8).
5. Essentially this argument has been used, for example by Oehme (O4), against the existence of moving branch points in the j-plane. The double dispersion relation is there taken for granted. Since in the relativistic domain neither the Mandelstam representation nor the meromorphy of the amplitude in the j-plane have been proved, it is a matter of conjecture whether branch points in the j-plane may be expected to be absent (in the "right" interpolation) on the basis of the double dispersion relation, or whether, on the basis of the branch points in j, the Mandelstam representation can be expected to be incorrect.
6. Removing the coordinates of particle 2 is not convenient for taking ℓ_2 along with j because, although there may still be completeness of the continued wave functions for negative ℓ, the integrals in the coefficients (for the nonsense terms) are not directly defined.
7. An alternative possibility is to put the diagonal elements of $V_1 + V_2$ into (17-6) and to take them out of (17-8).
8. There is, however, always the possibility that a divergence in the ℓ-summations causes further singularities. That has not been investigated at this writing.
9. This point has been made independently by J. B. Hartle in two papers listed in the Supplementary Bibliography; see also R. G. Newton, in a letter listed there.
10. Because of the lack of unitarity of $S^{(+)}$ for nonintegral values of j, as shown in (17-39), $\mathcal{K}$ is not Hermitian now, but

$$\mathcal{K}^{\dagger} = M\mathcal{K}M$$

However, that is of no consequence.
11. At proofreading time a symmetric treatment was introduced and carried rather far in a series of three preprints by R. L. Omnes (University of California, Lawrence Radiation Laboratory, Berkeley). The method has much to recommend itself over the one presented here. First indications are that the analytic interpolation of S based upon it, leads to no dynamical branch points in the j-plane. But at this writing that has not been conclusively established, nor has the Watson transform been shown to be possible with it.

Appendix A

BOUNDS ON THE GREEN'S FUNCTIONS

We want to prove here some bounds on the Green's function (3-5) for real values of k. The function g being even in λ, we may assume that $\eta = \mathrm{Re}\,\lambda \geq 0$.

$J_\lambda(z)$ is readily estimated by means of Hankel's integral[1]

$$J_\lambda(z) = \frac{(\frac{1}{2}z)^\lambda}{\Gamma(\frac{1}{2})\Gamma(\frac{1}{2}+\lambda)}\int_0^\pi d\varphi\, \sin^{2\lambda}\varphi\, \cos(z\cos\varphi) \tag{A-1}$$

Since

$$\int_0^\pi d\varphi\, \sin^{2\lambda}\varphi\, \cos(z\cos\varphi) = \int_0^\pi d\varphi\, \sin^{2\lambda}\varphi + \int_0^\pi d\varphi\, \sin^{2\lambda}\varphi \times [\cos(z\cos\varphi) - 1]$$

and[2]

$$\int_0^\pi d\varphi\, \sin^{2\lambda}\varphi = \frac{\Gamma(\frac{1}{2})\Gamma(\frac{1}{2}+\lambda)}{\Gamma(1+\lambda)} = O(\lambda^{-1/2}) \quad \text{as} \quad |\lambda| \to \infty$$

we conclude that

$$\left|\int_0^\pi\right| \leq C|\lambda|^{-1/2}$$

uniformly in z (for some C), and hence (for positive z)

$$|J_\lambda(z)| \leq C(\tfrac{1}{2}z)^\eta |\lambda|^{-1/2} / |\Gamma(\tfrac{1}{2} + \lambda)| \qquad \text{(A-2)}$$

Hankel's integral may also be used when $-\frac{1}{2} < \eta \leq 0$. Consequently for $\eta < \frac{1}{2}$ we have

$$\begin{aligned} |J_\lambda(z) J_{-\lambda}(z') \csc \pi\lambda| &\leq (z/z')^\eta C |\Gamma(\tfrac{1}{2} + \lambda)\Gamma(\tfrac{1}{2} - \lambda) \sin \pi\lambda|^{-1} |\lambda|^{-1} \\ &= (z/z')^\eta C' |\lambda|^{-1} \end{aligned}$$

and hence

$$|g(r, r')| \leq C|\lambda|^{-1}(r_</r_>)^{-\eta}(rr')^{1/2} \qquad \text{(A-3)}$$

When $-\frac{3}{2} < \text{Re}\,\lambda < -\frac{1}{2}$ and $|\text{Im}\,\lambda| \geq \nu_0 > 0$ we avail ourselves of the recurrence formula

$$J_\lambda(z) = 2(\lambda + 1)z^{-1} J_{\lambda+1} - J_{\lambda+2}$$

the right-hand side of which can be estimated by (A-2):

$$\begin{aligned} |J_\lambda(z)| &\leq C' \frac{(\frac{1}{2}z)^\eta}{|\lambda|^{1/2} |\Gamma(\frac{1}{2} + \lambda)|} + C'' \frac{(\frac{1}{2}z)^{\eta+2}}{|\lambda|^{1/2} |\Gamma(\frac{5}{2} + \lambda)|} \\ &\leq C''' \frac{(\frac{1}{2}z)^\eta \left(1 + (\frac{1}{2}z)^\eta\right)}{|\lambda|^{1/2} |\Gamma(\frac{1}{2} + \lambda)|} \end{aligned}$$

We proceed by induction and find for $\text{Re}\,\lambda < \frac{1}{2} + n$, $|\text{Im}\,\lambda| \geq \nu_0 > 0$, and positive z,

$$|J_{-\lambda}(z)| \leq C[1 + (\tfrac{1}{2}z)^{2n}] \frac{(\frac{1}{2}z)^{-\eta}}{|\lambda|^{1/2} |\Gamma(\frac{1}{2} - \lambda)|} \qquad \text{(A-4)}$$

This proves that the inequality

$$|g(r, r')| \leq C|\lambda|^{-1}(r_>/r_<)^\eta [1 + (\tfrac{1}{2}kr_>)^{2n}](rr')^{1/2} \qquad \text{(A-5)}$$

holds uniformly in the region $\nu \geq \nu_0 > 0$, $|\eta| < \frac{1}{2} + n$. It can thus be used for letting $\nu \to \pm\infty$ while η is fixed in $-\frac{1}{2} - n < \eta < \frac{1}{2} + n$. Since g is even in k, (A-5) holds both for positive and negative k.

We may use (A-2) and (A-4) for an estimate on the Hankel function. For positive z, $|\eta| < \frac{1}{2} + n$, $|\nu| \geq \nu_0 > 0$, we find by Stirling's formula

$$\left|H_\lambda^{(2)}(z)\right| \leq |\lambda|^{-1/2} e^{-(1/2)\pi|\nu|}[1 + (\tfrac{1}{2}z)^{2n}][C_1 e^{-\pi\nu}(z/2|\lambda|)^{\eta} + C_2(z/2|\lambda|)^{-\eta}] \quad \text{(A-6)}$$

In order to derive a bound useful when $\eta \to \infty$ we look directly at the integral equation

$$\mathcal{G}(r, r') = g_0(r, r') - k^2 \int_{r'}^{r} dr'' \, g_0(r, r'')\mathcal{G}(r'', r') \quad \text{(A-7)}$$

satisfied by the Green's function

$$\mathcal{G}(r, r') = \begin{cases} g(r, r') & r' < r \\ 0 & r' > r \end{cases}$$

where

$$g_0(r, r') = (rr')^{1/2}[(r/r')^{\lambda} - (r'/r)^{\lambda}]/2\lambda$$

By writing

$$\zeta(t) = F(r't, r')$$

$$F(r, r') = 2\lambda(rr')^{-1/2}(r'/r)^{\lambda}\mathcal{G}(r, r')$$

we get for $t > 1$

$$\zeta(t) = 1 - t^{-2\lambda} - \frac{(kr')^2}{2\lambda}\int_1^t dt' \, t'[1 - (t'/t)^{2\lambda}]\zeta(t')$$

$$= 1 - t^{-2\lambda} - (kr')^2\int_1^t dt' \int_1^{t'} dt'' \, (t''/t')^{1 + 2\lambda}\zeta(t'') \quad \text{(A-8)}$$

Consequently for all Re $\lambda \geq 0$

$$|\zeta(t)| \leq 1 + |kr'|^2 \int_1^t dt' \int_1^{t'} dt'' |\zeta(t'')|$$

Since both (A-6) and

$$\xi(t) = 1 + |kr'|^2 \int_i^t dt' \int_i^{t'} dt'' \, \xi(t'')$$

can always be solved by iteration it follows that

$$|\zeta(t)| \le \xi(t) = \cosh |k| r'(t - 1)$$

We, therefore, have the uniform bound

$$|g(r, r')| \le C|\lambda|^{-1}(rr')^{1/2}(r_>/r_<)^{|\eta|} e^{|k|(r_> - r_<)} \tag{A-9}$$

for all values of r, r', k, and λ.

Notes and References

1. See Whittaker and Watson (W6), p. 366.
2. This follows at once from Hankel's integral by letting $z \to 0$ and using the value of J_λ near $z = 0$.

Appendix B

LIMITATIONS ON THE PHASE-SHIFT DERIVATIVE

The continuous connection of S-matrix elements of different angular momenta implies certain relations between successive phase shifts which we want to derive here.

If we define

$$\Delta \equiv \arg F(\lambda, k) \tag{B-1}$$

and the phase shift is defined by

$$\delta \equiv \tfrac{1}{2} \arg S \tag{B-2}$$

then by (5-18) and (5-4) for real λ and k,

$$\delta = \Delta + \tfrac{1}{2}\pi(\lambda - \tfrac{1}{2}) \tag{B-3}$$

Integrate (7-3), with $\psi = \phi$, from r = 0 to r = ∞, and use (5-1). That yields for positive k and λ

$$-|F|^2 \,\partial\Delta/\partial\lambda = 2\lambda k \int_0^\infty dr\, r^{-2} \phi^2 > 0 \tag{B-4}$$

and, consequently,

$$\frac{\partial\Delta}{\partial\lambda} < 0$$

By (B-3) that implies

$$\frac{\partial\delta}{\partial\lambda} < \tfrac{1}{2}\pi \qquad \text{(B-5)}$$

and a fortiori[1]

$$\delta_{\ell+1} - \delta_\ell < \tfrac{1}{2}\pi \qquad \text{(B-6)}$$

The inequality (B-5) is well known in the semiclassical approximation. Since the WKB phase shift δ is connected to the classical deflection function Θ by

$$\Theta = 2\partial\delta/\partial\ell$$

(B-5) states the simple fact that $\Theta < \pi$. (It must be remembered that Θ is so defined that "orbiting" is described by a large negative Θ.)

Equation (B-4) tells us explicitly that $\partial\delta/\partial\lambda \to 0$ as $k \to \infty$, since in that limit ϕ approaches ϕ_0. That all the phase shifts must approach the same multiple of 2π at infinite energy is, of course, a consequence of the fact that the S-matrix has been so defined that it approaches unity as $E \to \infty$ for all λ, not just for integral ℓ. Only within the context of such a restriction on the phase-shift definition does the inequality (B-5) have any meaning. We may assume then that all phase shifts have been defined to vanish at infinite energy.

Consider now a case in which the p-wave has a sharp resonance at some energy E_0 in the vicinity of which the s- and d-waves are smoothly varying functions of the energy. Let the p-wave below resonance be positive and less than $\frac{1}{2}\pi$, so that $\sin^2\delta_1 = 1$ before $\sin^2\delta_1 = 0$; i.e., it looks as indicated in Figure B-1. Equation (B-6) applied to $\ell = 0$ just above E_0 then says

$$\delta_0 > A > \tfrac{1}{2}\pi \qquad \text{(B-7)}$$

which implies that there exists either an s-wave bound state[2] or else an s-wave resonance below E_0. This physically quite intuitive result is a simple extension of the well-known fact that the p-wave cannot support a bound state unless the s-wave has one at a lower energy. It should be noted that it refers directly to physically observable resonances in the sense that $\sin^2\delta = 1$, and not merely to S-matrix poles, which may or may not be visible as resonances.

In the same situation described above we may also apply (B-6) to $\ell = 1$ just below E_0. Then we get

$$\delta_2 < A \qquad \text{(B-7')}$$

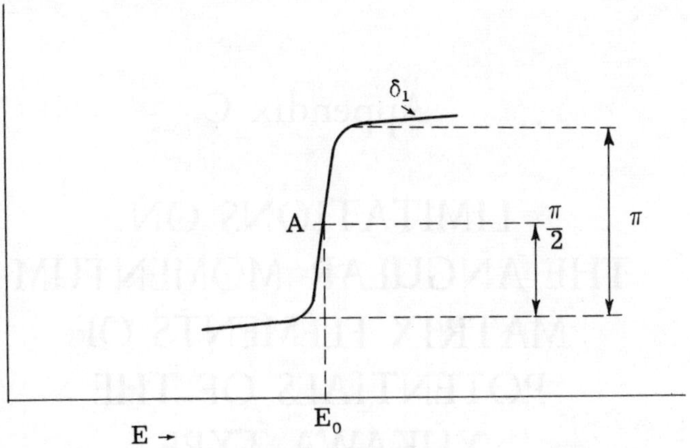

Figure B-1

Schematic representation of a p-wave phase shift as a function of the energy near a sharp resonance.

The two inequalities (B-7) and (B-7') may serve to determine whether or not an experimentally given resonance is caused by a local, single channel potential.

It is easy to generalize[3] (B-6) to the case of two spin-$\frac{1}{2}$ particles in the triplet state of parity $(-)^{j+1}$. In that instance we get for $j \geq 1$

$$\delta_{j+1} - \delta_j < \pi \tag{B-8}$$

where δ is the sum of the eigenphase shifts. No restriction is known for the difference between the sum of the $j = 1$ phase shifts, and the $j = 0$ phase shift.

Notes and References

1. This was first derived by Regge (R1).
2. We use the Levinson theorem.
3. For the derivation, see Desai and Newton (D3).

Appendix C

LIMITATIONS ON THE ANGULAR MOMENTUM MATRIX ELEMENTS OF POTENTIALS OF THE YUKAWA TYPE

We want to prove here (17-19). Assume that V_{12} is of the Yukawa type (3-8), so that

$$V_{12}(|\mathbf{r}_1 - \mathbf{r}_2|) = \int d\mu\ \rho(\mu) e^{-\mu|\mathbf{r}_1 - \mathbf{r}_2|} |\mathbf{r}_1 - \mathbf{r}_2|^{-1}$$
$$= 4\pi \int d\mu\ \rho(\mu) G(i\mu; \mathbf{r}_1, \mathbf{r}_2) \qquad \text{(C-1)}$$

where G is the well-known, free, two-particle Green's function. Therefore[1]

$$V_{12}(|\mathbf{r}_1 - \mathbf{r}_2|) = -2i(r_1 r_2)^{-1/2} \sum_{\ell m} (-)^{\ell} Y_{\ell}^{m}(\mathbf{r}_1) Y_{\ell}^{m*}(\mathbf{r}_2)$$
$$\times \int d\mu\ \rho(\mu) J_{\ell + (1/2)}(i\mu r_<) H^{(2)}_{\ell + (1/2)}(-i\mu r_>) \qquad \text{(C-2)}$$

Inserting this in (17-9) and (17-4) we obtain

$$W_{\ell_1\ell_2, \ell_1'\ell_2'}(j; E_2, E_2'; r) = -2i \sum_{\substack{\ell m \\ m_1 m_2 m_1' m_2'}} C_{\ell_1\ell_2}(jMm_1m_2) C_{\ell_1'\ell_2'}(jMm_1'm_2')$$
$$\times A^{m_1 m_1' m}_{\ell_1 \ell_1' \ell} A^{m_2' m_2 m*}_{\ell_2' \ell_2 \ell} \int d\mu \mu \rho(\mu)$$
$$\times \left[r^{-1/2} J_{\ell + (1/2)}(i\mu r) \int_{r_2 > r} dr_2\ r_2^{-1/2} \right.$$
$$\times H^{(2)}_{\ell + (1/2)}(-i\mu r_2) \psi^*_{\ell_2} \psi_{\ell_2'}$$

$$+ r^{-1/2} H^{(2)}_{\ell + (1/2)}(-i\mu r) \int_{r_2 < r} dr_2\, r_2^{-1/2}$$

$$\times J_{\ell + (1/2)}(i\mu r_2) \psi^*_{\ell_2} \psi_{\ell_2'} \Big] \qquad \text{(C-3)}$$

where[2]

$$A^{m_1 m_1' m}_{\ell_1 \ell_1' \ell} \equiv \int d\Omega\, Y^{m_1^*}_{\ell_1}(\mathbf{r}) Y^{m_1'}_{\ell_1'}(\mathbf{r}) Y^{m}_{\ell}(\mathbf{r})$$

$$= (-)^{j + m_1'} \left[\frac{(2\ell_1 + 1)(2\ell_1' + 1)}{4\pi(2s + 1)!} (2s - 2\ell_1)!(2s - 2\ell_1')! \right.$$

$$\left. \times (2s - 2\ell)! \right]^{1/2} \frac{s!\, \cos \pi s}{(s - \ell_1)!(s - \ell_1')!(s - \ell)!}$$

$$\times C_{\ell_1 \ell_1'}(\ell m m_1 - m_1')$$

$$= 0 \qquad \text{unless} \qquad |\ell_1 - \ell_1'| \leq \ell \leq \ell_1 + \ell_1' \qquad \text{(C-4)}$$

(with $2s = \ell_1 + \ell_1' + \ell$). The integrand in the first integral in (C-3) is $O(r_2^{\ell_2 + \ell_2' + 1 - \ell})$ as $r_2 \to 0$; and since, because of the second factor of A and (C-4), only $\ell \leq \ell_{12} + \ell_2'$ contribute to the sum, the integral is finite as $r \to 0$. Consequently the first term in the bracket is $O(r^{\ell})$ and, therefore, because of the first factor of A and (C-4), $O(r^{|\ell_1 - \ell_1'|})$.

The integrand in the second integral in the bracket is $O(r_2^{\ell_2 + \ell_2' + \ell + 1})$ and, therefore, the second term is $O(r^{\ell_2 + \ell_2' + 2})$ as $r \to 0$. But because of the two factors of A and (C-4) we must have $|\ell_1 - \ell_1'| \leq \ell_2 + \ell_2'$; otherwise at least one of the A-factors vanishes. Hence the second term in the bracket is dominated by the first, and (17-19) follows. The result could, of course, break down if $\rho(\mu)$ is not sufficiently well behaved as $\mu \to \infty$.

We may take part of (C-4) explicitly into account by restricting the sum on ℓ in (C-3) to

$$\max\,[|\ell_1 - \ell_1'|, |\ell_2 - \ell_2'|] \leq \ell \leq \ell_2 + \ell_2'$$

or, after introducing $\ell_1 = j + t$,

$$\max\,[|t - t'|, |\ell_2 - \ell_2'|] \leq \ell \leq \ell_2 + \ell_2'$$

Subsequently j may be made continuous and complex, and the argument leading to (17-19) goes through as before.

Notes and References

1. See, for example (N8).
2. This follows from the result of Gaunt (G20), p. 194, Eq. (9) and a closed form by Racah for the Clebsch-Gordan coefficients; see for example, Edmonds (E1), p. 44, Eq. (3.6.10).

BIBLIOGRAPHY

The bibliography is split into four parts. The first contains the papers on complex angular momenta in nonrelativistic Schrödinger theory; the second, those dealing with them in relativistic theory and with applications. There are some papers which straddle both; they have been put in the category suggested by their emphasis. An attempt has been made to make the list as complete as possible, but omissions, particularly in the relativistic category, have no doubt crept in; I apologize to the authors whose work I overlooked. The cut-off date was May 1963. A number of papers of whose existence I knew in the form of preprints or otherwise but which were published at a later date are, nevertheless, included. The third part is a list of relevant papers that were published or came to my attention after the manuscript was finished. It takes into account all journals to which I had access by January 10, 1964, which includes PR; PRL; Ann Phys; and JETP (transl.) through December 15, 1963; NC through Nov. 1; JMP, Nov.; Progr Theo Phys, Oct.; PL, Dec. 1; Nucl Phys, November; and JETP (Russian) through November 1963. The fourth part is a list of other papers and books referred to in the text.

In order to make the bibliography useful for those who want to study specific points, the title of all papers are included. The following abbreviations have been used:

Ampl	Amplitude	Disp	Dispersion
Anal	Analytic, Analyticity	E	Energy
AM	Angular Momentum	Eq	Equation
Approx	Approximation	H	High
Asy	Asymptotic	Nonrel	Nonrelativistic
Beh	Behavior	P	Pole
C	Complex	Pert	Perturbation
Cont	Continuation	Pl	Plane
Diffr	Diffraction	Pot	Potential

Prop	Property	Sing	Singularity
R	Regge	SM	S-Matrix
Rel	Relativistic, relation	Theo	Theory
Rep	Representation	Traj	Trajectory
Scatt	Scattering	U	Unitarity

In addition, the journals have been abbreviated:

Ann Phys	Annals of Physics (New York)
CERN	Proceedings of the 1962 International High Energy Physics Conference at CERN, Geneva; publisher CERN, Geneva, 1962
JETP	Journal of Experimental and Theoretical Physics of the Academy of Sciences of the USSR; in brackets after the original Russian reference, there appears the reference to the translation in Soviet Physics, JETP
JMP	The Journal of Mathematical Physics
NC	Il Nuovo Cimento
PL	Physics Letters
PR	The Physical Review
PRL	Physical Review Letters
prep	preprint (unpublished)
UCRL	a preprint from the Lawrence Radiation Laboratory at the University of California (Berkeley)

Nonrelativistic Theory

(A1) Ahmadzadeh, A., P. G. Burke, and C. Tate, UCRL 10140 (1962): R Traj for a Single Attractive Yukawa Pot.

(A2) Ahmadzadeh, A., P. G. Burke, and C. Tate, PR **131**, 1315 (1963): R Traj for Yukawa Pot.

(A3) Ahmadzadeh, A., and I. A. Sakmar, PL **5**, 145 (1963): An Approx Method for R Traj and Its Implications on the Spin 2 Particle of the Chew-Frautschi Diagram.

(B1) Barut, A. O., and F. Calogero, PR **128**, 1383 (1962): Sing in AM of the Scatt Ampl for a Class of Soluble Pot.

(B2) Belinfante, J. G., and B. C. Unal, JMP **4**, 372 (1963): Pot Scatt.

(B3) Berendt, G., NC **27**, 550 (1963): A Remark about RP for Hard Core Pot.

(B4) Bethe, H. A., and T. Kinoshita, PR **128**, 1418 (1962): Beh of RP in a Pot at Large E.

(B5) Blankenbecler, R., and M. L. Goldberger, PR **126**, 766 (1962): Beh of Scatt Ampl at HE, Bound States, and Resonances.

(B6) Bollini, C. G., and J. J. Giambiagi, NC **26**, 619 (1962) and NC **28**, 341 (1963): R Traj for the Square Well Pot.

(B7) Bottino, A., A. M. Longoni, and T. Regge, NC **23**, 954 (1962): Pot Scatt for CE and AM.

(B8) Bottino, A., and A. M. Longoni, NC **24**, 353 (1962): Holomorphy Domain of the SM in Pot Scatt.

(B9) Brander, O., PL **4**, 218 (1963): On AM Anal in Hard Core Pot.

(B10) Burke, P. G., and C. Tate, CERN, 507: Calc of R Traj by Using Disp Rel.

(C1) Calogero F., NC **28**, 66 (1963): Anal Cont and Asy Beh of the SM in AM in Pot Scatt

(C2) Calogero F., NC **28**, 761 (1963): Asy Beh of the SM in Pot Scatt for Large Imaginary Values of the AM.

(C3) Calogero, F., J. M. Charap, and E. J. Squires, Ann Phys **25**, 325 (1963): Cont in Total AM of the Partial Wave Scatt Ampl for Particles with Spin.

(C4) Calogero, F., and J. M. Charap, Ann Phys **26**, 55 (1964): On the Born Approx in the Pot Scatt of Particles with Arbitrary Spin.

(C5) Calogero, F., and J. M. Charap, Ann Phys **26**, 44 (1964): Anal Prop in E of the C J Partial Wave Ampl in the Scatt of Particles with Spin.

(C6) Cassandro M., M. Cini, G. Jona-Lasinio, and L. Sertorio, NC **28**, 1351 (1963): Pert Expansions of RP Traj for Yukawa Pot.

(C7) Challifour, J., and R. J. Eden, JMP **4**, 359 (1963): RP and Branch Cuts for Pot Scatt.

(C8) Chan, Hong-Mo, prep (1963): Real Unitary Rep of the Many Channel SM for C l and E.

(C9) Charap, J. M., and E. J. Squires, PR **127**, 1387 (1962): Factorization of the Residues of R P.

(C10-12) Charap, J.M., and E. J. Squires, Ann Phys **20**, 145 (1962); **21**, 8 (1963); **25**, 143 (1963): On CAM in Many-Channel Pot Scatt Problems, I, II and III.

(C13) Cheng, H., PR **127**, 647 (1962): Meromorphic Prop of the SM in the C Pl of AM.

(C14) Cheng, H., PR **130**, 1283 (1963): Disp Rel for the R Parameters.

(C15) Cheng, H., and R. Nunez-Lagos, NC **26**, 177 (1962): The Uniqueness of the Anal Cont of Partial Wave Ampl in the C Pl of AM.

(C16) Cornwall, J. M., and M. A. Ruderman, PR **128**, 1474 (1962): Mandelstam Rep and RP with Absorptive E-Dependent Pot.

(D1) de Alfaro, V., E. Predazzi, and C. Rossetti, NC **30**, 522 (1963): A Pert Expansion for Large AM.

(D2) de Alfaro, V., T. Regge, and C. Rossetti, NC **26**, 1029 (1962): Dynamical Eq and AM.

(D3) Desai, B. P., and R. G. Newton, PR **129**, 1437 (1963): AMP of the Nonrel SM for Spin $\frac{1}{2}$ Particles.

(D4) Desai, B. P., and R. G. Newton, PR **129**, 1445 (1963): Rep of the SM in Terms of Its AMP.

(D5) Desai, B. P., and R. G. Newton, PR **130**, 2109 (1963): Threshold Motion of RP.

(D6) Drummond, I. T., Ann Phys **23**, 284 (1963): R Cuts and Three Particle States in a Nonrel Model.

(F1) Favella, L., and M. T. Reineri, NC **23**, 616 (1962): Prop of the SM As a Function of the CAM for the Many-Channel Case and for the Dirac Eq.

(F2) Fenster, S., Nucl Phys **38**, 638 (1962): An Investigation of Coulomb Scatt Ampl in the CAMPl.

(F3) Froissart, M., JMP **3**, 922 (1962): CAM in Pot Scatt.

(G1) Gell-Mann, M., PRL **8**, 263 (1962): Factorization of Coupling to RP.

(J1) Jaffe, A. M., and Y. S. Kim, PR **127**, 2261 (1962): CAM in Two-Channel Problems.

(J2) Jaffe, A. M., and Y. S. Kim, PR **129**, 2818 (1963): Asy Beh of the SM for H AM.

(J3) Jones, E., UCRL 10700: Anal of RP Terms.

(K1) Kaufman, A. M., NC **27**, 804 (1963): Elimination of the Background Integral in the R Formula.

(K2) Kaus, P., NC **29**, 598 (1963): R Traj for Pot Scatt at Negative AM.

(K3) Kaus, P., and C. J. Pearson, NC **28**, 500 (1963): Jost Function and Determinantal Method in Pot Scatt.

(K4) Kazes, E., NC **27**, 995 (1963): Soluble Models in Many Body Scatt and CAM.

(K5) Khuri, N. N., PR **130**, 429 (1963): An Extension of the R Rep.

(L1) Lovelace, C., and D. Masson, CERN, 510; NC **26**, 472 (1962): Calculation of RP by Continued Fractions.

(M1) Mandelstam, S., Ann Phys **19**, 254 (1962): An Extension of the R Formula.

(M2) Martin, A., PL **1**, 72 (1962): Remarks on the Prolongation of a Scatt Ampl in the CAMPl.

(M3) Mitra, A. N., and J. D. Arnand, PR **130**, 2117 (1963): Separable Pot in the Cl-Pl.

(N1) Newton, R. G., JMP **3**, 867 (1962) and **4**, 1342 (1963): Nonrel SMP for CAM.

(N2) Newton, R. G., NC **29**, 400 (1963): The total AMPl in the Nonrel Three Body Problem.

(N3) Newton, R. G., PL **4**, 11 (1963): Discontinuities across Cuts in CAMPl.

(P1) Patashinskii, A. Z., V. L. Pokrovskii, and I. M. Khalatnikov, JETP **43**, 1117 (1962) [**16**, 788 (1963)]: RP in Nonrel Quantum Mechanics.

(P2) Predazzi, E., and T. Regge, NC **24**, 518 (1962): The Maximum Anal Principle in the AM.

(P3) Prosperi, G. M., NC **24**, 957 (1962): On the Uniqueness of the Anal Cont of the SM in AM.

(R1) Regge, T., NC **14**, 951 (1959): Introduction to C Orbital M.

(R2) Regge, T., NC **18**, 947 (1960): Bound States, Shadow States, and Mandelstam Rep.

(R3) Regge, T., CERN, 503: Topics on CAM.

(R4) Regge, T., and G.A. Viano, NC **25**, 709 (1962): The Interpolation Problem in the Theo of CAM.

(S1) Singh, V., PR **127**, 632 (1962): Anal in the CAMPl of the Coulomb Scatt Ampl.

(S2) Squires, E.J., NC **25**, 242 (1962): On the Continuation of the Partial Wave Ampl to C l.

(T1) Tani, S., JMP **4**, 1258 (1963): RP in HE Pot Scatt.

(T2) Taylor, J.R., PR **127**, 2257 (1962): Anal of the Position and Residues of RP.

Relativistic Theory and Applications

(A4) Amati, D., S. Fubini, and A. Stanghellini, PL **1**, 29 (1962): Asy Prop of Scatt and Multiple Production.

(A5) Amati, D., S. Fubini, and A. Stanghellini, CERN, 560: Theo of HE Scatt and Multiple Production.

(A6) Amati, D., A. Stanghellini, and K. Wilson, NC **28**, 639 (1963): Theo of Fermion RP.

(A7) Amati, D., M. Cini, and A. Stanghellini, PL **4**, 270 (1963) and NC **30**, 193 (1963): Diffr Scatt in the Multiperipheral Model.

(A8) Arbuzov, B.A., et al. PL **2**, 150 (1962): The Asy Beh of the Scatt Ampl and the Renormalization Group Method.

(A9) Arbuzov, B.A., et al., PL **2**, 305 (1962); **4**, 272 (1963): RP and Pert Theo.

(A10) Azimov, Ya. I., PL **3**, 195 (1962): The Influence of Spin as the Position of RP.

(B11) Balázs, L.A.P., PRL **10**, 170 (1963): Pion Resonances, RP, and the Chew-Frautschi Saturation Principle.

(B12) Bardakci, K., PR **127**, 1832 (1962): CAM in Field Theo (included in this volume).

(B13) Bardakci, K., PR **130**, 369 (1963): N/D Method for C Partial Waves.

(B14) Barut, A.O., PR **126**, 1873 (1962): Virtual Particles.

(B15) Barut, A.O., PR **128**, 1959 (1962): Anal in AM of the Rel Many-Channel SM from Disp Rel and U.

(B16) Barut, A.O., I. Muzinich, and D.N. Williams, PR **130**, 442 (1963): Construction of Invariant Scatt Ampl for Arbitrary Spin and Anal Cont in Total AM.

(B17) Barut, A.O., and D. Zwanziger, PR **127**, 974 (1962): CAM in Rel SM Theo.

(B18) Berestetsky, V.B., PL **3**, 175 (1963): On the Removal of the "Ghost" on the Vacuum P Traj.

(B19) Bertocchi, L., S. Fubini, and M. Tonin, NC **25**, 626 (1962): Integral Eq for HE Pion-Pion Scatt.

(B20) Blankenbecler, R., L.F. Cook, and M.L. Goldberger, PRL **8**, 463 (1962): Is the Photon on Elementary Particle?

(B21) Budini, P., PRL **10**, 384 (1963): RP in Renormalizable Field Theo.

(C17) Challifour, J., and R.J. Eden, PR **129**, 2349 (1963): R Surfaces and Sing in the Rel Theo.

(C18) Cheng, H., and D. Sharp, Ann Phys **22**, 481 (1963): On the Dynamical Determination of the RP Parameters.

(C19) Chew, G. F., CERN, 525: Strong Interaction Theo without Elementary Particles.

(C20) Chew, G. F., PR **129**, 2363 (1963): Self-consistent SM with R Asy Beh.

(C21) Chew, G. F., and S. Frautschi, PRL **5**, 580 (1960): Unified Approach to H and Low E Strong Interactions on the Basis of the Mandelstam Rep.

(C22) Chew, G. F., and S. Frautschi, PRL **7**, 394 (1961): Principle of Equivalence for All Strongly Interacting Particles within the SM Framework.

(C23) Chew, G. F., and S. Frautschi, PRL **8**, 41 (1962): R Traj and the Principle of Maximum Strength for Strong Interactions.

(C24) Chew, G. F., S. Frautschi, and S. Mandelstam, PR **126**, 1202 (1962): RP in π-π Scatt (included in this volume).

(C25) Contogouris, A. P., PL **3**, 103 (1962): Possible Tests of the Elementarity of the Photon and the Electron.

(C26) Contogouris, A. P., S. Frautschi, and H. S. Wong, PR **129**, 974 (1963): RP and Inelastic Scatt at HE.

(D7) Domokos, G., NC **23**, 1175 (1962): On the Asy Beh of the Elastic $\pi\pi$ and πN Scatt Ampl.

(D8) Domokos, G., CERN, 553: RP and HE Scatt.

(D9) Drell, S. D., CERN, 897: HE Physics.

(F4) Frautschi, S. C., NC **28**, 409 (1963): Strong Damping of Large M Transfer and Its Consequences for HE Inelastic Processes.

(F5) Frautschi, S. C., M. Gell-Mann, and F. Zachariasen, PR **126**, 2204 (1962): Experimental Consequences of the Hypothesis of RP (included in this volume).

(F6) Frazer, W. F., PR **131**, 491 (1963): Some Experimental Consequences of RP.

(F7) Freund, P. G. O., PL **3**, 123 (1962): How Different is the R Traj of the ρ-Meson from a Straight Line?

(F8) Freund, P. G. O., NC **28**, 263 (1963): N/D Calculation of the Pomeranchuk and ρ-R Traj.

(F9) Freund, P. G. O., and R. Oehme, PR **129**, 2361 (1963): Lower Bound for the Leading R Traj.

(F10) Freund, P. G. O., and R. Oehme, PRL **10**, 199 and 315 (1963): Vector Mesons and the Pomeranchuk Traj.

(F11) Froissart, M., PR **123**, 1053 (1962): Asy Beh and Subtractions in the Mandelstam Rep.

(F12) Frye, G., PRL **8**, 494 (1962): Remark on Diffr Scatt.

(F13) Frye, G., PR **129**, 1453 (1963): Two Pomeranchuk-R Traj.

(G2) Gatland, I. R., and J. W. Moffat, PR **129**, 2812 (1963): Sing in the AMPl.

(G3) Gell-Mann, M., CERN, 533: Applications of RP.

(G4-5) Gell-Mann, M., and M. L. Goldberger, PRL **9**, 275 (1962) and **10**, 39 (1963) and with F. E. Low and F. Zachariasen, PL **4**,

265 (1963): Elementary Particles of Conventional Field Theo As RP.

(G6) Gribov, V.N., JETP **41**, 667 (1961)[**14**, 478 (1962)]: Possible Asy Beh of Elastic Scatt.

(G7) Gribov, V.N., JETP **41**, 1962 (1961)[**14**, 1395 (1962)]: Partial Waves with C Orbital AM and the Asy Beh of the Scatt Ampl.

(G8) Gribov, V.N., JETP **42**, 1260 (1962)[**15**, 873 (1962)]: Anal Prop of the Partial Wave Ampl and the Asy Beh of the Scatt Ampl.

(G9) Gribov, V.N., CERN, 547: Fermion RP and Asy Beh of Meson-Nucleon Large Angle Scatt.

(G10) Gribov, V.N., CERN, 515: Partial Waves with CAM and their Moving Sing.

(G11) Gribov, V.N., JETP **43**, 1529 (1962)[**16**, 1080 (1963)]: Fermion RP and the Asy Beh of Meson-Nucleon Large Angle Scatt.

(G12) Gribov, V.N., B.L. Joffe, I. Ya. Pomeranchuk, and A.P. Rudik, JETP **42**, 1419 (1962)[**15**, 984 (1962)]: Some Consequences of the Moving P Hypothesis for Processes at HE.

(G13) Gribov, V.N., and I. Ya. Pomeranchuk, PRL **8**, 343 (1962): CAM and the Relations between the Cross Sections of Various Processes at HE.

(G14) Gribov, V.N., and I. Ya. Pomeranchuk, PL **2**, 239 (1962) and CERN, 522: Limitations on the Rate of Decrease of Ampl in Various Processes.

(G15) Gribov, V.N., and I. Ya. Pomeranchuk, PRL **9**, 238 (1962) and CERN, 543: RP and Landau Sing.

(G16) Gribov, V.N., and I. Ya. Pomeranchuk, PRL **8**, 412 (1962): Spin Structure of the Meson-Nucleon and Nucleon-Nucleon Scatt Ampl at HE.

(G17) Gribov, V.N., and I. Ya. Pomeranchuk, JETP **43**, 308 (1962) [**16**, 220 (1963)]: Some Prop of the Elastic Scatt Ampl at HE.

(G18) Gribov, V.N., and D.V. Volkov, CERN, 552: RP in N-N and $\overline{\text{N}}$-N Scatt Ampl.

(G19) Guralnik, G.S., and C.R. Hagen, PR **130**, 1259 (1963): RP in Rel Wave Eq.

(H1) Hadjioannou, F., R.J.N. Phillips, and W. Rarita, PRL **9**, 183 (1962): RP Model for HE p-p and $\overline{\text{p}}$-p Scatt.

(H2) Hadjioannou, F., and A.H. Zimmerman, PL **3**, 220 (1963): Coupling of the Pomeranchuk Particle to the Pion and Its Decay Width.

(I1) Igi, K., PRL **9**, 76 (1962): π-N Scatt Length and Sing in the C J-Pl.

(I2) Igi, K., PR **130**, 820 (1963): Two Vacuum P and Pion Nucleon Scatt.

(I3) Islam, J.N., P.V. Landshoff, and J.C. Taylor, PR **130**, 2560 (1963): Sing of the R Ampl.

(I4) Iwao, S., and G.A. Viano, PL **3**, 9 (1962): Some [Experimental] Evidence of R Traj.

(K6) Kanavatz, V. P., I. I. Levintov, and B. V. Morosov, PL **4**, 196 (1963) and JETP **45**, 679 (1963)[**18**, 467 (1964)]: Comparison of π-p and p-p Elastic Scatt on the Basis of a Model with Three RP.

(K7) Kastrup, H. A., PL **4**, 56 (1963): On the Relationship between the Scale Transformation and the Asy R Beh of the Rel Scatt Ampl.

(K8) Khuri, N. N., PRL **10**, 420 (1963): A Crossing Symmetric Watson-Sommerfeld Transformation.

(K9) Khuri, N. N., and B. M. Udgaonkar, PRL **10**, 172 (1963): Nucleon as RP and the $J = \frac{1}{2}$, $T = \frac{1}{2}\pi N$ Phase Shifts.

(K10) Kibble, T. W. B., PR **131**, 2282 (1963): Feynman Rules for R Particles.

(L2) Lee, B. W., and R. F. Sawyer, PR **127**, 2266 (1962): RP and HE Limits in Field Theo.

(L3) Lee, B. W., and R. F. Sawyer, PR **127**, 2274 (1962): Leading R Traj in the $\lambda\varphi^4$ Theo.

(L4) Levy, M., PRL **9**, 235 (1962): Electromagnetic Radiative Corrections and the Elementary Nature of the Photon.

(L5) Levy, M., PR **130**, 791 (1963): HE Beh of Scatt of Ampl in Quantum Electrodynamics.

(L6) Liu, L. S., and K. Tanaka, PR **129**, 1876 (1963): R Traj in Field Theo.

(L7) Lovelace, C., NC **25**, 730 (1962): Diffr Scatt and Mandelstam Rep.

(M4) Mandelstam, S., CERN, 739: Pion and Nucleon Physics.

(M5) Mandelstam, S., Ann Phys **21**, 302 (1963): RP as Consequences of Anal and U.

(M6) Marquit, E., PL **4**, 101 (1963) and **5**, 96 (1963): On the Experimental Verification of the Single R-Pomeranchuk P Approx for HE Electron Scatt.

(M7) Martin, A., CERN, 566: Limitations Imposed by U on the Imaginary Part of a Scatt Ampl and Consequences of Its HE Beh.

(M8) Matthews, P. T., Proc Phys Soc (London) **80**, 1 (1962): RP and Diffr Scatt (included in this volume).

(N4) Nambu, Y., and M. Sugawara, PRL **10**, 304 (1963): Nonshrinking Diffr Scatt.

(N5) Nakanishi, N., PR **130**, 1230 (1963): Partial Wave Bethe-Salpeter Eq.

(N6) Newton, R. G., PL **4**, 201 (1963): Remark on the "Ghost" Problem in the Vacuum P Traj.

(O1) Oehme, R., PRL **9**, 358 (1962): Moving P and Elementary Particles.

(O2) Oehme, R., NC **25**, 183 (1962): RP in Rel Schrödinger Theo.

(O3) Oehme, R., PR **130**, 424 (1963): R Traj and Elementary P.

(O4) Oehme, R., NC **28**, 736 (1963): The Problem of Branch Point Traj in the CAMPl.

(O5) Oehme, R., and G. Tiktopoulos, PL **2**, 86 (1962): Compl AM in Rel Disp Theo.

(O6) Okubo, S., NC **28**, 47 (1963): CAM and Domain of Holomorphy.

(P4) Pignotti, A., PRL **10**, 416 (1963): Does the f_0 Particle Lie on the Pomeranchuk Traj?

(P5) Polkinghorne, J.C., PR **128**, 2459 (1962): CAM and U in Crossed Channels.

(P6) Polkinghorne, J.C., PL **4**, 24 (1963): Cancelling Cuts in the RPl.

(P7) Polkinghorne, J.C., JMP **4**, 503 (1963): HE Beh in Pert Theo.

(P8) Predazzi, E., T. Regge, and C. Rossetti, PRL **8**, 493 (1962): HE Limit of Scatt Ampl.

(P9) Prosperi, G.M., NC **26**, 541 (1962): On the Anal Continuation of the SM in AM.

(S3) Shirkov, D.V., PL **3**, 273 (1963): On the Structure of the Vacuum Traj.

(S4) Singh, V., PR **129**, 1889 (1963): RP in πN Scatt and in $\pi + \pi \to N + \overline{N}$.

(S5) Suranyi, P., JETP **42**, 1425 (1962) [**15**, 988 (1962)]: Beh of the Real Part of the Scatt Ampl at Very HE.

(T3) Ter-Martirosian, K.A., CERN, 556: Partial Wave Anal and the HE Beh of Many Particle Ampl.

(U1) Überall, H., PL **3**, 323 (1963) and **4**, 264 (1963): RP Hypothesis and Polarization in πp and Kp Scatt.

(U2) Udgaonkar, B.M., PRL **8**, 142 (1962): HE Cross Sections, Pomeranchuk Theorems, and RP.

(U3) Udgaonkar, B.M., and M. Gell-Mann, PRL **8**, 346 (1962): HE Nuclear Scatt and RP.

(W1) Wagner, W.G., PRL **10**, 202 (1963), and **10**, 386 (1963): Simplicity of R Asy Ampl.

(W2) Wagner, W.G., and D.H. Sharp, PR **128**, 2899 (1962): M Meson and a Generalization of the Pomeranchuk Relation.

(W3) Wong, D., PR **126**, 1221 (1962): RP and Resonances in Strong Interactions.

Supplementary Bibliography

Ahmadzadeh, A. prep (UCRL): A Modified Khuri Series and its Convergence for a Single Yukawa Pot.

Ahmadzadeh, A., and I.A. Sakmar, PRL **11**, 439 (1963): RP Hypothesis and π-p Diffr Experiments.

Akhiezer, I.A., JETP **44**, 697 (1963) [**17**, 472 (1963)]: Restrictions Imposed on R Traj by Maximal Anal.

Arutyunian, V.M., I.I. Goldman, and G.A. Nagorsky, JETP **45**, 246 (1963)[**18**, 172 (1964)]: RP for Scatt on a δ-Pot.

Azimov, Ya. I., and A.A. Anselm, JETP **44**, 686 (1963) [**17**, 464 (1963)]: RP and Asy Beh of Ampl in Pert Theo.

Azimov, Ya. I., A.A. Anselm, and V.M. Shekhter, JETP **44**, 361 (1963) [**17**, 246 (1963)]: The RP Traj for Weak Coupling.

Azimov, Ya. I., A.A. Anselm, and V.M. Shekhter, JETP **44**, 1078 (1963) [**17**, 726 (1963)]: Anal Prop of RP Traj.
Banerjee, H., PR **131**, 2810 (1963): Remarks on the Anal Cont of the Partial-Wave Ampl.
Bardakci, K., and D.A. Geffen, PR **132**, 1361 (1963): Sing of a Rel Scatt Ampl in the CAM Pl.
Barrett, G., and G. Barton, NC **29**, 703 (1963): Goldberger-Treiman Formulae with R Phase Shifts.
Barut, A.O., and J. Dilley, JMP **4**, 1401 (1963): Behavior of the Scatt Ampl for Large AM.
Bastai, A., L. Bertocchi, and M. Tonin, NC **29**, 247 (1963): R Traj in the Weak-Coupling Limit.
Beltrametti, E.G., and G. Luzzatto, NC **29**, 1003 (1963): Rotation Matrices Corresponding to CAM.
Berestetsky, V.B., JETP **44**, 1603 (1963) [**17**, 1079 (1963)]: Asy Beh of Scatt Ampl and the Problem of "Ghosts" in the Traj of Vacuum RP.
Berkov, A.V., E.D. Zhizhin, V.D. Mur, and Yu.P. Nikitin, JETP **45**, 1585 (1963): RP in the Photoproduction Ampl.
Bose, S.K., and S.N. Biswas, PR **133**, B789 (1964): N* RP and Pion-Nucleon (3, 3) Phase Shifts.
Bose, S.K., and M. DerSarkissian, NC **30**, 878 (1963): Prop of the Deuteron P Traj and Low Energy Neutron-Proton Scatt.
Bransden, B.H., et al. prep (NIRL): Pion-Pion Scatt in the Strip Approx, I.
Brown, L., D.I. Fivel, B.W. Lee, and R.F. Sawyer, Ann Phys **23**, 187 (1963): Fredholm Method in Pot Scatt and Applications to CAM.
Calogero, F., and J.M. Charap, prep (Imp. Coll. London): Asy Beh for Large Imaginary Values of AM of the Ampl for the Scatt of a Dirac Particle on a Central Scalar Pot.
Carruthers, P., PRL **10**, 540 (1963): Dynamical Basis for R Traj in the Pion Nucleon System.
Chan, C.H., PL **5**, 274 (1963): On the Non-shrinking π-p Diffr Peak near 10 GeV.
Cheng, H., PR **132**, 931 (1963): Discussion on the Dynamical Eq for R Parameters.
Cheng, H., and D. Sharp, PR **132**, 1854 (1963): Formulation and Numerical Solution of a Set of Dynamical Eq for the RP Parameters.
Chew, G.F., and C.E. Jones, prep (UCRL): New Form of Strip Approx.
Childers, R.W., and W.G. Holladay, PR **132**, 1809 (1963): RP and Photoproduction of Pions.
Choudhury, M.H., prep (Tait Inst., Edinburgh): On the Anal Prop and Asy Beh of Partial Wave Ampl in Pot Scatt.
Ciafaloni, M., NC **29**, 420 (1963): Levinson's Theorem and RP.
Ciulli, S., G.R. Ghika, and M. Stihi, prep (Institut de Fisica Atomica, Academia Republicii Populare Romine, Bucharest): RP in the Presence of a Hard Core.

Contogouris, A. P., F. Hadjioannou, and T. Kinoshita, NC **29**, 192 (1963): RP and the Production of HE particles by γ-Rays.

Cornwall, J. M., PRL **11**, 21 (1963): Total Cross Sections and Slope of R Traj.

Cornwall, J. M., K. J. Mahanthappa, and V. Singh, PR **131**, 1882 (1963): RP and C Sing.

Cosenza, G., L. Sertorio and M. Toller, prep (Univ. of Rome): Singular Integral Eq in Diffr Scatt and in Bound State Problems.

Dai Yuan-ben, Scientia Sinica **12**, 1395 (1963): The R Beh of the Scatt Ampl for a Highly Singular Pot.

De Alfaro, V., M. Flamberti, E. Predazzi, and C. Rossetti, NC **29**, 1367 (1963): Mathematical Structure of a Model for Asy Nonforward Scatt Ampl.

Desai, B., PRL **11**, 59 (1963): Shrinkage of the Diffr Pattern and Short Range Forces.

Desai, B., prep (Univ. of Wisconsin): Diffr Width in Terms of f° and the Residue of the Pomeranchuk P.

Deser, S., G. Furlan, and G. Mahoux, PL **5**, 333 (1963): Renormalization Group and R Beh.

Dombay, N., prep: RP Theo of the Photoproduction of Pions.

Domokos, G., and P. Suranyi, Nucl Phys **48**, 529 (1963): Three Particle States in the Rel Theo of CAM.

Durso, J. W., and P. Signell, prep: RP and Pot with Cores.

Eden, R. J., PR **132**, 912 (1963): Legendre Transforms and Khuri Rep of Scatt Ampl.

Feinberg, E. L., and D. S. Chernavsky, JETP **45**, 1252 (1963): R Narrowing of the Diffr Cone and the Role of Multimeson Interactions.

Finn, A. C., PR **132**, 836 (1963): A Theorem on the Shrinking of Diffr Peaks.

Fivel, D., PR **125**, 1085 (1962): New Formulation of Disp Rel for Pot Scatt.

Flamm, D., NC **29**, 1080 (1963): R Traj for a Class of Weak Short Range Pot.

Frautschi, S. C., P. E. Kaus, and F. Zachariasen, prep (Cal Tech): A Method for the Self-consistent Determination of RP Parameters.

Freedman, D. Z., prep: Model for the Nucleon and Baryon R Traj.

Freund, P. G. O., and R. Oehme, PL **5**, 353 (1963) and **7**, 167 (1963): Shrinking and Non-Shrinking Diffr Peaks.

Freund, P. G. O., and R. Oehme, PL **5**, 362 (1963): Vector Mesons as RP in Pert Theo.

Fried, H. M., and J. G. Taylor, JMP **4**, 727 (1963): Propagator Ghosts and RP.

Frolov, G. V., JETP **44**, 1746 (1963)[**17**, 1173 (1963)]: Pert Theo and Fermion RP in Electrodynamics.

Gatland, I. R., and J. W. Moffat, PR **132**, 442 (1963): Diffr Scatt and Sing in the AM Pl.

Gell-Mann, Goldberger, Low, Marx, and Zachariasen, PR **133**, B145 (1964): Elementary Particles of Conventional Field Theo as RP, III.

Gell-Mann, Goldberger, Singh, and Zachariasen, PR **133**, B161 (1964): Elementary Particles of Conventional Field Theo as RP, IV.

Geshkenbein, B. V., and B. L. Ioffe, JETP **45**, 346 (1963)[**18**, 240 (1964)]: On the Traj of R Vacuum P.

Gorshkov, V. G., M. P. Rekalo, and G. V. Frolov, JETP **45**, 285 (1963)[**18**, 199 (1964)]: Fermion RP and the Compton Effect.

Gribov, V. N., L. Okun, and I. Ya. Pomeranchuk, JETP **45**, 1114 (1963): On Processes Determined by Fermion RP.

Gribov, V. N., and I. Ya. Pomeranchuk, JETP **43**, 1970 (1962)[**16**, 1387 (1963)]: RP and Landau Sing.

Hagedorn, R., Acta Phys Austriaca **17**, 18 (1963): A Qualitative Survey on HE Elastic Scatt and RP.

Hartle, J. B., prep (Cal Tech): CAM in Three-Particle Pot Scatt.

Hartle, J. B., prep (Cal Tech): The Watson-Sommerfeld Transf for Many-Particle Scatt Ampl.

Igi, K., and V. L. Teplitz, prep: Experimental Test for R Cuts.

Islam, M. M., NC **30**, 579 (1963): Pion as a RP.

Islam, M. M., and R. Pinon, NC **30**, 837 (1963): Pion as a RP, II.

Iso, C., Ann Phys **23**, 304 (1963): Weak Interactions Mediated by R Particles.

Itabashi, K., Progr Theor Phys **29**, 724 (1963): RP Hypothesis and HE Beh of the Single Pion Photoproduction.

Iwao, S., NC **28**, 1248 (1963): $\overline{K}$-N Scatt in the Mandelstam Rep. II - R Traj of K* Meson.

Jaksic, B., Acta Phys Austriaca **17**, 29 (1963): Asy Beh of Phase Shift for Large λ.

Jones, C. E., and J. A. Poirer, prep (UCRL 10677): Basic Theo and Applications of RP.

Keller, J. B., S. I. Rubinow, and M. Goldstein, JMP **4**, 829 (1963): Zeros of Hankel Functions and P of Scatt Ampl.

Khalfin, L. A., JETP **45**, 631 (1963)[**18**, 433 (1964)]: The Hypothesis of RP in Quantum Field Theo and Threshold Sing of Inelastic Processes.

Khriplovich, I. B., JETP **44**, 2079 (1963)[**17**, 1398 (1963)]: Limitations on the Asy Values of Cross Sections Imposed by the RP Hypothesis.

Khuri, N. N., PR **132**, 914 (1963): RP, Power Series, and a Crossing Symmetric Sommerfeld-Watson Transformation.

Koba, Z., Fortschr. der Physik **11**, 119 (1963): Recent Theo Considerations on Ultra HE Nuclear Collisions.

Kolkunov, V. A., JETP **45**, 1123 (1963): Nonrel RP Traj.

Konisi, G., and T. Ogimoto, Progr Theo Phys **29**, 908 (1963): Anal in Coupling Constant, AM and E of the SM for Pot Scatt.

Kretzschmar, M., prep (Max Planck Inst., Munich): A New R Rep for Pot Scatt.

Lendyel, V. I., and J. Mathews, PL **5**, 286 (1963): Some Remarks about a Second Pomeranchuk Traj.

Lepore, J. V., and R. J. Riddell, PRL **10**, 550 (1963): Essential Sing of a Partial Wave Ampl.

Logunov, A. A., et al., Nucl Phys **44**, 275 (1963): RP in Quantum Electrodynamics.

Malyuta, Yu., M., JETP **44**, 1317 (1963)[**17**, 888 (1963)]: RP in Quantum Field Theo.

Malyuta, Yu. M., JETP **45**, 1167 (1963): R Traj for the Positronium Atom.
Mandelstam, S., prep: Cuts in the AM Pl, I and II.
Mandelstam, S., prep: The R Formalism for Rel Particles with Spin.
Martin, A., prep: On the Beh of the Partial Wave Ampl for Large AM in Pot Scatt.
McMillan, M., and E. Predazzi, NC **25**, 838 (1962): Electromagnetic Form Factors in the R Rep.
McMillan, M., NC **29**, 1043 (1963): Separable Non-local Pot and RP.
McMillan, M., prep: R Cuts in a Nonrel Three Body Problem Involving Separable Pot.
Minami, S., and K. Mori, NC **30**, 458 (1963): Diffr Scatt at HE and Possibility of new R Traj.
Muzinich, I. J., PRL **11**, 88 (1963): ρ-Meson R Traj and HE Charge Exchange Scatt.
Nakanishi, Noboru, PR **133**, B214 (1964): Pert-Theo Integral Rep and the HE Beh of the Scatt Ampl.
Newton, R. G., PL **8**, 210 (1964): AM Cont in the Three Body Problem without Cuts.
Nikanorov, V. I., JETP **44**, 2184 (1963) [**17**, 1466 (1963)]: Contribution of RP to Total Cross Sections at HE.
Nilsson, J., PL **7**, 86 (1963): The Renormalization Group and R Beh.
Nussinov, S., NC **28**, 1491 (1963): A Possible Indication for RP Beh of the Pion.
Pac, P. Y., Progr Theor Phys **30**, 201 (1963): A Note on R Traj in $\lambda\varphi^4$ Theo.
Patashinskii, A. Z., V. L. Pokrovskii, and I. M. Khalatnikov, JETP **44**, 2062 (1963) [**17**, 1387 (1963)]: RP in Quasiclassical Potential Wave Problems.
Patashinskii, A. Z., V. L. Pokrovskii, and I. M. Khalatnikov, JETP **45**, 760 (1963)[**18**, 522 (1964)]: Investigation of SM in CAM Space in the Quasiclassical case.
Phillips, R. J. N., PL **5**, 159 (1963): Diffr Shrinking and R Traj.
Polkinghorne, J. C., JMP **4**, 1393 (1963): Sing of R Traj and Asymptotes to Landau Curves.
Polkinghorne, J. C., JMP **4**, 1396 (1963): HE Beh in Pert Theo, II.
Polkinghorne, J. C., PL **7**, 217 (1963): Production Processes and Moving R Cuts.
Read, A. L., J. Orear, and H. A. Bethe, NC **29**, 1051 (1963): Exact Form for Scatt Ampl in RP Theo.
Rekalo, M. P., V. G. Gorshkov, and G. V. Frolov, JETP **45**, 672 (1963)[**18**, 462 (1964)]: Photoproduction of π Mesons on Nucleons and Fermion RP.
Riazuddin and Fayyazuddin, prep: Three Meson Model for p-p Scatt and RP.
Ringhofer, K., and P. Urban, Acta Phys Austriaca **17**, 96 (1963): Komplexe Energie und Komplexer Drehimpuls bei Vorhandensein von Nichtzentralpotenzialen.
Salecker, H., NC **29**, 92 (1963): On RP in Quantum Electrodynamics.

Sawyer, R. F., PR **131**, 1384 (1963): CAM in Pert Theo.
Shapiro, I. S., Nucl Phys **48**, 58 (1963): Restrictions on RP Traj.
Squires, E. J., prep (Tait Inst., Edinburgh): On the Nature of the Sing of a Partial Wave Scatt Ampl at the Negative Integral Value of J.
Solovev, L. D., and O. A. Khrustalev, JETP **44**, 758 (1963) [**17**, 512 (1963)]: Infrared Sing and R Traj in Electrodynamics.
Suranyi, P., PL **6**, 59 (1963): On the Leading Sing in the AM Pl in Pert Theo.
Suzuki, M., Progr Theor Phys **29**, 851 (1963): Application of R Hypothesis to Multiple Meson Production.
Swift, A. R., and B. W. Lee, PR **131**, 1857 (1963): CAM in Spinor Bethe-Salpeter Eq.
Tadic, D., NC **29**, 183 (1963): RP in HE Neutrino Reactions.
Teplitz, V. L., PL **6**, 73 (1963): Experimental Test for R Cuts.
Trueman, T. L., and T. Yao, PR **132**, 2741 (1963): HE Scatt Ampl in Pert Theo.
Überall, H., NC **29**, 947 (1963): HE π-Meson-Nucleon Backscatt using RP Hypothesis.
Vaks, V. G., and A. I. Larkin, JETP **45**, 800 (1963)[**18**, 548 (1964)]: RP in the Nonrel Problem with Non-local and Singular Interaction.
Van Hieu, Nguyen, JETP **45**, 544 (1963)[**18**, 374 (1964)]: RP and the Asy Beh of the Cross Sections of some Weak Interaction Processes.
Volkel, A. H., Acta Phys Austriaca **17**, 3 (1963): CAM in the Nonrel Pot Scatt.
Volkov, D. V., JETP **45**, 742 (1963)[**18**, 509 (1964)]: Factorization of RP of Scatt Ampl of Particles with Spin at the RP.
Volkov, D. V., and V. N. Gribov, JETP **44**, 1068 (1963) [**17**, 720 (1963)]: RP in Nucleon-Nucleon and Nucleon-Antinucleon Scatt Ampl.
Volkov, D. V., and A. F. Bakai, PL **5**, 223 (1963): On Quantum Electrodynamics with a Reggeized Photon.
Wilkin, C., NC **31**, 377 (1964): Cuts and P in the AM Pl.
Wilson, K. G., Acta Phys Austriaca **17**, 37 (1963): RP and Multiple Production.
Zwanziger, D., PR **131**, 2818 (1963): Rep of the Lorentz Group Corresponding to Unstable Particles.

Other References

(B22) Bateman Manuscript Project, "Higher Transcendental Functions" (A. Erdelyi, ed.), McGraw-Hill, New York, 1953.
(B23) Bateman Manuscript Project, "Tables of Integral Transforms" (A. Erdelyi, ed.), McGraw-Hill, New York, 1953.
(B24) Blatt, J. M., and V. Weisskopf, "Theoretical Nuclear Physics," Wiley, New York, 1952.
(B25) Boas, R. P., "Entire Functions," Academic Press, New York, 1954.
(C27) Caratheodory, C., "Funktionentheorie," Birkhäuser, Basel, 1950.

(C28) Chew, G. F., "Theory of Strong Interactions," W. A. Benjamin, New York, 1961.

(E1) Edmonds, A. R., "Angular Momentum in Quantum Mechanics," Princeton Univ. Press, Princeton, N. J., 1957.

(F14) Franz, W., Z. Naturforsch. **9a**, 705 (1954).

(G20) Gaunt, J. A., Phil. Trans. Roy. Soc. London **A228**, 151 (1929).

(G21) Goodrich, R. F., and N. D. Kazarinoff, Proc. Camb. Phil. Soc. **59**, 167 (1963), and Michigan Math. Journal **10**, 105 (1963).

(I5) Imai, I., Z. Physik **137**, 31 (1954).

(N7) Newton, R. G., PR **100**, 412 (1955).

(N8) Newton, R. G., JMP **1**, 319 (1960). [Reprinted in "Quantum Scattering Theory" (M. Ross, ed.), Indiana Univ. Press, Bloomington, Indiana, 1963.]

(N9) Newton, R. G., JMP **2**, 188 (1961).

(N10) Nicholson, J. W., Phil. Mag. **19**, 516 (1910); **20**, 157 (1910); and Messenger Math. **37**, 84 (1907).

(P10) Poincaré, H., Rend. Circ. Mat. Palermo **29**, 169 (1910).

(P11) Pol, Balth. van der, and H. Bremmer, Phil. Mag. **24**, 141 and 825 (1937).

(S6) Sommerfeld A., "Partial Differential Equations of Physics," Academic Press, New York, 1949.

(T4) Titchmarsh, E. C., "The Theory of Functions," Oxford Univ. Press, New York, 1950.

(W4) Watson, G. N., Proc. Roy. Soc. (London) **95**, 83 (1918).

(W5) Watson, G. N., "Bessel Functions," Cambridge Univ. Press, New York, 1958.

(W6) Whittaker, E. T., and G. N. Watson, "Modern Analysis," Cambridge Univ. Press, New York, 1948.

REPRINTS

Reprinted from THE PHYSICAL REVIEW, Vol. 126, No. 6, 2204–2218, June 15, 1962
Printed in U. S. A.

Experimental Consequences of the Hypothesis of Regge Poles*

S. C. FRAUTSCHI
Newman Laboratory of Nuclear Studies, Cornell University, Ithaca, New York

AND

M. GELL-MANN AND F. ZACHARIASEN
California Institute of Technology, Pasadena, California

(Received January 8, 1962)

In the nonrelativistic case of the Schrödinger equation, composite particles correspond to Regge poles in scattering amplitudes (poles in the complex plane of angular momentum). It has been suggested that the same may be true in relativistic theory. In that case, the scattering amplitude in which such a particle is exchanged behaves at high energies like $s^{\alpha(t)}[\sin\pi\alpha(t)]^{-1}$, where s is the energy variable and t the momentum transfer variable. When $t=t_R$, the mass squared of the particle, then α equals an integer n related to the spin of the particle. In contrast, we may consider the case of a field theory in which the exchanged particle is treated as elementary and we examine each order of perturbation theory. When $n>1$, we can usually not renormalize successfully; when $n\leq 1$ and the theory is renormalizable, then the high-energy behavior is typically $s^n(t-t_R)^{-1}\phi(t)$. Thus an experimental distinction is possible between the two situations. That is particularly interesting in view of the conjecture of Blankenbecler and Goldberger that the nucleon may be composite and that of Chew and Frautschi that all strongly interacting particles may be composite dynamical combinations of one another. We suggest a set of rules for finding the high-energy behavior of scattering cross sections according to the Regge pole hypothesis and apply them to π-π, π-N, and N-N scattering. We show how these cross sections differ from those expected when there are "elementary" nucleons and mesons treated in renormalized perturbation theory. For the case of N-N scattering, we analyze some preliminary experimental data and find indications that an "elementary" neutral vector meson is probably not present. Various reactions are proposed to test the "elementary" or "composite" nature of other baryons and mesons. Higher energies may be needed than are available at present.

I. INTRODUCTION

IN conventional Lagrangian field theory, particles of spin higher than one give rise to difficulties.

If we treat a particle as "elementary," by analogy with the electron and photon in quantum electrodynamics, we assign it a field and consider a Lagrangian in which there is a free-field term for the particle and also coupling terms to other fields. We expand in a perturbation series, renormalizing masses and coupling strengths, and look at the behavior of each order. When the spin of the particle is higher than one (and, in some cases, when it equals one) the resulting theory is unrenormalizable or divergent in each order.[1] The divergences are connected, loosely speaking, with a singular behavior at high energies of scattering amplitudes in which the particle of high spin is exchanged.

Now objects of high spin obviously exist in nature, and therefore from the point of view of renormalizable field theory they have to be regarded as "composite." Somehow, when a composite particle of high spin is exchanged, the singular behavior of the scattering amplitudes is avoided. Regge,[2] investigating the nonrelativistic Schrödinger equation, has found what is no doubt the mechanism by which composite states of high spin make themselves respectable. This mechanism can apply just as well to states of spin 0, $\frac{1}{2}$, or 1, and one is led naturally to the conjecture[3] that all dynamical bound and resonant states follow the Regge type of behavior.

For spins 0 and $\frac{1}{2}$, however, and sometimes for spin 1 as well, we have the alternative possibility of considering a bound or resonant state as coming from an "elementary" particle in the sense described above. In many cases, one can exhibit, in every order of the resulting renormalizable field theory, the high-energy behavior of amplitudes in which the "elementary" particle is exchanged. This perturbation theory behavior is very different from that of the Regge case. We shall use the words "elementary" and "composite" to describe the two situations, even though the applicability of these words depends on perturbation theory in one case and on conjecture in the other.

Recently, Chew and Frautschi[4] have suggested that *all* strongly interacting particles[5] may exhibit the Regge behavior that we believe to be typical of composite states. In a sense, then, all baryons and mesons would be bound states of one another. It is made plausible that under this hypothesis all the mass ratios and

---

* Work supported in part by the Alfred P. Sloan Foundation and the U. S. Atomic Energy Commission. The research was begun under the auspices of the High-Energy Physics Study Group (HEPS) at the Lawrence Radiation Laboratory of the University of California at Berkeley in the summer of 1961. All the authors were at that time members of HEPS.

[1] For the case of the graviton, having mass zero and spin 2 and obeying Einstein's nonlinear equation that satisfies the gauge invariance of general relativity, the question of renormalizability has not been settled.

[2] T. Regge, Nuovo cimento 14, 951 (1959); 18, 947 (1960).

[3] S. Mandelstam has suggested and emphasized repeatedly since 1960 that the Regge behavior would permit a simple description of dynamical states (private discussions). Similar remarks have been made by R. Blankenbecler and M. L. Goldberger and by K. Wilson.

[4] G. F. Chew and S. C. Frautschi, Phys. Rev. Letters 7, 394 (1961). See also reference 14.

[5] It is also possible that the other particles are composite in this sense. The most fascinating possibilities are those involving the electron, muon, and photon. Quantum electrodynamics would still be correct at low energies and momenta, but would be gradually cut off at high momentum transfers by the Regge mechanism without violating causality.

coupling constants of the strongly interacting particles could, in principle, be calculated.

We are concerned here with the possibility of testing directly by experiment the hypothesis that the various baryons and mesons obey the Regge conditions. It is often possible to compare the predictions of the "elementary" and "composite" pictures of particular baryons and mesons for the high energy behavior of scattering amplitudes in which they are exchanged. If s and t are the energy and momentum transfer variables, then the two predictions are essentially a form $s^{\alpha(t)}$ in the composite case and s^n in the elementary case, where n is a fixed integer depending on the spin of the exchanged particle, while $\alpha(t)$ is variable and smaller than n in the physical region for the scattering.

Let us consider these statements in more detail. Stable particles appear as poles in S-matrix elements at real values of energy or momentum transfer variables. Correspondingly, unstable particles (or resonances) give poles on unphysical sheets of the S matrix at complex values of the same variables. Consider a two-particle scattering process $a+b \to c+d$, for which the energy variable is s (center-of-mass energy squared), and the corresponding crossed reaction $a+\bar{c} \to \bar{b}+d$, for which the energy variable is t. We may speak of the s reaction and the t reaction, respectively. In the physical region for the s reaction, $s > s_{\text{threshold}} > 0$ and $t < t_{\max}$ where $t_{\max} \to 0$ as $s \to \infty$, while in the physical region for the t reaction we have $t > t_{\text{threshold}} > 0$ and $s < s_{\max}$ where $s_{\max} \to 0$ as $t \to \infty$. The cosine x_t of the scattering angle in the t reaction is linearly related to the energy variable of the s reaction. In particular, if q_t and p_t are the center-of-mass momenta of $a+\bar{c}$ and $\bar{b}+d$, respectively, then for large s we have

$$x_t \approx -s(2q_t p_t)^{-1}. \tag{1.1}$$

Suppose, for simplicity, that a, b, c, and d are spinless and that a particle of spin l gives a pole in the t variable. In the invariant amplitude $T(s,t)$, the residue of the pole is then evidently a number times $P_l(x_t)$:

$$T(s,t) = [CP_l(x_t)/t - t_R] + \text{other terms}. \tag{1.2}$$

Thus, in the s reaction, the contribution to the scattering amplitude of the pole (occurring at an *unphysical* value of the momentum transfer variable t) has the energy dependence s^l at large s.

As we indicated earlier, it is possible in many cases to show, for the *renormalizable* theories of elementary particles of spin ≤ 1, that in each order of perturbation theory the high energy behavior characteristic of the pole term persists for all values of t. (See Sec. VI for details.)

For fixed *physical* (i.e., negative) values of the momentum transfer t in the s reaction, if this energy dependence of the pole contribution is not cancelled by other terms, then any value of l greater than 1 gives us a rate of energy variation of $T(s,t)$ at large s that is embarrassing for the following reasons:

(1) The experimental situation seems to be that the most singular behavior for $T(s,t)$ (or its analog for the case of particles with spin) is exhibited by the imaginary part of elastic scattering amplitudes for $t=0$ and that the variation in that case is exactly or approximately linear with s, corresponding (with the use of the optical theorem) to constant or approximately constant total cross section.

(2) Froissart,[6] using the Mandelstam representation, has shown (for the case of spinless particles a, b, c, d) that the invariant amplitude cannot grow faster than $s \ln^2 s$ for large s and fixed t.

The situation described by Regge avoids these difficulties. He treated the nonrelativistic Schrödinger equation for one particle in a potential that is a superposition of Yukawa potentials. Let t be the energy variable and $x_t = \cos\theta_t$. One may examine the behavior of the scattering amplitude for large x_t, even though this limit is not connected with high energy in a crossed reaction, since there is no nonrelativistic crossing relation. Regge has found that in this simple case there is a beautiful mechanism that reduces the singularity of the behavior of the scattering amplitude at large $\cos\theta_t$ as t decreases and becomes negative. If there are resonances or bound states, the scattering amplitude at large x_t is dominated by a sum of terms of the form[7]

$$\frac{\beta(t)}{\sin\pi\alpha(t)} P_{\alpha(t)}(-x_t) \underset{s\to\infty}{\longrightarrow} \frac{c(t)s^{\alpha(t)}}{\sin\pi\alpha(t)}, \tag{1.3}$$

where each term represents, in general, a family of resonances and/or bound states of *variable angular momentum*. We have used the asymptotic form (1.1) of x_t and the fact that $P_\alpha(y) \propto y^\alpha$ at large y.

We shall discuss (1.3) further in the next section but for the moment let us just note the relationship to the simple resonance formula (1.2). For values of t below threshold t_0 (that is, below zero kinetic energy in the Schrödinger problem), Regge's α is real and increasing with t. A bound state of angular momentum l occurs at a value $t_R < t_0$ if $\alpha(t_R) = l$, since near t_R we have

$$\frac{\beta(t_R)}{\pi\alpha'(t_R)} \frac{P_l(x_t)}{t - t_R}, \tag{1.4}$$

which just corresponds to (1.2).

At the bound state, then, we have the same situation as always, with the scattering amplitude varying like s^l at large s. However, as t decreases from t_R, so does $\alpha(t)$, and the dependence on s at large s keeps getting less singular.

---

[6] M. Froissart, Phys. Rev. **123**, 1053 (1961). Froissart's proof does not apply to the exchange of massless particles like the graviton.

[7] Below threshold, each term may actually be proportional to $(-1)^\alpha P_\alpha(x_t)$ or some other function that is *asymptotically* the same as $P_\alpha(-x_t)$.

In the relativistic problem, if Regge's mechanism operates, it can give precisely the desired effects. By the time we reach negative values of t and enter the physical region for the crossed reaction, α can have decreased to a value ≤ 1 so that we have an acceptable high energy behavior in the s reaction even though the spin of the resonance at $t=t_R$ is greater than one.

Moreover, even for spin 0 (and similarly for spin $\frac{1}{2}$ and spin 1), where the asymptotic law s^l for fixed l leads to no trouble, the still less singular Regge situation is an alternative possibility. These two situations are just the ones we described earlier under the names "elementary" and "composite," respectively. Evidently they can be distinguished by experiments. In the physical region, the "elementary" picture makes the pole contributions persist at high energies with the same energy dependence as at the pole; this is in the spirit of the "peripheral model" of high-energy scattering. The "composite" picture, in contrast, makes the peripheral terms much weaker at high energies. The Regge description also makes important predictions for diffraction scattering.

In Sec. II, we discuss the Regge mechanism in detail and make specific conjectures as to how it enters the relativistic problem. We present these conjectures as a set of rules for calculating the high-energy behavior of scattering amplitudes.

In Sec. III, we illustrate the use of the rules by treating π-π scattering; the problem of diffraction scattering arises here, as elsewhere, and we discuss it.

In Sec. IV, we apply the rules to π-N scattering and show how the nature of the nucleon pole can be tested by experiment.

In Sec. V, we treat N-N scattering and analyze some experimental data, which seem consistent with the "composite" hypothesis for mesons and, in particular, seem to be difficult to reconcile with the existence of an "elementary" neutral vector meson.

In Sec. VI, we treat the "elementary particle" situation that is contrasted with the Regge pole hypothesis; we base our discussion on the field theory perturbation expansion and explore the connection with the "peripheral model." Finally, we list tests of the Regge property of various baryons and mesons, including strange particles.

II. REGGE POLES

We have mentioned the problem of extending the scattering amplitude for the nonrelativistic Schrödinger equation to large values of $x_t=\cos\theta_t$. Regge solved this problem by the mathematical method of Watson and Sommerfeld, involving complex angular momenta. Let us describe the method briefly.

The usual phase shift expansion,

$$T(x_t,t)=\sum_{l=0}^{\infty}(2l+1)P_l(x_t)A(l,t), \qquad (2.1)$$

where $A(l,t)$ is proportional to $\sin\delta_l\exp i\delta_l$, does not converge for large x_t. To obtain an expression that does converge, one considers the solution of the radial Schrödinger equation for arbitrary complex l, obtaining an analytic continuation of $A(l,t)$. The phase shift expansion can now be rewritten in the form of a contour integral,

$$T(x_t,t)=\frac{1}{2\pi i}\oint dl \times(2l+1)P_l(-x_t)A(l,t)\pi(\sin\pi l)^{-1}, \qquad (2.2)$$

over a contour just surrounding the positive real l axis. The residues from the poles of $\pi(\sin\pi l)^{-1}$ give back the terms of the sum (2.1).

For a superposition of Yukawa potentials, Regge shows that one may distort the contour in (2.2) to the vertical line from $l=-\frac{1}{2}-i\infty$ to $l=-\frac{1}{2}+i\infty$ without encountering any singularities other than simple poles of $A(l,t)$, when t is above threshold t_0. These "Regge poles" occur at complex values of l, called $\alpha_n(t)$, at which the Schrödinger equation (for energy variable $=t$) has solutions corresponding formally to resonant states with zero width. The position $\alpha_n(t)$ in the complex l plane of a given Regge pole (the nth one) varies continuously with t. We use here only values of α_n to the right of the vertical line at $\mathrm{Re}\,l=-\frac{1}{2}$.

For each $t>t_0$, we distort the contour, pick up the Regge poles, and obtain in place of (2.2) the expression

$$T(x_t,t)=\frac{-1}{2\pi i}\int_{-\frac{1}{2}-i\infty}^{-\frac{1}{2}+i\infty} dl \times(2l+1)P_l(-x_t)A(l,t)\pi(\sin\pi l)^{-1} +\sum_n \beta_n(t)P_{\alpha_n}(-x_t)(\sin\pi\alpha_n)^{-1}, \qquad (2.3)$$

which represents the scattering amplitude for all values of x_t and allows us to extract the asymptotic form that we want at large x_t. Note the Regge pole contributions have the form (1.2); if they are present they dominate the line integral in (2.3), which is bounded by a constant times $x_t^{-\frac{1}{2}}$ at large x_t.

For energies below threshold the specific representation (2.3) is not quite correct, but $A(l,t)$ continues to have simple poles at positions $\alpha_n(t)$ in the complex l plane; these positions are now on the real axis and represent formally the angular momenta of bound states at value t of the energy variables. The *asymptotic* behavior of $T(x_t,t)$ for large x_t is presumably still dominated by the Regge terms:

$$T(x_t,t) \underset{x_t\to\infty}{\approx} \sum_n \beta_n(t)P_{\alpha_n}(-x_t)(\sin\pi\alpha_n)^{-1}. \qquad (2.4)$$

To get a bound state more and more below threshold, we need more and more attraction. For real l between $-\frac{1}{2}$ and 0, $l(l+1)$ is negative and gives a "centrifugal attraction" that is greatest at $l=-\frac{1}{2}$, where $l(l+1)\hbar^2/2mr^2$ just balances the kinetic energy $(\hbar/2r)^2 \times(1/2m)$ coming from the uncertainty principle. Thus if the potential gives attraction at small distances, a bound state should be possible at $l=-\frac{1}{2}$ for some value of t below threshold. As t increases, we need less "centrifugal attraction" to supplement the attractive potential, and so each $\alpha_n(t)$ should emerge[8] from the vertical line at $l=-\frac{1}{2}$ for some value of t below threshold and move to the right along the real l axis as t increases. At threshold, α_n is continuous, although it has a cusp.

For t above threshold, $\alpha_n(t)$ represents the angular momentum of a resonance of zero width and so must be complex. We shall see that α_n in fact acquires a positive imaginary part above threshold. When $\text{Im}\alpha_n$ is small, then $\text{Re}\alpha_n$ represents approximately the angular momentum of a resonance of positive width.

Genuine physical bound states and resonances are now very easy to discuss. As a given $\alpha_n(t)$ increases from $-\frac{1}{2}$ along the real l axis while t increases (below threshold) it may reach zero; there is a genuine bound s state at this value of t, say t_R. The contribution of this Regge term to the asymptotic scattering amplitude (2.4) near $t=t_R$ is just

$$\frac{\beta_n(t_R)}{\pi\alpha'(t_R)}\frac{P_0(x_t)}{t-t_R}, \tag{2.5}$$

as in (1.3). If α_n attains higher integral values below threshold, these correspond to bound p states, d states, etc., all belonging to a single family with a given number of radial nodes in the wave function.

Above threshold, if $\text{Re}\alpha_n$ continues to increase and rises through integral values while $\text{Im}\alpha_n$ is still small, then there are resonances in the family. Say $\text{Re}\alpha_n$ rises through $\alpha_n=l$ at $t=t_R$ above threshold with $\text{Re}\alpha_n'(t_R)=\epsilon_R$; and say $I_R=\text{Im}\alpha_n$ is small there. Nearby, the contribution of the Regge term to the scattering amplitude (2.3) is approximately

$$\frac{\beta_n(t_R)}{\pi\epsilon_R}\frac{P_l(x_t)}{t-t_R+iI_R\epsilon_R^{-1}}, \tag{2.6}$$

which is just what we expect.

Before we pass on to the relativistic problem, we must consider a slight generalization of the nonrelativistic case, namely the addition of an exchange potential to the direct potential in the Schrödinger equation. The potentials for the radial Schrödinger equation are then different for states of even and odd angular momentum. Each of the two mathematical problems can be treated à la Regge and continued to arbitrary l. However, when the solution of the even-wave Schrödinger equation has a bound or resonant state at odd integral l, or vice versa, we must not expect this to lead to a pole in t in the physical scattering amplitude $T(x_t,t)$. We show in the Appendix that the necessary cancellation comes about as follows: with exchange scattering, each asymptotic Regge term takes on the form

$$\beta_n(t)(\sin\pi\alpha_n)^{-1}\tfrac{1}{2}[P_{\alpha_n}(-x_t)\pm P_{\alpha_n}(x_t)], \tag{2.7}$$

instead of (2.4). The Regge terms corresponding to physical states of even l take the $+$ sign in (2.7); we shall refer to these terms as having positive signature. Likewise, the terms corresponding to physical states of odd l have negative signature. If the exchange scattering disappears, then two Regge terms of opposite signature coalesce, giving back the form of (2.3).

We now suppose that for the relativistic problem the behavior of the invariant scattering amplitude $T(x_t,t)$ is likewise dominated by terms like (2.6). For the general case of the t reaction $a+\bar{c}\rightarrow\bar{b}+d$ (and the corresponding s reaction $a+b\rightarrow c+d$), with arbitrary spins for the particles involved, we conjecture the following rules for finding the form of a given Regge term:

(1) Consider a complete set of linearly independent invariant scattering amplitudes $A_i(s,t)$ free of kinematic singularities and zeros in s and t. For example, in π-π scattering there are three of these, for the three isotopic spin states; in π-N scattering there are four, since there are two values of the isotopic spin and also the possibility of spin flip or no spin flip.

(2) For the t reaction, take any set of values of the conserved quantum numbers except j, the total angular momentum. Then, as a function of j, construct the contribution to the amplitudes A_i of a hypothetical exchanged particle with these quantum numbers; the "particle" is introduced for mathematical convenience only and may occur at any value M^2 of t. For each A_i, this contribution will be a sum of terms containing Legendre functions of x_t (or derivatives thereof) with indices depending on j. At large s, each such function of x_t is asymptotic to a power of s, where the exponent varies with j like $j+\text{const}$. Thus the contribution to A_i takes the form

$$c_i s^{(j-\nu_i)}/(t-M^2),$$

asymptotically in s; there may, of course, be constraints on the c_i.

(3) Write $j=\alpha$ for integral spin in the t reaction or $j=\alpha+\frac{1}{2}$ for half-integral spin and continue to complex α. Then each Regge term has, asymptotically in s, a dependence on s such as described in rule (2), with α depending on t, and with $[(1\pm e^{-i\pi\alpha})/2\sin\pi\alpha]c_i(t)$ appearing as an over-all factor in place of $c_i(t-M^2)^{-1}$. The reason for choosing this form is clear from (2.6) and (1.1). (See also the discussion in the Appendix.) Each Regge term is associated with a definite set of conserved quantum numbers in the t reaction (except j)

[8] By using other representations of the scattering amplitude, it may be possible to follow the poles and the corresponding α's into the region to the left of $\text{Re}l=-\frac{1}{2}$. M. Froissart, M. Goldberger, and S. Mandelstam (private communication).

and with a definite signature, which may be ± 1 for any set of these quantum numbers.[9] We see that when the signature is positive (negative), there is no pole for odd (even) integral α.

A Regge term having the *same* α will then appear in *each* reaction in which this set of quantum numbers can occur; that is analogous to the fact that a given resonance occurs in many reactions. The coefficients, generalizations of β in (2.6), will of course vary from one process to another. We always exhibit explcitly the factor

$$\frac{1\pm e^{-i\pi\alpha(t)}}{2\sin\pi\alpha(t)},$$

which is independent of the particular process in which the quantum numbers are exchanged.

It is attractive to suppose, as in the nonrelativistic potential problem, that each $\alpha(t)$ eventually becomes negative as t decreases. There are, however, some cases in which this assumption raises difficult questions. For example, there are many known systems, such as nuclei, for which the ground state spin is greater than $\frac{3}{2}$. Take the case of spin 2. The corresponding Regge term must have positive signature and $\alpha=2$ at the energy of the ground state. As t decreases further, α will have to pass through zero if it is to attain a negative value. That would put us in the absurd position of having a state of spin zero below the ground state, unless *all* coefficients $c(t)$ for this Regge term vanish at the point where α is zero.

From the point of view of nonrelativistic quantum mechanics, it is presumably the Pauli principle that prevents the existence of the spin zero state, given the nuclear dynamics responsible for the ground state of spin two. That would suggest that perhaps it *is* possible to continue the Regge pole down to a point where $\alpha=0$, but the c's vanish because the corresponding wave function vanishes after antisymmetrization.

We shall consider, in our discussion of diffraction scattering, a Regge α (called α_P) for a state of positive signature such that $\alpha_P=1$ at $t=0$. If α_P is to reach negative values, it must pass through zero at a *negative* value of t, giving a physical state of negative mass squared; again, we can be saved if all the c's vanish at the same point.

Whether or not the α's become negative, they are presumably ≤ 1 in the physical region $t<0$ for the s reaction, even though Froissart's proof may not apply when there are anomalous thresholds such as exist in nuclei, and there are no known experimental limitations in the case when a heavy nucleus is exchanged. There are, however, nuclei in which the ground state spin is 3, for example. Hence the α's must pass through 1 at a value of t above zero but below that of the spin 3 ground state, but since no spin 1 state exists, the c's should in this case all vanish at the place where $\alpha=1$. This indicates it is not absurd to expect that the c's may vanish in other situations when α's pass through zero.

Let us now apply our rules (1), (2), and (3) to some particular scattering problems.

III. PION-PION SCATTERING

For π-π scattering, the independent amplitudes of rule (1) can be taken to be the three isotopic spin amplitudes $T^I(s,t)$ with $I=0$, 1, 2 for the reaction in which s is the total energy squared.

A prominent feature of the scattering process is the $I=1$, $J=1^-$ resonance at about 750 Mev, called ρ. Let us start by considering, for the purposes of rule (2), the quantum numbers in the t reaction of this state: $I=1, P=-1, G=+1$. Suppose the ρ meson is a physical manifestation of a Regge term with these quantum numbers and signature -1. The exchange of a particle with $I=1$, $P=-1$, $G=+1$, spin j ($j=1, 3, 5$, etc.) and mass M, contributes to (T^0,T^1,T^2) a term

$$(-2,-1,1)P_j(x_t)C/(t-M^2), \tag{3.1}$$

and rule (3) gives us for the Regge term for large x_t the form

$$(-2,-1,1)s^{\alpha}\frac{1-\exp[-i\pi\alpha(t)]}{2\sin\pi\alpha(t)}c(t), \tag{3.2}$$

where we might use the more explicit notation $\alpha_\rho(t)$ and $c_{\pi\pi\rho\pi\pi}(t)$. To avoid having variable dimensions for the quantity c, it is useful to put

$$c(t)=4m_\pi^2(2m_\pi^2)^{-\alpha_\rho(t)}b(t). \tag{3.3}$$

Near $t=m_\rho^2$, we have information about α and b. We may, if we like, define m_ρ^2 to be the value of t for which $\mathrm{Re}\alpha_\rho=1$. Setting

$$\begin{aligned}\epsilon_\rho&=\mathrm{Re}\alpha_\rho'(m_\rho^2),\\ I_\rho&=\mathrm{Im}\alpha_\rho(m_\rho^2),\end{aligned} \tag{3.4}$$

and treating the imaginary part as small, then in the neighborhood of m_ρ^2 the expression (3.2) gives us approximately

$$(-2,-1,1)s\frac{2b(m_\rho^2)}{\pi\epsilon_\rho}\frac{(-1)}{t-m_\rho^2+iI_\rho\epsilon_\rho^{-1}}, \tag{3.5}$$

to be compared with the contribution to π-π scattering of the exchange of a single virtual, slightly unstable ρ particle in field theory or dispersion theory:

$$(-2,-1,1)P_1(x_t)[-2\gamma_{\rho\pi\pi}^2(m_\rho^2-4m_\pi^2)]\times\frac{(-1)}{t-m_\rho^2+i\Gamma_\rho m_\rho}, \tag{3.6}$$

$$\underset{s\to\infty}{\longrightarrow}(-2,-1,1)8\gamma_{\rho\pi\pi}^2 s\frac{(-1)}{t-m_\rho^2+i\Gamma_\rho m_\rho},$$

[9] The signature has sometimes been confused with parity in the literature. Even when parity is not conserved, the poles are still absent at every other integral value of α because of the signature.

where $\gamma_{\rho\pi\pi}^2/4\pi$ is an effective coupling constant of ρ to π and π. If we make the approximation that $\rho \to 2\pi$ is the dominant decay mode of ρ, then the width Γ_ρ is given[10] by

$$\Gamma_\rho m_\rho = \tfrac{1}{3}(\gamma_{\rho\pi\pi}^2/4\pi)(m_\rho^2-4m_\pi^2)^{\frac{3}{2}} m_\rho^{-1}, \qquad (3.7)$$

so that the experimental value of $\gamma_{\rho\pi\pi}^2/4\pi$ is around unity. Evidently in (3.5) and (3.6) we make the identifications (for small Γ_ρ)

$$b(m_\rho^2)/\pi\epsilon_\rho = 4\gamma_{\rho\pi\pi}^2, \qquad I_\rho\epsilon_\rho^{-1} = \Gamma_\rho m_\rho. \qquad (3.8)$$

Using (3.7) and (3.8) we obtain a result that comes just from the assumption of the pure decay $\rho \to 2\pi$:

$$\frac{\pi I_\rho}{b(m_\rho^2)} = \frac{(m_\rho^2-4m_\pi^2)^{\frac{3}{2}} m_\rho^{-1}}{48\pi}. \qquad (3.9)$$

If the charge exchange amplitudes for π-π scattering are dominated by the Regge term containing the ρ meson for large s, then a charge exchange cross section will be, for example,

$$\frac{d\sigma^{I=0}}{dt} - \frac{d\sigma^{I=2}}{dt} \underset{s\to\infty}{\longrightarrow} 3F_{\rho\pi\pi}(t)\left(\frac{s}{2m_\pi^2}\right)^{2\alpha_\rho(t)-2}, \qquad (3.10)$$

where

$$F_{\rho\pi\pi}(t) = \frac{1}{16\pi}\left|b_{\rho\pi\pi}(t)\left(\frac{1-e^{-i\pi\alpha_\rho(t)}}{\sin\pi\alpha_\rho(t)}\right)\right|^2 \qquad (3.11)$$

and we have restored some of the subscript indices for b.

In the physical region for the s reaction $\alpha(t)$ is no doubt <1. This is quite different from the situation for an elementary ρ in the lowest order of perturbation theory; however, it seems unlikely that the ρ could be elementary in any case, since the perturbation expansion of an elementary $J=1$, $I=1$ particle is not renormalizable. Later, for example, in Sec. V where we discuss N-N scattering, such distinctions will take on more importance, since in N-N scattering the exchange of a $J=1$, $I=0$ particle, which can be renormalized, is possible.

We have already indicated that the Regge approach can provide an explanation of the experimental result that total cross sections become constant at high energies if we assume the existence of a particular α, called α_P, with even signature and such that $\alpha_P(0)=1$. Let us associate α_P with the set of quantum numbers describing the vacuum. Then its existence also guarantees the validity of the Pomeranchuk theorems, which state that particle and antiparticle total cross sections become equal at high energies, and that all two-body inelastic cross sections vanish, provided the α_P Regge term dominates the amplitude for small momentum transfers. Froissart has shown that no α may be greater than one[6] for $t\leqslant 0$; to assure the Pomeranchuk statement, then, we must assume no other α, associated with a different set of quantum numbers, equals one for $t\leqslant 0$.

[10] M. Gell-Mann and F. Zachariasen, Phys. Rev. **124**, 953 (1961).

The form in which this Pomeranchuk Regge term will appear at high energies in the π-π problem is, by rule (3),

$$(1,1,1)(s/2m_\pi^2)^{\alpha_P(t)} \times\left\{\frac{1+\exp[-i\pi\alpha_P(t)]}{2\sin\pi\alpha_P(t)}\right\}4m_\pi^2 b_{P\pi\pi}(t). \qquad (3.12)$$

Near $t=0$, we have $\alpha_P(t)\approx 1$, while other α's from other Regge terms such as that associated with the ρ meson which was discussed before, are presumably less than 1. The entire π-π amplitude is then dominated by (3.12); hence, as $t\to 0$ we find the amplitude becomes pure imaginary, and

$$T^I(s,0) \underset{s\to\infty}{\longrightarrow} -(1,1,1)isb_{P\pi\pi}(0). \qquad (3.14)$$

The optical theorem for π-π scattering states that

$$\mathrm{Im}T^I(s,0) \underset{s\to\infty}{\longrightarrow} -s\sigma_T^I, \qquad (3.15)$$

where σ_T^I is the asymptotic total π-π cross section in the isotopic spin I channel. Therefore

$$\sigma_T^I = b(0). \qquad (3.16)$$

The differential cross section for π-π scattering at high energies which results from (3.13) may be written

$$\frac{d\sigma^I}{dt} \to F_{P\pi\pi}(t)\left(\frac{s}{2m_\pi^2}\right)^{2\alpha_P(t)-2}, \qquad (3.17)$$

if we define

$$F_{P\pi\pi}(t) = \frac{1}{16\pi}\left|b_{P\pi\pi}(t)\left(\frac{1+e^{-i\pi\alpha_P(t)}}{\sin\pi\alpha_P(t)}\right)\right|^2. \qquad (3.18)$$

These equations are valid for all t for which the "Pomeranchuk" Regge term dominates; therefore, they should certainly be valid for small t. For larger negative t however, there is in principle nothing to stop a different α from being bigger than α_P. If this happens, the form (3.17) is still valid, but with a different $F_{\pi\pi}(t)$ and the newly dominant α replacing α_P.

The "Pomeranchuk" Regge term can be exchanged in all elastic scattering amplitudes, since it goes with the quantum numbers of the vacuum. Therefore, all elastic differential cross sections will, for sufficiently large energies, and for momentum transfers at which α_P dominates all other α's, have the energy dependence of (3.17) with the same exponent $\alpha_P(t)$. The coefficient

$F_{P\pi\pi}(t)$ in (3.17) will, of course, not be the same for different processes.[11]

For small t, we may write $\alpha_P(t)=1+t\alpha_P'(0)$, in which case (3.17) becomes

$$\frac{d\sigma^I}{dt}\longrightarrow F_{P\pi\pi}(t)\exp[-2|t|\alpha_P'(0)\ln(s/2m_\pi^2)]. \quad (3.19)$$

For very large energies, the most rapid variation with t will come from the exponential, so there will be an exponential diffraction peak with a width that decreases logarithmically with increasing energy.

IV. PION-NUCLEON SCATTERING

The discussion in this case is much the same as for the π-π problem in the forward direction at high energies; the only real difference arises from the nucleon spin. However, in the π-N case, because of the non-identity of the particles, we no longer have the symmetry between the forward and backward high energy behavior that was true of the π-π problem. We must therefore discuss these two limits separately.

In accordance with rule (1) we may choose the amplitudes describing the π-N process to be $A^{\pm}$ and $B^{\pm}$ where the invariant amplitude is written

$$T=A^+\delta_{\sigma'\sigma}+A^-[\tau_{\sigma'},\tau_\sigma]/2 +(B^+\delta_{\sigma'\sigma}+B^-[\tau_{\sigma'},\tau_\sigma]/2)(q'+q)/2. \quad (4.1)$$

Here σ', σ and q', q are the final and initial charges and 4-momenta of the pions.

First, we shall concentrate on the high energy forward limit $s\rightarrow\infty$, t fixed, where s is the total c.m. energy squared for π-N scattering, and t is the total c.m. energy squared for the process $\pi+\pi\rightarrow N+\bar{N}$. As in the π-π problem, the ρ meson will appear in the t reaction, as will the Pomeranchuk term. The quantum numbers of the ρ meson are $I=1$, $P=-1$, $G=+1$, so using rule (2) of Sec. II and the known form of the partial wave expansion for the $\pi+\pi\rightarrow N+\bar{N}$ process,[12] we may write the form of the relevant meson pole term:

$$A^{(-)}=\frac{C^{(1)}P_j(x_t)+m_N(M^2-4m_\pi^2)^{\frac{1}{2}}(M^2-4m_N^2)^{-\frac{1}{2}}C^{(2)}x_tP_j'(x_t)}{t-M^2},$$
$$B^{(-)}=C^{(2)}P_j'(x_t)/(t-M^2). \quad (4.2)$$

There is no contribution to $A^{(+)}$ or $B^{(+)}$ since these amplitudes correspond to a pure $I=0$ state in the t reaction. The cosine of the scattering angle in the t reaction is

$$x_t=-(s-m_N^2-m_\pi^2+\tfrac{1}{2}t)/2q_tp_t,$$

where for this problem we have

$$q_t^2=\tfrac{1}{4}t-m_\pi^2,\quad p_t^2=\tfrac{1}{4}t-m_N^2.$$

Asymptotically, we still have (1.1).

At large s, $P_j(x_t)$ goes like s^j and $x_tP_j'(x_t)$ like js^j, while $P_j'(x_t)$ goes like js^{j-1}. Applying rule (3) and taking out some factors for convenience, we have for the asymptotic Regge term the form:

$$-A^{(-)}\rightarrow\frac{1-e^{-i\pi\alpha_\rho(t)}}{2\sin\pi\alpha_\rho(t)}\left(\frac{s}{2m_\pi m_N}\right)^{\alpha_\rho(t)} \times 2m_\pi[b_{\pi\pi\rho NN}^{(1)}(t)-\alpha_\rho(t)b_{\pi\pi\rho NN}^{(2)}(t)]+\cdots,$$
$$-B^{(-)}\rightarrow\frac{1-e^{-i\pi\alpha_\rho(t)}}{2\sin\pi\alpha_\rho(t)}\left(\frac{s}{2m_\pi m_N}\right)^{\alpha_\rho(t)-1} \times 2\alpha_\rho(t)b_{\pi\pi\rho NN}^{(2)}+\cdots. \quad (4.3)$$

For simplicity, we shall usually drop the π and N subscripts on $b^{(1)}$ and $b^{(2)}$.

The appearance of two unknown functions of t, $b_\rho^{(1)}(t)$ and $b_\rho^{(2)}(t)$, reflects the fact that there are two possible states of the N-$\bar{N}$ system in the t reaction, for example $^3S_1$ and $^3D_1$, and without a complete solution to the dynamics of the process, there is an unknown mixing parameter between these two.

The α_ρ here is, of course, the same α_ρ as we found in the π-π problem. The position and width of the ρ meson are expressed in terms of this α. The functions $b_\rho^{(1)}$ and $b_\rho^{(2)}$, on the other hand, are characteristic of the particular process in question. As in the π-π problem, these functions when evaluated at m_ρ^2 may be related to the coupling constants $\gamma_{\rho\pi\pi}$ and $\gamma_{\rho NN}$ and the "anomalous moment" $\mu_{\rho NN}$ of the ρ meson coupling to pions and nucleons. Specifically, we find

$$b_\rho^{(1)}(m_\rho^2)/\pi\epsilon_\rho=2\gamma_{\rho NN}\gamma_{\rho\pi\pi},$$
$$b_\rho^{(2)}(m_\rho^2)/\pi\epsilon_\rho=2\gamma_{\rho NN}\gamma_{\rho\pi\pi}-4m_N\mu_{\rho NN}\gamma_{\rho\pi\pi}. \quad (4.4)$$

At large s and for $t<0$, so that we are in the physical region for the s reaction, this Regge term contributes to the no-spin-flip and spin-flip scattering amplitudes as follows:

$$f^-\rightarrow\frac{m_N}{4\pi s^{\frac{1}{2}}}\left(\frac{1-e^{-i\pi\alpha_\rho}}{2\sin\pi\alpha_\rho}\right)\left(\frac{s}{2m_\pi m_N}\right)^{\alpha_\rho}2m_\pi b_\rho^{(1)}+\cdots,$$
$$\tilde{f}^-\rightarrow\frac{1}{16\pi}\left(\frac{1-e^{-i\pi\alpha_\rho}}{2\sin\pi\alpha_\rho}\right)\left(\frac{s}{2m_\pi m_N}\right)^{\alpha_\rho}2m_\pi(b_\rho^{(1)}-\alpha b_\rho^{(2)})+\cdots. \quad (4.5)$$

[11] Note the presence of the factor $1/2m_\pi^2$ in the quantity raised to the power $2\alpha_P(t)-2$ is purely arbitrary. In π-N and N-N scattering, we shall use $2m_\pi m_N$ and $2m_N^2$, which are equally arbitrary. In general, any constant raised to the power $2\alpha_P(t)-2$ can be absorbed into $F(t)$.

[12] W. R. Frazer and J. R. Fulco, Phys. Rev. **117**, 1603 (1960).

The no-spin-flip amplitude f is defined, for large s, by

$$f^{\pm}=-\frac{m_N}{4\pi s^{\frac{1}{2}}}\left(A^{\pm}+\frac{s}{2m_N}B^{\pm}\right),$$

and the spin-flip amplitude by

$$\tilde{f}^{\pm}=\frac{1}{16\pi}(-A^{\pm}+s^{\frac{1}{2}}B^{\pm}). \tag{4.6}$$

Hence, the differential cross section is

$$\frac{d\sigma^{\pm}}{d\Omega}=\frac{1}{16\pi^2}\times\left(\frac{m_N^2}{s}\left|A^{\pm}+\frac{s}{2m_N}B^{\pm}\right|^2+\frac{\sin^2\theta}{16}|A^{\pm}-s^{\frac{1}{2}}B^{\pm}|^2\right). \tag{4.7}$$

The asymptotic charge exchange π-N cross section is thus

$$\frac{d\sigma^{-}}{dt}\to\left(\frac{s}{2m_\pi m_N}\right)^{2\alpha_\rho-2}F_{\rho\pi N}(t), \tag{4.8}$$

where we have

$$F_{\rho\pi N}(t)=\frac{1}{16\pi}\left\{|b^{(1)}|^2-\frac{t}{4m_N^2}|b^{(1)}-\alpha b^{(2)}|^2\right\}\times\left|\frac{1-e^{-i\pi\alpha_\rho}}{\sin\pi\alpha_\rho}\right|^2. \tag{4.9}$$

In the t reaction without charge exchange we expect to find the "Pomeranchuk" Regge term. The form which this term takes is, according to our rules,

$$\begin{aligned}A^{(+)}&\to\frac{1+e^{-i\pi\alpha_P(t)}}{2\sin\pi\alpha_P(t)}\left(\frac{s}{2m_\pi m_N}\right)^{\alpha_P(t)}\times 2m_\pi[b_{\pi\pi PNN}{}^{(1)}(t)-\alpha_P(t)b_{\pi\pi PNN}{}^{(2)}(t)]+\cdots,\\ B^{(+)}&\to\frac{1+e^{-i\pi\alpha_P(t)}}{2\sin\pi\alpha_P(t)}\left(\frac{s}{2m_\pi m_N}\right)^{\alpha_P(t)-1}\times 2\alpha_P(t)b_{\pi\pi PNN}{}^{(2)}(t),\end{aligned} \tag{4.10}$$

much as in (4.3).

At high energies in the physical region for the s reaction, this Regge term contributes to the no-flip and flip amplitudes as follows:

$$\begin{aligned}f^{(+)}&\to-\frac{m_N}{4\pi s^{\frac{1}{2}}}\left(\frac{1+e^{-i\pi\alpha_P}}{2\sin\pi\alpha_P}\right)\left(\frac{s}{2m_\pi m_N}\right)^{\alpha_P}\times 2m_\pi b_P{}^{(1)}+\cdots,\\ \tilde{f}^{(+)}&\to-\frac{1}{16\pi}\left(\frac{1+e^{-i\pi\alpha_P}}{2\sin\pi\alpha_P}\right)\left(\frac{s}{2m_\pi m_N}\right)^{\alpha_P}\times 2m_\pi(b_P{}^{(1)}-\alpha b_P{}^{(2)})+\cdots.\end{aligned} \tag{4.11}$$

As $t\to 0$, we have $\alpha_P(0)=1$ and therefore

$$f^{(+)}\to(s^{\frac{1}{2}}/8\pi)ib_P{}^{(1)}(0)+\cdots. \tag{4.12}$$

Assuming as always that the "Pomeranchuk" Regge term dominates, we may then use the optical theorem, which states for large s that

$$\mathrm{Im}f^{(+)}=(s^{\frac{1}{2}}/8\pi)\sigma_T{}^{(+)}, \tag{4.13}$$

to relate $b_P{}^{(1)}(0)$ to the asymptotic total π-N cross section. Thus, we find

$$b_P{}^{(1)}(0)=\sigma_T{}^{(+)}. \tag{4.14}$$

At any $t<0$ for which the "Pomeranchuk" Regge term dominates the entire amplitude, we may write

$$\frac{d\sigma^{(+)}}{dt}=F_{\pi NP}(t)\left(\frac{s}{2m_\pi m_N}\right)^{2\alpha_P(t)-2}, \tag{4.15}$$

where we define

$$F_{\pi NP}(t)=\frac{1}{16\pi}\left\{|b_P{}^{(1)}|^2-\frac{t}{4m_N^2}|b_P{}^{(1)}-\alpha b_P{}^{(2)}|^2\right\}\times\left|\frac{1+e^{-i\pi\alpha_P}}{\sin\pi\alpha_P}\right|^2. \tag{4.16}$$

Let us now turn to a discussion of backward high-energy Regge terms. These will be Regge terms associated with the u reaction, where u is the crossed momentum transfer. The u reaction is then also π-N scattering. The partial wave expansion for this process is well known,[13] and in accordance with rule (2) we consider the hypothetical pole terms

$$\begin{aligned}A&=C\left(\frac{W+m_N}{E+m_N}P_{j+\frac{1}{2}}'(x_u)+\frac{W-m_N}{E-m_N}P_{j-\frac{1}{2}}'(x_u)\right)(u-M^2)^{-1},\\ B&=C\left(\frac{1}{E+m_N}P_{j+\frac{1}{2}}'(x_u)-\frac{1}{E-m_N}P_{j-\frac{1}{2}}'(x_u)\right)(u-M^2)^{-1},\end{aligned} \tag{4.17}$$

for states with $j=l+\frac{1}{2}$, and

$$\begin{aligned}A&=C\left(\frac{W+m_N}{E+m_N}P_{j-\frac{1}{2}}'(x_u)+\frac{W-m_N}{E-m_N}P_{j+\frac{1}{2}}'(x_u)\right)(u-M^2)^{-1},\\ B&=C\left(\frac{1}{E+m_N}P_{j-\frac{1}{2}}'(x_u)-\frac{1}{E-m_N}P_{j+\frac{1}{2}}'(x_u)\right)(u-M^2)^{-1},\end{aligned} \tag{4.18}$$

for states with $j=l-\frac{1}{2}$.

In this reaction, a single C suffices to describe each pole term since there is no mixing between states possible as long as parity is conserved. For the moment, we are ignoring isotopic spin. The notation in (4.17)

[13] S. C. Frautschi and J. D. Walecka, Phys. Rev. **120**, 1486 (1960).

and (4.18) is the following:

$$\begin{aligned} x_u &= -(s-m_N^2-m_\pi^2+2E_u\omega_u)/2q_u^2, \\ q_u^2 &= u/4-\tfrac{1}{2}(m_N^2+m_\pi^2)+(m_N^2-m_\pi^2)^2/4u, \\ E_u &= (u+m_N^2-m_\pi^2)/2u^{\frac{1}{2}}, \\ \omega_u &= (u-m_N^2+m_\pi^2)/2u^{\frac{1}{2}}, \\ W_u &= E_u+\omega_u=u^{\frac{1}{2}}. \end{aligned} \tag{4.19}$$

Applying rule (3) to a Regge family with positive signature and negative parity or negative signature and positive parity (counting the intrinsic nucleon parity as $+1$ and that of the pion as -1), we use (4.17) and obtain for the high-energy contribution to A and B something of the form

$$\begin{aligned} A &\to \frac{[1\pm e^{-i\pi\alpha(u)}]}{2\sin\pi\alpha(u)}\left(\frac{s}{2m_Nm_\pi}\right)^{\alpha(u)}(W_u+m_N)b(u) \\ &\qquad +\cdots, \\ B &\to \frac{[1\pm e^{-i\pi\alpha(u)}]}{2\sin\pi\alpha(u)}\left(\frac{s}{2m_Nm_\pi}\right)^{\alpha(u)}b(u)+\cdots. \end{aligned} \tag{4.20}$$

Correspondingly, for a Regge family with positive signature and positive parity or negative signature and negative parity, we use (4.18) and find

$$\begin{aligned} A &\to \frac{[1\pm e^{-i\pi\alpha(u)}]}{2\sin\pi\alpha(u)}\left(\frac{s}{2m_Nm_\pi}\right)^{\alpha(u)}(W_u-m_N)b(u)+\cdots, \\ -B &\to \frac{[1\pm e^{-i\pi\alpha(u)}]}{2\sin\pi\alpha(u)}\left(\frac{s}{2m_Nm_\pi}\right)^{\alpha(u)}b(u)+\cdots. \end{aligned} \tag{4.21}$$

There are a number of stable and unstable states in the π-N process which we may associate with Regge terms of this sort, namely the nucleon itself and the various π-N resonances: the 33 resonance, the presumed $d_{\frac{3}{2}}$, $I=\frac{1}{2}$ resonance at 1520 Mev, and the presumed $f_{\frac{5}{2}}$, $I=\frac{1}{2}$ resonance at 1680 Mev.

If the nucleon is due to a Regge term,[14] this term must be of the form (4.21) with even signature and $\alpha(m_N^2)=0$. Furthermore, the nucleon has $I=\frac{1}{2}$, so the Regge term must appear with coefficient $(1,-1)$ in the $((+),(-))$ amplitudes. Let us take $b(u)$ to have the sign given by (4.21) for the $(+)$ amplitude. It is easy to compare this Regge term near $u=m_N^2$ with the usual nucleon pole and relate $b(m_N^2)$ to the usual pion-nucleon coupling constant:

$$b(m_N^2)/\pi\epsilon=g_{NN\pi}^2, \tag{4.22}$$

where we define $\epsilon=\alpha'(m_N^2)$. Since $u=m_N^2$ is below threshold in the u reaction α is real there. The contribution of this Regge term to the high energy no-spin-flip and spin-flip amplitudes in the physical region[15] for the s reaction is easily seen to be, for large s and fixed u,

$$\begin{aligned} f^\pm &\to \pm\frac{1}{8\pi}\left(\frac{1+e^{-i\pi\alpha}}{2\sin\pi\alpha}\right)\left(\frac{s}{2m_\pi m_N}\right)^{\alpha}b(u)(W_u-2m_N)+\cdots, \\ \tilde{f}^\pm &\to \mp\frac{s^{\frac{1}{2}}}{16\pi}\left(\frac{1+e^{-i\pi\alpha}}{2\sin\pi\alpha}\right)\left(\frac{s}{2m_\pi m_N}\right)^{\alpha}b(u)+\cdots. \end{aligned} \tag{4.23}$$

Note that we expect α in (4.23) to be less than zero for u in the physical region for the s reaction, while if the nucleon is elementary it can be shown in each order of perturbation theory[16] that the form (4.23) is correct but with exponent$=0$ for all u. If the nucleon Regge term were to dominate in the limit, then we would have an immediate method for testing whether the nucleon is "elementary." In general, however, we cannot be sure that this particular Regge term will dominate, because there is no reason to believe that the Regge α's associated with the various π-N resonances are smaller than the nucleon α in the physical region. Of course, if *all* these Regge α's are considerably less than zero in the physical region, then the difference from the "elementary" case will still be obvious. In any case, the variation of the α's with t can still distinguish the Regge situation.

Of the higher resonances, we might expect that the $f_{\frac{5}{2}}$, $I=\frac{1}{2}$ resonance is associated with the *same* α as the nucleon,[14] since the quantum numbers of the two states are the same. Thus we should have not only $\alpha(m_N^2)=0$ but also $\mathrm{Re}\alpha(m_{f_{\frac{5}{2}}}^2)=2$. This requires a rate of change of α of about $\alpha'\approx1(\mathrm{Bev})^{-2}$, which, as we shall see in Sec. V, is of the same order of magnitude as the slope which seems to be experimentally indicated for the Pomeranchuk α_P.

There should then be two additional α's, associated with the $p_{\frac{3}{2}}$, $I=\frac{3}{2}$ and the $d_{\frac{3}{2}}$, $I=\frac{1}{2}$ resonances. We shall close this section by indicating the form of the Regge term associated with the 33 resonance. We use (4.20) with odd signature and $\alpha(m_{33}^2)=1$. The form (4.20) must appear in the $[(+),(-)]$ amplitudes with coefficients (2,1). The width of the 33 resonance is given for small Γ, by

$$m_{33}\Gamma_{33}=I_{33}/\epsilon_{33}, \tag{4.24}$$

where $\epsilon_{33}=\mathrm{Re}\alpha'(m_{33}^2)$, $I_{33}=\mathrm{Im}\alpha(m_{33}^2)$. We can evaluate the coefficients b at resonance by using unitarity and the condition of a single dominant decay mode $(33)\to N+\pi$. We obtain a relation analogous to (3.9)

---

[14] R. Blankenbecler and M. L. Goldberger, Phys. Rev. **126**, 766 (1962).

[15] Backward scattering in the s reaction corresponds to a maximum value of u that decreases from $u=(m_N-m_\pi)^2$ at threshold to $u=0$ at infinite s. R. Blankenbeder, L. Cook, and M. L. Goldberger have pointed out to us that between this maximum value of u and $u=0$ the quantity $|x_u|$ is less than unity. But asymptotic expansions such as (4.23) are valid in the limit of large s for fixed u and we can take such a limit only for negative u; in that case $|x_u|$ becomes large at high energies.

[16] M. Gell-Mann and F. Zachariasen, Phys. Rev. **123**, 1065 (1961).

for $\rho \to 2\pi$, namely

$$\frac{\pi I_{33}}{b_{33}} = -\frac{1}{4\pi} \frac{q_u^3(E_u+m_N)}{m_\pi m_N}\bigg|_{u=m_{33}^2} \qquad (4.25)$$

It should be remarked that for this Regge term one cannot say that we must have $\alpha<0$ in the physical region, but only $\alpha<1$ on the basis of assuming decreasing α's. Nevertheless, we may hope that for sufficiently large negative u this α will go negative as well.

V. NUCLEON-NUCLEON SCATTERING: EXPERIMENTAL DATA

From the preceding analysis of the π-π and π-N cases, we can easily see the general features of the N-N problem without going through the details.

The scattering amplitude without isotopic spin exchange ($I=0$ in the t reaction) contains the Pomeranchuk term and dominates the amplitude in which $I=1$ is exchanged; the latter can be studied conveniently only in backward n-p scattering, unless "elementary" mesons contribute.

Consider the nonexchange amplitude for fixed $t<0$ and large s. Suppose only Regge terms contribute. Because of the dominance of α_P (at least near $t=0$) the main phenomenon is the diffraction peak and the cross section has the form

$$d\sigma/dt \to F_{NNP}(t)(s/2m_N^2)^{2\alpha_P(t)-2}, \qquad (5.1)$$

where $F(t)$ is relatively slowly varying.[11] The corresponding scattering amplitude goes like $s^{\alpha_P(t)}$.

Now suppose there is an elementary neutral vector meson with $I=0$, which might be identified with the observed ω^0. In field theory we may couple it to a conserved vector current and construct a renormalizable perturbation series; in each order, the diagrams corresponding to the exchange of an ω^0 with a dressed propagator and a dressed vertex at each end give a contribution to the scattering amplitude that persists at large s with the form

$$s(t-m_\omega^2)^{-1}\phi(t), \qquad (5.2)$$

where $\phi(t)$ includes the effect of the vertex function at each end and the modification of the propagator by interactions. We see that the amplitude has a real part going like s^1 at high energies with the exponent unity independent of t. This behavior is in sharp contrast with that of a "Pomeranchuk" Regge term, which is pure imaginary in the forward direction and goes like $s^{\alpha(t)}$ with α decreasing from unity away from the forward direction.

If we describe the ω^0 (or other vector meson) as a member of a Regge family with parameter $\alpha_\omega(t)$, then the term contributed to the N-N amplitude by the exchange of this family goes like $s^{\alpha_\omega(t)}$ at high energies. But Reα_ω equals unity only at $t=m_\omega^2$ and as t decreases to zero (to reach the physical region for the s reaction) α_ω falls well below unity, so that in the region of the diffraction peak the exchange of the ω family is overshadowed by the Pomeranchuk amplitude.

There are various experimental ways to test for an ω^0 acting as an elementary particle does in perturbation theory. The thoroughness with which these tests must be carried out depends on the effective strength of the ω^0 coupling to nucleons.

First, one can compare the high-energy forward scattering cross section (eliminating the Coulomb effect for p-p collisions) with that calculated from the optical theorem for the imaginary part of the amplitude alone.[17] A real part of the forward amplitude with the same linear behavior in s as the imaginary part would come from the exchange of an "elementary" vector meson. In fact, that is just the behavior we expect for the exchange of a photon, treating it as elementary.

Second, one may search for a persistent real part of the nuclear forward scattering amplitude by looking for interference with the Coulomb amplitude, especially in nucleon-nucleus collisions.

Third, one may examine the form of the diffraction peak for a fixed high energy. In field theory, there is no known reason for the function $\phi(t)$ in (5.2) to fall off very rapidly (e.g., exponentially) as t decreases from zero. If we look at the cross section and see a diffraction peak like that given by (5.1), which for small t is $d\sigma/dt = F(t)\exp[-2|t|\alpha_P'(0)\ln(s/2m_N^2)]$, we can set a rough limit on the strength with which a term decreasing approximately like $(m_\omega^2-t^2)^{-2}$ could be present.

A fourth slightly different approach to the data, which can in principle test for "elementary" mesons of either spin zero or spin one (and of either isotopic spin), is the following. For each fixed momentum transfer t, we examine the s dependence of the cross section at large s and try to find the dominant power law. This method improves rapidly with energy at high momentum transfers. At two sufficiently high energies s_1 and s_2 we should have

$$\frac{d\sigma}{dt}(s_1,t)\bigg/\frac{d\sigma}{dt}(s_2,t) \approx (s_1/s_2)^{2[L(t)-1]}, \qquad (5.3)$$

where $L(t)$ is the dominant power at momentum transfer t, whether that is a Regge $\alpha(t)$ or the *fixed* angular momentum of an "elementary" meson (1 for a vector and 0 for a scalar or pseudoscalar meson). It would be desirable to have higher energies than are at present

---

[17] See, for example, B. Cork, W. A. Wenzel, and C. W. Causey, Jr., Phys. Rev. **107**, 859 (1957), and G. A. Smith, H. Courant, E. C. Fowler, H. Kraybill, J. Sandweiss, and H. Taft, *ibid.* **123**, 2160 (1961). These authors find extrapolated forward cross sections consistent with a pure imaginary forward amplitude between 2 and 6 Bev. W. M. Preston, R. Watson, and J. C. Street, *ibid.* **118**, 579 (1960), find some evidence for a real part.

available,[18] but a preliminary analysis has been made of the existing data.

For the first two methods discussed above, we do not have good enough data available. The experiment of Cocconi *et al.*[19] permits some application of the third and fourth methods. The diffraction peak seems to be quite clearly exponential in shape. It is evident that (5.3) gives a direct measure of $L(t)$. At small $|t|$ the errors in the experimental cross sections at different energies overlap, so $L(t)$ cannot yet be accurately determined in this range. For larger $|t|$, however, in the range 1–3 Bev^2, the cross sections at different energies are clearly separated, and yield roughly $L(-1\text{ Bev}^2)\approx 0$, $L(-2.7\text{ Bev}^2)\approx -0.7\pm 0.3$. Supposing that $L(t)$ is in fact $\alpha_P(t)$ in this range, we have a crude estimate of the rate at which $\alpha_P(t)$ changes. If this rate of change is maintained for positive t, we may expect α_P to pass through 2 at about $t\sim(1\text{ Bev})^2$. There would then be a spin two object with a mass around one Bev, and $I=0$, $P=+1$, $G=+1$.[20]

The data also seem to indicate that α_P has passed through zero near $t=-1$ Bev^2. Because of the even signature of the α_P terms, that means there is a ghost of mass squared around -1 Bev^2. As we have remarked before, the difficulty may be overcome by the vanishing of all the b's coupling the "Pomeranchuk" Regge term to any particle at this point.

An alternative possibility would be to separate the $I=0$, $J=0$ state in the t channel and determine it by the N/D method in such a way that the ghost does not appear. Still another possibility is that $\alpha_P\to 0$ as $t\to -\infty$. In either of these cases, however, we would have to ignore the slight indication from experiment that the leading α passes through zero near $t=-1$ Bev^2.

Using the above estimate for $\alpha_P(t)$, or $L(t)$, one may calculate from the data the variation with t of the coefficient $F_{NNP}(t)$ in Eq. (5.1). We find $F(t)$ decreases only by a factor of ~ 3 between $t=0$ and $t=-2.7$ Bev^2; that is almost nothing compared to the decrease of $d\sigma/dt$ due to the factor $(s/2m_N^2)^{2L-2}$, which is of the order 10^5.

This encourages the hope that most of the exponential behavior in t for small t comes from the coefficient $(s/2m_N^2)^{2L-2}$, and little from the $F(t)$. If we make that assumption, putting[11]

$$d\sigma/dt\approx F(0)\exp[-2|t|\alpha_P'(0)\ln(s/2m_N^2)] \quad (5.4)$$

for small t, we find $\alpha_P'(0)\ln(s/2m_N^2)\approx 3.75$ from the data $0<-t\lesssim 1$ Bev^2, 30 Bev$^2\lesssim s\lesssim 40$ Bev^2. Thus we get $\alpha_P'(0)\sim 1.3$ Bev^{-2}, which is roughly consistent with our earlier estimates.

The above discussion has all been for noncharge-exchange scattering. It is evident, however, that similar statements may be made for charge exchange scattering. The differences will be the absence of the "Pomeranchuk" Regge term and of other Regge terms corresponding to $I=0$ exchange. There remain terms for the exchange of $I=1$ vector or pseudoscalar mesons, such as ρ or π. If we define forward scattering to be the case where the proton is undeflected in angle, then $\rho^\pm$ and $\pi^\pm$ Regge terms will show up in the backward charge exchange scattering at high energies.

It is important to remark that the "Pomeranchuk" Regge term occurs in the scattering whenever a state with the quantum numbers (other than j) of the vacuum can be exchanged, even in spin-flip and genuinely inelastic processes. For example, we can see from (4.11) and (4.16) that in spin-flip π-N scattering without isotopic spin-flip, the contribution to the high energy cross section is of the form

$$\frac{d\sigma}{dt}\approx F(t)\left(\frac{s}{2m_\pi m_N}\right)^{2\alpha_P(t)-2}, \quad (5.5)$$

but with $F(t)\propto -t$ near $t=0$, since the angular distribution contains a factor $\sin^2\theta_s$. In N-N scattering also, there is a contribution of the "Pomeranchuk" Regge term to spin-flip scattering, but that is not yet of great experimental interest.

A phenomenon that has been studied experimentally[18] is inelastic diffraction scattering of protons on protons. Consider, for example, a reaction

$$N+N\to N+N^*, \quad (5.6)$$

where N^* is an unstable nucleon isobar. In such a reaction, the maximum value of t in the physical region is not zero, but a negative quantity $t_{\max}$. For large s, we have

$$t_{\max}\approx -m_N^2(m_{N^*}^2-m_N^2)^2/s^2.$$

Now whenever N^* is such that the "Pomeranchuk" Regge family can be exchanged, we have for (5.6) the contribution[21]

$$d\sigma/dt\approx F(t)(s/2m_N^2)^{2\alpha_P(t)-2}, \quad (5.7)$$

to the asymptotic cross section. Since t is less than zero in the physical region, $\alpha_P(t)$ is less than unity and $2\alpha_P(t)-2$ is less than zero. Thus inelastic scattering is reduced (at high energy in the forward direction) compared to elastic scattering.

In reaction (5.6), the 33 isobar can never be reached in the exchange of the Pomeranchuk channel, since the latter has $I=0$. The second and third resonances can,

[18] This is especially true of the application of the method to particles other than nucleons, since the range of presently available energies is then even lower.

[19] G. Cocconi, A. N. Diddens, E. Lillethun, G. Manning, A. E. Taylor, T. G. Walker, and A. M. Wetherell, Phys. Rev. Letters 7, 450 (1961); we wish to thank Dr. Cocconi, Dr. Wetherell, and Dr. Taylor for illuminating discussions of this work. A theoretical discussion of inelastic N-N scattering is given by S. Drell and Z. Hiida, *ibid.* 7, 199 (1961).

[20] C. Lovelace (to be published).

[21] When a reaction involves particles that are unstable or have anomalous thresholds, certain complications may arise in the complex angular momentum plane. See B. M. Udgaonkar and M. Gell-Mann, Phys. Rev. Letters 8, 346 (1962).

however, be reached. If they are $d_{\frac{3}{2}}$ and $f_{\frac{5}{2}}$ states respectively of π and N, then they require the exchange of at least 1 and 2 units of angular momentum, respectively, in the forward direction. As a consequence, $F(t)$ contains a factor $[\alpha_P(t)]^2$ for the second resonance and $[\alpha_P(t)]^2[\alpha_P(t)-1]^2$ for the third resonance near $t=t_{\max}$, while the characteristic diffraction peak function $(s/2m_N^2)^{2\alpha_P(t)-2}$ should appear in each case as in (5.7). For small t, then, the ratio of the lowest inelastic peak to the elastic one should be roughly constant, while the ratio of the next inelastic peak to the elastic one should go approximately like t^2. All these results are consistent with the observations of Cocconi *et al.*[19] but further experimental work is needed if the interpretation we have given is to be properly tested.

VI. REGGE POLES AND "ELEMENTARY" PARTICLES

We have discussed at some length the effect on scattering amplitudes of the Regge pole hypothesis. However, our treatment of the contrasting situation has not so far been very thorough; we shall now go into it in more detail.

Take, for example, the $B^{\pm}$ amplitudes in π-N scattering that we considered in Sec. IV. In pseudoscalar pion-nucleon field theory, to each order in the π-N coupling constant, the $B^{\pm}$ amplitudes obey the Mandelstam representation[22] in the following form[10,23]:

$$B^{\pm}=\frac{g_{NN\pi}^2}{s-m_N^2}\mp\frac{g_{NN\pi}^2}{u-m_N^2}+\frac{1}{\pi}\int\frac{b_1(s')ds'}{s'-s}$$
$$\mp\frac{1}{\pi}\int\frac{b_1(u')du'}{u'-u}+\frac{1}{\pi^2}\int\int\frac{B_{13}^{\pm}(s',t')ds'dt'}{(s'-s)(t'-t)}$$
$$\mp\frac{1}{\pi^2}\int\int\frac{B_{13}^{\pm}(u',t')dt'du'}{(t'-t)(u'-u)}$$
$$+\frac{1}{\pi^2}\int\int\frac{B_{12}^{\pm}(u',s')du'ds'}{(u'-u)(s'-s)}. \quad (6.1)$$

There are no subtractions, but there are pole terms and single integrals in addition to the double integrals. Using the fact that an unsubtracted dispersion integral vanishes as its argument approaches infinity, we may explore the behavior of (6.1) as $s\to\infty$ with u fixed (asymptotic scattering at backward angles, such as we discussed in Sec. IV). Since $t\to-\infty$ as $s\to\infty$, all the terms in (6.1) vanish except the pole term and single integral term in u:

$$B^{\pm}\xrightarrow[s\to\infty,\ u\text{ fixed}]{}\mp\frac{g_{NN\pi}^2}{u-m_N^2}\mp\frac{1}{\pi}\int\frac{b_1(u')du'}{u'-u}. \quad (6.2)$$

[22] There may be extra terms if there are singularities such as those discussed by R. J. Eden, P. V. Landshoff, J. C. Polkinghorne, and J. C. Taylor, J. Math. Phys. **2**, 656 (1961).
[23] S. Mandelstam, Phys. Rev. **115**, 1741 (1959).

In the π-N field theory, the asymptotic form (6.2) has a very simple interpretation.[10] It is the contribution to $B^{(\pm)}$ of the sum of all crossed Feynman diagrams in which there is a stretch of bare nucleon line between the emission of the final pion and the absorption of the initial one. Thus, it may be written in terms of the renormalized nucleon propagator $S_{FC}(p)$ and the renormalized pion-nucleon vertex operator Γ_{5c}.

The pole term comes from the matrix element

$$\bar{u}_f(p_f)\gamma_5\frac{1}{p-m_N}\gamma_5u_i(p_i)=\bar{u}_f(p_f)\gamma_5\frac{p+m_N}{p^2-m_N^2}\gamma_5u_i(p_i), \quad (6.3)$$

where p_i and p_f are the initial and final nucleon four-momenta and p is the intermediate nucleon four-momentum, with $p^2=u$ and $(p_i-p)^2=(p-p_f)^2=m_\pi^2$. The complete expression (6.2) comes in a similar way from the matrix element

$$\bar{u}_f(p_f)\Gamma_{5c}(p_f,p)S_{FC}(p)\Gamma_{5c}(p,p_i)u_i(p_i)$$
$$\equiv\bar{u}_f(p_f)\gamma_5\frac{p\chi(p^2)+m_N\psi(p^2)}{p^2-m_N^2}\gamma_5u_i(p_i), \quad (6.4)$$

so that we have

$$\frac{g_{NN\pi}^2}{u-m_N^2}+\frac{1}{\pi}\int\frac{b_1(u')du'}{u'-u}=\frac{g_{NN\pi}^2}{u-m_N^2}\chi(u). \quad (6.5)$$

The occurrence of the nucleon pole and single integral terms as additions to the double integrals is connected with the assumption of an elementary nucleon treated in perturbation theory. Unstable or bound dynamical isobars of the nucleon would not occur in each order of the expansion, but would appear only when infinite sets of terms of the expansion are summed. We can only conjecture how they would manifest themselves, but presumably it would be as Regge poles, with contributions at large s going like $s^{\alpha(u)}$ rather than s^0 as in (6.2). Moreover, at sufficiently large negative u, we expect the α's to become negative, so that the Regge contributions would vanish as $s\to\infty$, while a term like (6.2) persists.

It has been emphasized in reference 10 that the detection of terms such as (6.2) is a way of measuring off-energy-shell quantities in field theory, namely propagators and vertex functions. To the extent that all particles correspond to Regge poles, this possibility of measuring off-shell matrix elements disappears, as we might expect in a pure S-matrix theory.

Another point made in reference 10 is the connection between propagators or vertices and broken symmetries. In formal Lagrangian field theory, one conventionally describes a broken symmetry by the equality of bare quantities (for example, the bare masses of neutron and proton) when the physical quantities are not equal. In renormalized perturbation theory, one can convert the relation between formal bare quantities to a relation between the asymptotic forms of quantities like renormalized propagators and vertices for large values of their arguments. Thus it was proposed that comparison of quantities like $\chi(u)$ for large u in various reactions involving different baryons and mesons would provide a test of broken symmetries in strong interactions by means of measurements of S-matrix elements for strong processes. Again, if all baryons and mesons are just Regge poles, this possibility disappears and one must reconsider the whole question of the meaning of broken symmetry.[24] The same kind of argument applies even to familiar cases like isotopic spin conservation.

The most important aspect of high energy limits like (6.2), characteristic of many processes in renormalized perturbation theory, is their connection with the "peripheral model" of high energy collisions.[25] To discuss "peripheralism," let us choose another example, namely the charge exchange amplitude $P(s,t)$ in N-N scattering associated with the invariant $\gamma_5^{(1)}\gamma_5^{(2)}$, where the upper indices refer to the two nucleons. In the perturbation expansion of renormalized π-N field theory, we have, much as in (6.2), the result

$$P(s,t) \xrightarrow[s\to\infty,\ t\text{ fixed}]{} \frac{g_{NN\pi}^2}{t-m_\pi^2}+\frac{1}{\pi}\int\frac{b_1(t')dt'}{t'-t}, \qquad (6.6)$$

where the right-hand side may once again be interpreted as the product of a propagator and two vertex functions. This time we have the pion propagator $\Delta_{FC}(t)$ and the vertex $\gamma_5 V_c(t)$ for emission of an off-shell pion between two free nucleon lines:

$$\frac{g_{NN\pi}^2}{t-m_\pi^2}+\frac{1}{\pi}\int\frac{b_1(t')dt'}{t'-t}=g_{NN\pi}^2[V_c(t)]^2\Delta_{FC}(t). \qquad (6.7)$$

Now the peripheral model emphasizes the dominance at high energies of this exchange of one off-shell pion. (Moreover, the same kind of term is assumed to dominate many other reactions.) But the situation is quite different if the pion belongs to a Regge family; in that case, we have an asymptotic amplitude proportional to $s^{\alpha(t)}/\sin\pi\alpha(t)$, which agrees with (6.7) only at $t=m_\pi^2$, where $\alpha=0$. In the physical region for N-N scattering ($t\leq 0$), α is negative and the amplitude falls to zero at high energies instead of remaining constant. Of course, at moderate energies ($\sim$1 Bev) or even substantially higher if $|t|$ is kept small, the contribution of the one-pion pole is still expected to play an important role in the physical region.

Similar considerations apply to the amplitude $\mathcal{V}(s,t)$, in N-N scattering without isotopic spin exchange, that multiplies the invariant $\gamma_\alpha^{(1)}\gamma_\alpha^{(2)}$. Renormalized perturbation theory for a neutral vector meson such as ω^0, or else "peripheralism," suggests an asymptotic form

$$\gamma_{NN\omega}^2[V_{c\omega}(t)]^2\Delta_{FC\omega}(t), \qquad (6.8)$$

analogous to (6.7). We saw in Sec. V that this asymptotic form is very different from what is produced by Regge poles alone.

There are other amplitudes (such as $A^\pm$ in π-N scattering) which obey the Mandelstam representation with subtractions, even in renormalized perturbation theory. For those cases, we cannot make any clear cut statement about the asymptotic behavior for large s. Moreover, if we consider field theory apart from the perturbation expansion, or merely allow for the possibility that the sum of the series acts differently from each individual term, then we do not know how many subtractions there are in the Mandelstam representation even for $B^\pm$ in π-N scattering or P or $\mathcal{V}$ in N-N scattering. If additional subtractions are necessary, then many new kinds of asymptotic behavior are possible, including the type characteristic of Regge poles. After all, the Regge pole hypothesis is only a special case of the situation with subtractions. Thus if the experiments show that the nucleon, pion, etc., are all members of Regge families, then we still cannot rigorously exclude a field theory that treats these particles as "elementary" in a broad sense. However, if the nonsingular character of the amplitudes according to the Regge hypothesis really permits the calculation of all coupling constants and mass ratios, then there is not much point in calling the particles "elementary."

In conclusion, let us list a number of reactions in which the Regge pole hypothesis can be tested for various baryons and mesons.

N: $\pi+N\to N+\pi$,
$\gamma+N\to N+\pi$,
$\pi+N\to N+\omega$, etc.,

$Y=\Lambda, \Sigma$: $\pi+N\to Y+K$,
$K+N\to N+K$,
$\gamma+N\to Y+K$, etc.,

π: $N+N\to N+N$ (charge exchange),
$\gamma+N\to\pi+N$,
$\pi+N\to\rho+N$
$K+N\to K^*+N$, etc.,

K: $\pi+N\to K^*+Y$,
$\gamma+N\to K+Y$, etc.,

ω: $N+N\to N+N$,
$\pi+N\to\rho+N$,
$\gamma+N\to\pi^0+N$, etc.

ACKNOWLEDGMENTS

It is a pleasure to thank Geoffrey F. Chew for numerous enlightening conversations and the Lawrence

---

[24] M. Gell-Mann, Phys. Rev. **125**, 1067 (1962).

[25] G. Salzman, *Proceedings of the 1960 Annual International Conference on High-Energy Physics at Rochester* (Interscience Publishers, Inc., New York, 1960); S. Drell, Revs. Modern Phys. **33**, 458 (1961).

Radiation Laboratory of the University of California at Berkeley for its hospitality to the HEPS group.

APPENDIX

We should like to discuss the effect of an exchange potential in the Schrödinger equation on the form of the Regge terms, and in particular to justify Eq. (2.7).

A trivial justification is the following: consider the scattering amplitude $T(q,x)$, where q is the momentum and x is the cosine of the scattering angle, and write it as the sum of an even part and an odd part in x:

$$T(q,x)=T_+(q,x)+T_-(q,x). \tag{A1}$$

Now if $V_d(\mathbf{r})$ is the direct potential and $V_e(\mathbf{r})$ the exchange potential, then the effective potential for the even partial waves is $V_E=V_d+V_e$, while that for the odd partial waves is $V_O=V_d-V_e$. Now suppose we solve the Schrödinger equation for all partial waves with the potential V_E, obtaining the scattering amplitude $T_E(q,x)$; likewise, with V_O, we obtain the amplitude $T_O(q,x)$. Then we have

$$\begin{aligned}T_+(q,x)&=\tfrac{1}{2}[T_E(q,x)+T_E(q,-x)],\\ T_-(q,x)&=\tfrac{1}{2}[T_O(q,x)-T_O(q,-x)].\end{aligned} \tag{A2}$$

Now each amplitude T_E and T_O has its own Regge pole terms, and these appear symmetrized or antisymmetrized in $T(q,x)$. Hence we have (2.7).

We may look at the same nonrelativistic problem in another way, which is more relevant to the relativistic theory. The scattering amplitude may be assumed to have certain analyticity properties, as a function of the energy and the momentum transfer, which are summarized by the statement that it satisfies the Mandelstam representation. These analyticity properties, together with the assumption that the amplitude also satisfies the usual unitarity condition, allow the construction of an integral equation for the amplitude, in which the potential itself appears as an inhomogeneous term. For potentials which are superpositions of Yukawa potentials, it has been shown[26] that the unitarity condition and the analyticity properties completely define the scattering amplitude, at least when the Mandelstam representation has no subtractions. This assumption is, presumably, just the statement that there are no bound states or resonances. If bound states or resonances do exist, they appear through Regge terms and the Mandelstam representation will require subtractions. Nevertheless, it is plausible to assume that the unitarity condition and the analyticity properties still completely determine the problem.

The unitarity condition for the scattering amplitude $T(q,x)$ may be written

$$\mathrm{Im}T(q,x)=\frac{q}{4}\int_{-1}^{1}dx_1\int_{-1}^{1}dx_2\sum_l(2l+1)P_l(x)P_l(x_1)P_l(x_2)\times T(q,x_1)^*T(q,x_2). \tag{A3}$$

The normalization here is defined so that

$$T(q,x)=\textstyle\sum_l(2l+1)P_l(x)(\sin\delta_l e^{i\delta_l}/q). \tag{A4}$$

We now write $T(q,x)$ as in (A1), as a sum of even and odd parts in x. Using the facts that $P_l(-x)=(-1)^lP_l(x)$ and

$$\{\tfrac{1}{2}[1\pm(-1)^l]\}^2=\tfrac{1}{2}[1\pm(-1)^l],$$

it is easy to see that the unitarity condition is true separately for T_+ and T_-, so that we have

$$\mathrm{Im}T_\pm(q,x)=\frac{q}{4}\int_{-1}^{1}dx_1\int_{-1}^{1}dx_2\sum_l(2l+1)P_l(x)P_l(x_1)P_l(x_2)\times T_\pm(q,x_1)^*T_\pm(q,x_2). \tag{A5}$$

Since the analyticity properties of $T_\pm$ are essentially the same as those of T itself, there are, as a result, two separate scattering problems which differ only in the potential term. First suppose only a direct potential exists. It is a function of $2q^2(1-x)=\Delta^2$ and we will write it $V_d(\Delta^2)$. Then the two potentials for T_+ and T_- are

$$V_\pm=\tfrac{1}{2}[V_d(\Delta^2)\pm V_d(\bar{\Delta}^2)], \tag{A6}$$

where $\bar{\Delta}^2=2q^2(1+x)$. If the Regge terms are found for the T_+ and T_- amplitudes in this case, the same α's and β's must occur in each. For T_+, we find the Regge terms in the form

$$(\beta/\sin\pi\alpha)\tfrac{1}{2}[P_\alpha(-x)+P_\alpha(x)], \tag{A7}$$

and for T_-,

$$(\beta/\sin\pi\alpha)\tfrac{1}{2}[P_\alpha(-x)-P_\alpha(x)], \tag{A8}$$

with the same α and β, so that in $T=T_++T_-$ the Regge terms are simply

$$(\beta/\sin\pi\alpha)P_\alpha(-x). \tag{A9}$$

If, however, an exchange potential is introduced as well, the situation changes. An exchange potential is a function of $\bar{\Delta}^2$, and we may call it $V_e(\bar{\Delta}^2)$. The two effective potentials for the T_+ and T_- amplitudes now become

$$\begin{aligned}V_\pm&=\tfrac{1}{2}\{[V_d(\Delta^2)+V_e(\bar{\Delta}^2)]\pm[V_d(\bar{\Delta}^2)+V_e(\Delta^2)]\}\\ &=\tfrac{1}{2}\{[V_d(\Delta^2)\pm V_e(\Delta^2)]\pm[V_d(\bar{\Delta}^2)\pm V_e(\bar{\Delta}^2)]\}.\end{aligned} \tag{A10}$$

Now the $V_\pm$ are no longer of the form (A6), in that the potential corresponding to $V_d(\Delta^2)$ in (A6) is no longer the same in V_+ as it is in V_-. Therefore, we can no longer expect the Regge α's and β's appearing in (A7)

[26] R. Blankenbecler, M. Goldberger, N. N. Khuri, and S. Treiman, Ann. Phys. (New York) **10**, 62 (1960).

to be the same as those in (A8), and as a result, the Regge terms in T will now be of the form

$$\frac{\beta_+}{\sin\pi\alpha_+}\left(\frac{P_{\alpha_+}(-x)+P_{\alpha_+}(x)}{2}\right)+\frac{\beta_-}{\sin\pi\alpha_-}\left(\frac{P_{\alpha_-}(-x)-P_{\alpha_-}(x)}{2}\right), \quad \text{(A11)}$$

instead of as in (A9).

In the relativistic problem, if we discuss spinless particles and make the strip approximation, the mathematics is essentially identical with that we have gone through above. Without the strip approximation, in terms of a "generalized potential,"[27] the equations still look very similar and it is reasonable to expect that the results obtained here remain valid. We shall therefore assume that in the general case the form (A11) is correct at large x.

We will be interested in high energies in the crossed channel. If s is the square of the total c.m. energy in the crossed channel, and q is the initial and final c.m. momentum in the original channel (we take equal masses for convenience), then large s means $x\approx -s/2q^2$. The Regge terms in this limit then become

$$\frac{\beta}{(2q^2)^\alpha}\frac{1}{\sin\pi\alpha}\frac{[s^\alpha\pm(-s)^\alpha]}{2}. \quad \text{(A12)}$$

[27] G. F. Chew and S. C. Frautschi, Phys. Rev. 124, 264 (1961).

Now β is essentially the residue of the lth partial wave amplitude at a pole $l=\alpha$ in the complex angular momentum plane; we may therefore expect that as a function of q, β behaves like $(2q^2)^\alpha$ near each threshold. It will be convenient to factor this dependence out of β, and furthermore to write $(-s)^\alpha$ as $s^\alpha e^{-i\pi\alpha}$. Thus, the Regge terms may be written

$$\frac{b}{\sin\pi\alpha}\left(\frac{s}{2m^2}\right)^\alpha\left(\frac{1\pm e^{-i\pi\alpha}}{1}\right), \quad \text{(A13)}$$

as in rule (3) of Sec. II.

The choice of phase, $(-s)^\alpha=s^\alpha e^{-i\pi\alpha}$ rather than $s^\alpha e^{+i\pi\alpha}$, is the one suggested by the analyticity of the scattering amplitude in the upper half of the complex u plane; note that the direct potential in the t channel is associated with the cut in u. Of course, we could have absorbed a factor $\pm e^{-i\pi\alpha}$ into b and gotten $(1\pm e^{+i\pi\alpha})/2$ instead of $(1\pm e^{-i\pi\alpha})/2$ in (A13). So our choice of phase reflects a belief that b as defined in (A13) has simple properties. In fact, we conjecture that it is real in a region extending down from threshold.

Note added in proof. We have been able to prove, assuming the Mandelstam representation, that $\alpha(t)$ and $b(t)$ are real analytic functions with only right-hand cuts. See also A. O. Barut and D. E. Zwanziger (to be published).

CORRECTION

The following correction is added by request of the authors:

The sign of B in (4.17), (4.18), (4.20), and (4.21) should be changed. The point about elementary particles in field theory having fixed angular momenta is not applicable to all cases. For a detailed discussion see (G4-5).

Reprinted from THE PHYSICAL REVIEW, Vol. 127, No. 5, 1832–1836, September 1, 1962
Printed in U. S. A.

Complex Angular Momentum in Field Theory*

K. BARDAKCI
School of Physics, University of Minnesota, Minneapolis, Minnesota
(Received April 23, 1962)

The notion of complex angular momentum is extended to relativistic scattering amplitudes satisfying the Mandelstam representation. The domain of analyticity in the complex angular momentum plane is enlarged by the use of unitarity relations, and the existence of Regge poles in a certain restricted domain is established.

I

THE concept of complex angular momentum, first introduced by Regge in connection with nonrelativistic potential scattering[1] has recently been applied to field theory.[2,3] The poles in the complex angular momentum plane that naturally arise in this approach, or the so-called Regge poles, may very well be of great importance in explaining the large number of experimentally observed resonances and also the high-energy behavior of cross sections.[2–4] In the case of potential scattering, the continuation in the complex angular momentum plane can be effected by simply considering the solutions of the Schrödinger equation for complex values of l. The proper analyticity domain in the l plane and the existence of the Regge poles can then be proved if the potential is restricted to a linear superposition of Yukawa potentials, and also some useful information about Regge poles can be derived by studying the properties of the Schrödinger equation in detail.[1,5] In field theory, it has been found that a suitable continuation in the complex angular momentum plane can be defined if the validity of the Mandelstam representation is assumed.[6–9] About the existence and the properties of Regge poles in field theory, however, so far nothing has been established rigorously except for some tentative results in the strip approximation.[7,8] In this paper, starting from the Mandelstam representation, we will show how a unique continuation in the l plane can be defined, and we will derive the form of the two-particle unitarity relation in the complex l plane. Then, using a slightly generalized form of Froissart's result[10] about the unitarity limit on the scattering amplitude and a simple analytic completion procedure, we will be able to enlarge the previous domain of analyticity in the l plane. We will show that this domain can further be enlarged except for Regge poles if one utilizes the two-particle unitarity relation below the inelastic threshold. Finally, we will discuss the physical consequences of these results. It must be emphasized that our results are rigorously valid if the Mandelstam representation is correct and there have been no approximations involved.

II

In what follows, we will restrict ourselves to the scattering of identical pseudoscalar particles of mass $m>0$. Although there is no real difficulty in extending our results to scalar particles, the absence of the Born term for pseudoscalar case will slightly simplify matters. At the end of the paper, we will also say a few words about the case of several particles of different masses and particles with spin. We now start with the following dispersion relation:

$$f(s,t)=\sum_{p=0}^{n}\rho_p(s)t^p+t^K\int_{4m^2}^{\infty}dt'\frac{A(s,t')}{t'^K(t'-t)}+u^K\int_{4m^2}^{\infty}du'\frac{A(s,u')}{u'^K(u'-u)}. \quad (1)$$

where $u=4m^2-s-t$, K is a suitable integer that will make the integrals convergent, and the mass spectrum starts at $4m^2$. The same spectral function occurs in both integrals because of crossing symmetry. Using the definition of partial-wave amplitudes, we get, with $z=\cos\theta=1+2t/(s-4m^2)$,

$$\begin{aligned}a_l(s)&=\frac{1}{2}\int_{-1}^{1}dz\,P_l(z)f\{s,\tfrac{1}{2}(z-1)(s-4m^2)\}\\&=\frac{1}{2}\int_{-1}^{1}dz\,P_l(z)\left\{\sum_{0}^{n}\rho_p(s)\left[\frac{z-1}{2}(s-4m^2)\right]^p\right.\\&\quad+[\tfrac{1}{2}(z-1)(s-4m^2)]^K\\&\quad\times\int_{4m^2}^{\infty}dt'\frac{A(s,t')}{t'^K[t'-\frac{1}{2}(z-1)(s-4m^2)]}\\&\quad+[-\tfrac{1}{2}(z+1)(s-4m^2)]^K\\&\quad\left.\times\int_{4m^2}^{\infty}du'\frac{A(s,u')}{u'^K[u'+\frac{1}{2}(z+1)(s-4m^2)]}\right\}. \quad (2)\end{aligned}$$

---

* Supported in part by the U. S. Atomic Energy Commission.
[1] T. Regge, Nuovo cimento **14**, 951 (1959).
[2] G. F. Chew and S. C. Frautschi, Phys. Rev. Letters **7**, 394 (1961).
[3] G. F. Chew, S. C. Frautschi, and S. Mandelstam, Phys. Rev. **126**, 1202 (1962).
[4] M. Gell-Mann, Phys. Rev. Letters **6**, 263 (1962).
[5] A. Bottino, A. Longoni, and T. Regge (to be published).
[6] M. Froissart, invited paper to La Jolla Conference on Strong and Weak Interactions.
[7] K. Bardakci (to be published).
[8] A. O. Barut and D. E. Zwanziger (to be published).
[9] E. J. Squires (to be published).
[10] M. Froissart, Phys. Rev. **123**, 1053 (1961).

For $l \geqq K$, the orders of integration in (2) can be interchanged, as the resulting integral is then convergent. If we also take $l > n$, the subtraction polynomial does not contribute. For $l > \max\{K,n\} = L$, we therefore have

$$Q_l(s) = -[1+(-1)^l]R(s,l),$$

where

$$R(s,l) = \frac{2}{s-4m^2}\int_{4m^2}^{\infty} dt\, Q_l\left(1+\frac{2t}{s-4m^2}\right)A(s,t). \quad (3)$$

$Q_l(x)$, the Legendre function of the second kind, asymptotically approaches a function of the form Cx^{-l-1}, where C depends only on l, for all x except for $x = \mp 1$.[11] It therefore follows that $Q_l(1+2t/(s-4m^2))$ is bounded by an expression of the form Ct^{-l-1} for large positive t. Hence, the integral in (3) converges for $l \geqq K$, as asserted previously. Furthermore, if N is the greatest lower bound of the values of Rel for which the integral in (3) converges, where $N \leqq K$ necessarily, then the function $R(s,l)$ is analytic for Re$l > N$, since the function Q_l is an analytic function in this region. We now turn to the analyticity properties of $R(s,l)$ as a function of s, keeping Re$l > N$. The region of singularities of $R(s,l)$ is then the union of the regions of singularities of $Q_l(1+2t/(s-4m^2))$ and $A(s,t)$. From the Mandelstam representation, it follows that $A(s,t)$ is analytic in the s plane except for cuts extending from $4m^2$ to ∞ and from $-4m^2$ to $-\infty$. $Q_l(1+2t/(s-4m^2))$ contributes a cut extending from $s=4m^2$ to $s=-\infty$. Therefore, $R(s,l)$ is cut along the real axis from $-\infty$ to ∞. The part of the cut extending from $s=0$ to $s=4m^2$ is, however, purely kinematical and can easily be removed. To this end, we define:

$$R(s,l) = \left(\frac{s-4m^2}{4m^2}\right)^l T(s,l), \quad (4)$$

where the factor $[(s-4m^2)/4m^2]^l$ is defined to have a branch cut along the negative real axis. The nature of the branch cut of $Q_l(1+2t/(s-4m^2))$ is such that part of it is eliminated by this procedure, and $T(s,l)$ has cuts extending from $-\infty$ to 0 and from $4m^2$ to $+\infty$. Furthermore, since the l'th partial wave vanishes at least like $(s-4m^2)^l$ at $s=4m^2$, this definition does not give rise to poles for $T(s,l)$ for integer values of l.

Next we come to the important question of the asymptotic behavior of $R(s,l)$ as $|l| \to \infty$. In reference 1, the asymptotic properties of $R(s,l)$ were obtained by Regge through a detailed analysis of the Schrödinger equation for nonrelativistic scattering, and his asymptotic estimate enabled him to write down a Watson-Sommerfeld representation for the scattering amplitude. In the relativistic case, Froissart[6] has shown that the existence of a dispersion relation like (1) in linear momentum transfer is sufficient to establish an asymptotic bound for $R(s,l)$ which leads to a slightly modified Watson-Sommerfeld integral. At this point, we would like to stress on the importance of the proper asymptotic behavior of this function, since if one relaxes this condition, given an arbitrary set of partial waves, it is always possible to interpolate them by an infinite number of analytic functions. In what follows, we restrict ourselves to real $s > 4m^2$. Using the standard estimate[11]

$$Q_l(x) \leqq (C/|l|^{1/2})\exp\{-[x+(x^2-1)^{1/2}]\,\mathrm{Re}l\}, \quad (5a)$$

where x= real and >1 and C is independent of l, we obtain:

$$|R(s,l)| \leqq \frac{2}{s-4m^2}\int_{4m^2}^{\infty} dt\,|A(s,t)|\left|Q_l\left(1+\frac{2t}{s-4m^2}\right)\right|$$

$$\leqq \frac{2}{s-4m^2}\int_{4m^2}^{\infty} dt\, C_1 t^N \frac{C_2}{|l|^{1/2}}\exp\left\{-\mathrm{Re}l\left[1+\frac{2t}{s-4m^2}+\left[\left(1+\frac{2t}{s-4m^2}\right)^2-1\right]^{1/2}\right]\right\}$$

$$\leqq \frac{C_3}{|l|^{1/2}}\exp\left\{-\mathrm{Re}l\left[1+\frac{8m^2}{s-4m^2}+\left[\left(1+\frac{8m^2}{s-4m^2}\right)^2-1\right]^{1/2}\right]\right\}. \quad (5b)$$

where all the constants in question have no l dependence. In deriving the final result, we treated $A(s,t)$ as an ordinary function and ignored all distribution theoretical subtlities. The result can, however, be justified by a more careful treatment.[10]

Equation (5a) shows that $R(s,l)$ goes to zero as $|l| \to \infty$ for physical s, although it should be noted that this is in general not true for nonphysical values of s. One can then derive the Watson-Sommerfeld representation exactly as in reference 1, with two minor modifications: There is an additional crossed channel and the line of integration is moved to Re$l=L$. The result is, with the restriction $s>4m^2$,

$$f(s,t) = \sum_{i=0}^{L}(2i+1)a_i(s)P_{(l)}(z) + \frac{1}{2i}\int_{L-i\infty}^{L+i\infty} dl\frac{2l+1}{\sin\pi l}R(s,l) \times [P_l(z)+P_l(-z)]. \quad (6)$$

This in turn implies Eq. (1), so that analyticity in the linear momentum space with only a finite number

[11] *Higher Transcendental Functions*, Bateman Manuscript Project (McGraw-Hill Book Company, Inc., New York, 1954), Vol. 1, Chap. 3.

of subtractions at infinity is completely equivalent to analyticity and asymptotic boundedness in the angular momentum space.

Next we turn to the questions of uniqueness of $R(s,l)$ and the two-particle unitarity relation. For this purpose, we need the following theorem from the complex variable theory.[12]

Given a function $h(w)$, which is analytic for $\mathrm{Re}w \geqq 0$ with the following additional restrictions:

(a) $H(w)$ is bounded as $|w| \to \infty$ uniformly in the angle $-\pi/2 \leqq \arg w \leqq \pi/2$.

(b) $h(n)=0$ for all positive integer n. Then it follows that $h(w)=0$ identically.

It is now easy to see that a function which interpolates the partial waves and which is asymptotically bounded and has the proper domain of analyticity in the l plane is necessarily unique, since if there were two such functions, their difference would vanish by the above theorem. As another application, let us write the two-particle unitarity relation in terms of the function $R(s,l)$ in the interval $4m^2 < s < b$, where b is the threshold for inelastic processes:

$$R(s+i\epsilon, l) - R(s-i\epsilon, l) + i[(s-4m^2)/s]^{1/2}, \quad R(s+i\epsilon, l)R(s-i\epsilon, l) = 0. \tag{7}$$

This relation was originally true only for integer l. The left side of it, however, satisfies the conditions of our theorem and the equation stays valid for complex values. Equation (7) and some other results derived so far have independently been obtained in references 8 and 9 by different methods.

So far, we have established that $R(s,l)$ is analytic in the product of a cut plane in the variable s and the region $\mathrm{Re}l > N$ in the l plane. However, Froissart has shown that the scattering amplitude is bounded by an expression of the form $Cs\ln^2 s$ for real $t \leqq 0$ and large s.[10] Using crossing symmetry, it follows that $A(s,t)$ is bounded by $Ct\ln^2 t$ for real negative s, so that the integral in (3) converges for $\mathrm{Re}l > 1$ if s is real and negative. This result can be extended to complex s as follows:

The scattering amplitude for large s is bounded by an expression $Cs^{[1+(N-1)\ \mathrm{Re}(t/4m^2)^{1/2}+\epsilon]}$ for all $\epsilon > 0$ and for a fixed t which falls inside the ellipse with foci ∓ 1 and semimajor axis $1+8m^2/(s-4m^2)$ in the $z=\cos\theta$ plane for large enough s. Correspondingly, $R(s,l)$ is analytic in the region $\mathrm{Re}l > 1+(N-1)\,\mathrm{Re}(s/4m^2)^{1/2}$, for $\mathrm{Re}(s/4m^2) \leqq 1$. (The square root is defined to have always a non-negative real part). For a proof of this result, we refer the reader to the Appendix.

The domain given above is certainly not the best possible domain, since it is not even a natural domain of holomorqhy. To see this,we note that for a large domain in the s plane, the corresponding domain in the l plane is $\mathrm{Re}l > N$. When s crosses the curve $\mathrm{Re}(s/4m^2)^{1/2}=1$, the domain in the l plane suddenly starts getting larger. Such a discontinuous behavior, however, violates the continuity theorem for the surface of singularities of an analytic function of several complex variables,[13] therefore, it cannot be a natural domain of holomorphy. We now proceed to construct the required domain of holomorphy.

The method essentially consists of mapping the cut plane with s variable, into a simpler domain conformally. In order to apply one of the standard results of analytic completion, we use the following conformal transformations:

$$\omega = (2/\pi)\arcsin[(s-2m^2)/2m^2], \tag{8}$$

where the function "arc sin" has a cut extending from $s=0$ to $s=-\infty$ and from $s=4m^2$ to $s=\infty$ and is defined to be $\pi/2$ at $s=4m^2$. Equation (8) maps the s-plane cut from $s=0$ to $s=-\infty$ and from $s=4m^2$ to $s=+\infty$ into the strip between the lines $\mathrm{Re}(w)=-1$ and $\mathrm{Re}(w)=1$ in the w plane. We now need a slightly modified form of a standard result in the theory of functions of several complex variables.[14]

Suppose that a function of two complex variables z_1 and z_2 is analytic in the union of two domains (A) and (B), where (A) is the product of a small strip containing the line $\mathrm{Re}z_1 = a_1$ in the z_1 plane and the region satisfying $\mathrm{Re}z_2 > a_2$ in the z_2 plane, and (B) is the product of the strip $a_1 \leqq \mathrm{Re}z_1 < b_1$ in the z_1 plane and the region $\mathrm{Re}z_2 > b_2$ in the z_2 plane, with the real numbers a_1, b_1, a_2, b_2 satisfying $a_1 < b_1$ and $a_2 < b_2$. Every such function is also analytic in the larger region given by

$$a_1 \leqq \mathrm{Re}z_1 < b_1, \quad \mathrm{Re}z_2 > a_2,$$
$$(b_2-a_2)\,\mathrm{Re}(a_1-z_1) + (b_1-a_1)\,\mathrm{Re}(z_2-a_2) > 0.$$

Moreover, this is a natural domain of holomorphy.

If we consider $T(s,l)$ defined in (4) as a function of l and w as given in (8), we see that it satisfies the conditions of the above theorem with $z_1=w$, $z_2=l$, $a_1=-1$, $b_1=1$, $a_2=1$, $b_2=N$, and the existence of neighborhood of analyticity around $\mathrm{Re}w=-1$, or equivalently, around $s \leqq 0$ is proved in the Appendix. Transforming back to the variable s, it follows that $T(s,l)$ is analytic in the domain given by $\mathrm{Re}l > 1$, with s not on the cuts from $s=0$ to $s=-\infty$ or from $s=4m^2$ to $s=\infty$, and

$$2\,\mathrm{Re}(l-1) - (N-1) \times \mathrm{Re}\left\{1 + \frac{2}{\pi}\arcsin\left(\frac{s-2m^2}{2m^2}\right)\right\} > 0. \tag{9}$$

[12] E. C. Titchmarch, *Theory of Functions* (The Clarendon Press, Oxford, 1932), p. 186.

[13] See Wightman's lectures on Analytic Functions of Several Complex Variables in *Relations de dispersion et particules élémentaries* (Hermann et Cie, Paris, 1960).

[14] H. Behnke and P. Thullen, *Theorie Der Funktionen Mehrerer Komplexer Veränderlichen* (Verlag Julius Springer, Berlin, 1934), Chap. 4. One can also get the same result by setting Levi's determinant (see reference 13) equal to zero. [M. Froissart (private communication)].

The next step is to enlarge the domain given by (9) using the two-particle unitarity relation. The main point is that it is possible to construct families of functions $K(s,l)$ with the property that the elastic part of the cut is eliminated, a result familiar from continuation to the second energy sheet. One such function is

$$K(s,l)=\frac{1}{T(s,l)}\times\frac{1}{2\pi}\int_{4m^2}^{b}\frac{ds'}{s'-s}\times\left(\frac{s'-4m^2}{s'}\right)^{1/2}\left(\frac{s'-4m^2}{4m^2}\right)^{l}, \quad (10)$$

where the integral is analytic for $\text{Re}l>0$. Since the part of the branch cut in the s plane from $s=4m^2$ to $s=b$ is absent in $K(s,l)$, as can easily be checked using (7), we can now replace $4m^2$ by b in (8) and use the mapping,

$$w=(2/\pi)\text{ arc sin}[(2s-b)/b]. \quad (11)$$

Before applying the analytic completion procedure, one must realize that $K(s,l)$ may have poles. Such isolated poles do not change the conclusion of the theorem, however,[15] and solving for $T(s,l)$ in terms of $K(s,l)$, we get:

The function $T(s,l)$ is meromorphic in the domain given by

$$2\,\text{Re}(l-1)-(N-1)\times\text{Re}\left[1+\frac{2}{\pi}\text{ arc sin}\left(\frac{2s-b}{b}\right)\right]>0, \quad (12)$$

when $\text{Re}l>1$ and s is not on the usual cut in the s plane. Combining this with the previous result about the domain of analyticity, we see that the strip in between the lines

$$2\,\text{Re}(l-1)-(N-1)\,\text{Re}\left[1+\frac{2}{\pi}\text{ arc sin}\left(\frac{s-2m^2}{2m^2}\right)\right]=0$$

and

$$2\,\text{Re}(l-1)-(N-1)\,\text{Re}\left[1+\frac{2}{\pi}\text{ arc sin}\left(\frac{2s-b}{b}\right)\right]-0,$$

is the region where the Regge poles can occur.

IV

Let us summarize some of the more important results of the preceding sections. The double dispersion relation enables one to prove analyticity in the l plane to the right of a certain line $\text{Re}l=N$. It is not possible to say anything more without invoking unitarity. The unitarity limit enables one to extend this domain to that given by (9), and the application of the two-particle unitarity relation further enlarges this region to that given by (12), except for Regge poles. If one could continue this procedure to the inelastic portion of the branch cut, one probably would be able to push the domain of analyticity up to the line $\text{Re}l=1$. At this point, however, such a program seems very difficult to carry out due to our lack of knowledge of inelastic processes.

It is of some interest to note that (9) sets an upper bound on the real part of the angular momentum of a Regge pole in terms of its energy. The relation is not, however, very useful since it contains an undetermined constant.

We now turn to some possible generalization of our results. In the case of scattering of scalar particles, one can divide $R(s,l)$ by the Born term and thereby eliminate the additional singularity due to that term, and the problem reduces to the one treated here with some minor modifications. When one deals with the scattering of particles with unequal masses, however, there are some nontrivial complications. If the double dispersion relation is valid, one can define two functions $R_1(s,l)$ and $R_2(s,l)$ corresponding to the t and u channels, respectively, and in general they can be analytic to the right of two different lines $\text{Re}l=N_1$ and $\text{Re}l=N_2$. The two particle unitarity relations in the s channel satisfied by these functions are:

$$R_1(s+i\epsilon,l)-R_1(s-i\epsilon,l)+i[(s-4m^2)/s]^{1/2}[R_1(s+i\epsilon,l)R_1(s-i\epsilon,l)+R_2(s+i\epsilon,l)R_2(s-i\epsilon,l)]=0,$$

$$R_2(s+i\epsilon,l)-R_2(s-i\epsilon,l)+i[(s-4m^2)/s]^{1/2}[R_1(s+i\epsilon,l)R_2(s-i\epsilon,l)+R_2(s+i\epsilon,l)R_1(s-i\epsilon,l)]=0. \quad (13)$$

The result (9) is still obtained when applied to each R separately, with N replaced by N_1 and N_2, respectively, and $4m^2$ replaced by the two-particle mass threshold in the s channel. If one further defines a matrix (R), given by

$$(R)\equiv\begin{pmatrix}R_1+R_2 & 0\\ 0 & R_1-R_2\end{pmatrix}, \quad (14)$$

the unitarity relation (7) can be written in the familiar form in terms of (R). Then the line of reasoning that led to (12) can be repeated, and (12) remains valid if N is replaced by the larger of N_1 and N_2 and $4m^2$ is replaced by the proper two-particle threshold in the s channel, provided this threshold is not an anomalous one.

[15] Here we are assuming that the analytic completion procedure previously used for a domain of holomorphy equally well applies to a domain of meromorphy. This has been proved by Kneser with the condition that the boundary of the domain of meromorphy be twice differentiable in a piece-wise fashion. [M. Froissart (private communication)]. Also, in the case of a finite number of poles, we can consider the intersection of the original domain with a domain of the form $|K(s,l)|\leq M$ (again a natural domain of holomorphy), where the positive constant M can be taken arbitrarily large. Unfortunately, the theorem has not apparently been proved in all generality. It is the feeling of the author that our discussion cove is the physically interesting cases.

The situation for particles with spin is not clear, and to the author's knowledge, no clear-cut mathematical definition of complex angular momentum has so far been given in this case.

ACKNOWLEDGMENTS

The author gratefully acknowledges Dr. Froissart's contributions which made this work in its final shape possible. He would also like to thank Professor Gasiorowicz for help and encouragement during the progress of this work.

APPENDIX

Here, we want to sketch very briefly the generalization of Froissart's result to complex values of t, since the argument is a quite straightforward extension of that given in reference (10). Exactly as in (10), analyticity in the t plane yields the following upper bound for the partial waves:

$$|a_l(s)| \leqq \frac{C}{s-4m^2} s^N \left[1+\frac{8m^2}{s-4m^2} + \left[\left(1+\frac{8m^2}{s-4m^2}\right)^2 -1\right]^{1/2}\right]^{-l}, \quad \text{(A1)}$$

which, for large s, goes over to

$$|a_l(s)| \leqq C s^{N-1} \exp[-2l(4m^2/s)^{1/2}]. \quad \text{(A2)}$$

On the other hand, the unitarity relations imply

$$|a_l(s)| \leqq 1. \quad \text{(A3)}$$

In the expansion

$$f(s,t) = \sum_{\rho=0}^{\infty} (2l+1) a_l(s) P_l(z), \quad \text{(A4)}$$

convergent for z inside the ellipse with foci at ∓ 1 and semimajor axis equal to $1+8m^2/(s-4m^2)$, we use the bound (A2) for $l > (s/8m^2)^{1/2}[\ln C + (N-1)\ln s]$ and bound (A3) otherwise. Combining this with the estimates:

$$|P_l(z)| \leqq D \max\{|[z+(z^2-1)^{1/2}]^{\pm l}|\}, \quad \text{(A5)}$$

or

$$|P_l(z)| \leqq D|\exp[2l(t/s)^{1/2}]|, \quad \text{(A6)}$$

again valid for large s, we obtain:

$$f(s,t) \leqq E s^{\{1+(N-1)\,\mathrm{Re}(t/4m^2)^{1/2}+\epsilon\}}. \quad \text{(A7)}$$

Here ϵ is an arbitrarily small positive quantity and it is used to get rid of polynomials in $\ln(s)$ irrelevant for our purpose. The result given in (A7) is of course only valid in the ellipse of convergence of (A4).

Reprinted from THE PHYSICAL REVIEW, Vol. 126, No. 3, 1202–1208, May 1, 1962
Printed in U. S. A.

Regge Poles in π-π Scattering*

GEOFFREY F. CHEW AND STEVEN C. FRAUTSCHI†
Lawrence Radiation Laboratory, University of California, Berkeley, California

AND

STANLEY MANDELSTAM
Department of Mathematical Physics, University of Birmingham, Birmingham, England

(Received December 21, 1961)

The connection between Regge poles, bound states and resonances, and asymptotic behavior in momentum transfer is reviewed within the framework of the analytically continued S matrix, and a convergent iteration procedure is given for calculating the position and residue of a Regge pole in terms of a given (generalized) potential. By examining the long-range potential in the $\pi\pi$ system, it is inferred that Regge poles should appear in the $I=0$ and $I=1$ states, and that the latter pole may be responsible for the ρ meson while the former may well dominate *high-energy* behavior at low-momentum transfer in the crossed channels. The connection of this possibility with forward coherent (diffraction) scattering in general is explored, and a number of experimental predictions are emphasized. Finally it is shown that the short-range forces due to exchange of 4, 6, $\cdots$ pions are likely to be repulsive and must be included in some form if a consistent solution is to be achieved.

I. INTRODUCTION

IN the S-matrix theory of strong interactions, dynamical resonances and bound states have been easily and naturally handled insofar as partial-wave (one-variable) dispersion relations are concerned, but they have been a source of confusion with respect to double-dispersion relations. Froissart[1] showed that partial waves with $J>1$ are completely determined by the double-spectral functions; at the same time, as emphasized in the original paper by Mandelstam,[2] resonances or bound states require subtractions in the double-spectral integrals if the usual convergence criteria are applied. The resolution of this dilemma was given by Regge for nonrelativistic potential scattering, where in fact all partial waves are determined by the double-spectral function (even though in the absence of a "crossed" channel, the considerations of Froissart are inapplicable). Regge's explanation is based on the occurrence of poles in the complex angular momentum plane and the association of such poles with resonances and bound states.[3]

The point at issue is essentially the asymptotic behavior of the scattering amplitude as $\cos\theta$ approaches infinity and the energy is kept fixed. This is a highly unphysical region but, as it is here that the double spectral function fails to vanish, the question is of interest to us. The number of subtractions in $\cos\theta$ which it is necessary to perform depends on the asymptotic behavior. As subtraction terms in $\cos\theta$ are just polynomials in this variable, they correspond to low partial waves, so that the number of partial waves which are undetermined by the double-spectral function depends on the number of subtractions necessary.

* Work done under the auspices of the U. S. Atomic Energy Commission.
† Present address: Laboratory of Nuclear Studies, Cornell University, Ithaca, New York.
[1] M. Froissart, Phys. Rev. 123, 1053 (1961).
[2] S. Mandelstam, Phys. Rev. 112, 1344 (1958).
[3] T. Regge, Nuovo cimento 14, 951 (1959); 18, 947 (1960). See also A. Bottino, A. M Longoni, and T. Regge (to be published).

In Born approximation, the potential scattering amplitude vanishes asymptotically for large $\cos\theta$, and it is reasonable to suppose that the complete amplitude has this behavior if the potential strength is sufficiently small. It is evident, however, that such a behavior cannot persist as the strength of an attractive force increases since, if there is a bound state of angular momentum l, the scattering amplitude contains a pole term with residue $P_l(\cos\theta)$, whose asymptotic behavior is $(\cos\theta)^l$. If we assume that the asymptotic behavior does not change suddenly when a bound state appears, we reach the conclusion that the asymptotic behavior becomes progressively more divergent as the strength of attraction increases. Regge's results give one great insight into the nature of this divergence, and show that it does not in fact necessitate undetermined subtraction terms.

Although the existence of Regge poles in the relativistic S matrix has not been established, it appears plausible that they should occur, and we propose here to discuss $\pi\pi$ scattering on such a basis. In particular, we shall show that the $I=1$, $J=1$ resonance can plausibly be associated with a Regge pole. It will also be argued that in the $I=0$ state there should be a Regge pole which does not correspond to any resonance or bound state yet discovered but which *may* be connected with high-energy diffraction scattering.

An important practical consequence of an approach in which Regge poles are recognized is that partial-wave calculations for $J\geqslant 1$ are no longer necessary. Computational difficulties associated with nonzero angular momentum in the N/D method thus can be avoided.

We list now those conclusions of Regge that are most important from our point of view.

(a) The elastic scattering amplitude at a fixed energy, if regarded as a function of l, may be analytically continued into the complex l plane for $\mathrm{Re}l>-\frac{1}{2}$. The only singularities are poles that for positive (physical) kinetic energies are confined to the upper half plane ($\mathrm{Im}l>0$); these poles migrate to the real axis for negative kinetic energies.

(b) On the basis of the Sommerfeld-Watson contour representation[4] in the complex l plane, the amplitude may be divided into two parts with different asymptotic behavior. The first part is an integral, along the vertical line $\mathrm{Re}l=-\frac{1}{2}$, that vanishes as $\cos\theta\to\infty$. The second part consists of pole contributions that generally do not vanish at infinity, these being of the form

$$\sum_i(\beta_i/\sin\pi\alpha_i)P_{\alpha_i}(-\cos\theta), \qquad \text{(I.1)}$$

where α_i is the position of the ith pole, in the complex l plane. It may be described as a complex-angular momentum for which there exists a bound state at the given energy. Both α_i and β_i depend on the energy. As stated above, each α_i is real for negative kinetic energy but acquires a positive imaginary part for physical energies. (The Sommerfeld-Watson representation is, strictly speaking, valid only for positive kinetic energy, but the conclusions employed here about the connection between Regge poles, bound states and resonances, and asymptotic behavior can be justified by an analytic continuation in E.)

If an individual (physical) partial wave is projected out of (I.1), using the formula[5]

$$\frac{1}{2}\int_{-1}^{+1}P_l(z)P_\alpha(-z)dz=\frac{1}{\pi}\frac{\sin\pi\alpha}{(\alpha-l)(\alpha+l+1)}, \qquad \text{(I.2)}$$

for l integer, $l\geqslant 0$, one finds

$$\frac{1}{\pi}\sum_i\frac{\beta_i}{(\alpha_i-l)(\alpha_i+l+1)}, \qquad \text{(I.3)}$$

a result that is immediately interpretable in terms of bound states and resonances. Consider a particular Regge pole and suppose that at some energy $E=E_m$, $\mathrm{Re}\alpha$ is equal to an integer $m\geqslant 0$. In the neighborhood of E_m we may write

$$\mathrm{Re}\alpha(E)\approx m+(E-E_m)(d\,\mathrm{Re}\alpha/dE)_{E_m},$$
$$\mathrm{Im}\alpha(E)\approx\mathrm{Im}\alpha(E_m), \qquad \text{(I.4)}$$

and

$$\beta(E)\approx\beta(E_m),$$

so the Regge pole contributes to the lth wave a term, for E near E_m,

$$\frac{1}{\pi}\frac{\beta(E_m)/[\alpha(E_m)+l+1]}{m-l+(E-E_m)(d\,\mathrm{Re}\alpha/dE)_{E_m}+i\,\mathrm{Im}\alpha(E_m)}, \qquad \text{(I.5)}$$

which, for $l=m$, has the familiar Breit-Wigner resonance form with a width

$$\Gamma=\mathrm{Im}\alpha(E_m)/(d\,\mathrm{Re}\alpha/dE)_{E_m}. \qquad \text{(I.6)}$$

For negative kinetic energy, $\mathrm{Im}\alpha$ vanishes and we have a bound state (i.e., a pole in E on the real E axis).

The above reasoning enables one to extend our previous result that if, at given energy, there existed a bound state of angular momentum l, the scattering amplitude would contain a term behaving asymptotically like $P_l(\cos\theta)$. We can now say that if there exists a resonance of angular momentum l (at a given energy), the amplitude will contain a term behaving asymptotically like $P_\alpha(\cos\theta)$, where α is complex and $\mathrm{Re}\alpha\sim l$. If the resonance is narrow, $\mathrm{Im}\alpha$ is small.

Regge was able to prove that $(d\,\mathrm{Re}\alpha/dE)_{E_m}$ is positive for a bound-state pole, and gave qualitative arguments to show that the same would be true for sharp

[4] A. Sommerfeld, *Partial Differential Equations in Physics* (Academic Press Inc., New York, 1949), p. 279.

[5] Formulas employed in this section involving P_α may be derived from standard integral representations for the Legendre functions, such as given for example in Courant-Hilbert, *Method of Mathematical Physics* (Interscience Publishers, Inc., New York, 1953), Vol. I, p. 501. Note that formula (I.2) is correct for integer l *only*.

resonances—which normally occur at low energies.[3] One may conjecture that when $(d\,\mathrm{Re}\alpha/dE)_{E_m}$ is negative one is not dealing with a resonance but with the familiar high-energy return of the phase shift through 90 deg that always occurs in potential scattering. We add the remark that an analysis of the Born series suggests that $\mathrm{Re}\alpha \leqslant -\frac{1}{2}$ at sufficiently large $|E|$.

For superpositions of Yukawa potentials, all Regge poles are connected with bound states and resonances, and thus may be presumed to have the following general behavior in the complex l plane with E real: For a repulsive potential there are no poles for $\mathrm{Re}l > -\frac{1}{2}$. For an attractive potential a particular pole passes through $\alpha = -\frac{1}{2}$ at some negative E, and moves to the right along the real axis as E increases. When E reaches zero the pole moves into the upper half plane, perhaps continuing its rightward movement temporarily but eventually swinging back through the vertical line, $\mathrm{Re}l = -\frac{1}{2}$. For weak potentials the pole will leave the axis before reaching even $l=0$, and there are no bound states. If $\mathrm{Re}\alpha$ never reaches zero, even for positive E, then there are also no resonances. As the potential strength increases the rightward excursion of the pole will be extended, both the portion on the real axis and the portion in the upper half plane. In other words, there will develop bound states and resonances of higher and higher l, and we note the familiar circumstance that if $l_{\max}$ is the maximum value of l for which a bound state or resonance occurs then all $l \leqslant l_{\max}$ have bound states or resonances. There may, of course, be several poles present at once.

Consider now the possibility of representing the $\cos\theta$ (or momentum transfer) dependence of the amplitude by an unsubtracted dispersion relation. The "background" contour integral vanishes $\{\lesssim[1/(\cos\theta)^{\frac{1}{2}}]\}$ as $\cos\theta \to \infty$ and presents no problem. The Regge poles (I.1) seem to cause trouble. However, it can be shown that $P_\alpha(-z)$ for arbitrary α is an analytic function in the z plane cut along the positive real axis from 1 to ∞,[6] and that the discontinuity across the cut is $-2i\sin\pi\alpha P_\alpha(z)$. Since $P_\alpha(z) \propto z^\alpha$ for $z \to \infty$, we may for $\mathrm{Re}\alpha < 0$ write the dispersion relation

$$P_\alpha(-z) = -\frac{\sin\pi\alpha}{\pi}\int_1^\infty dz'\,\frac{P_\alpha(z')}{z'-z}, \qquad \text{(I.7)}$$

and give such a formula a meaning for $\mathrm{Re}\alpha > 0$ by analytic continuation. Thus, one may, in such a sense, write unsubtracted dispersion relations in $\cos\theta$ (or, equivalently, momentum transfer), even when the asymptotic behavior of one or more pole contributions seems to require subtractions. Individual partial waves need not be separated, all being determined by the same spectral function. An alternative but equivalent statement is to say that formula (I.7) requires subtractions when $\mathrm{Re}\alpha \geqslant 0$, but the subtractions are not arbitrary, being determined by analytic continuation. Of course, since the form of a Regge pole term is known explicitly, there is never a need to express it as a Cauchy integral. We are eager here, however, to exhibit the relation with dispersion theory.

How much of the above is it reasonable to conjecture will hold for a relativistic $\pi\pi$ scattering amplitude? We think that with two modifications all the above arguments will stand. The first point is trivial: the nonrelativistic kinetic energy E should be replaced by the relativistic s, the square of the total energy in the barycentric system. The second is that the region of analyticity in the complex l plane need not include the point $l=0$, so the "background" portion of the amplitude—i.e., everything in addition to the Regge poles—is not necessarily expected to vanish as $\cos\theta \to \infty$. Thus we must keep in mind the possibility of making an S-wave subtraction and not determining the $l=0$ amplitude entirely through double-dispersion integrals. All higher partial amplitudes should be so determined, however, with Regge poles appearing in those isotopic-spin states where the force is attractive.

Our confidence in the generality of the Regge poles has a twofold base: (a) It is known that resonances and bound states correspond to poles in the complex-energy plane, relativistic or nonrelativistic, and Regge was able to make a one-to-one correspondence between poles in E for l real and fixed, and poles in l for E real and fixed.[3] In the relativistic case Froissart has established analyticity in a certain region of the l plane,[7] and it is intuitively appealing that this region can be enlarged as in potential theory, provided we allow isolated poles. (b) Two of the present authors[8] have proposed a definition of a relativistic generalized potential that leads to dynamical equations closely similar to the equations for nonrelativistic potential scattering.[9] We do not enlarge on this point here, since it has been discussed in reference 8 and will arise again in what follows.

In the following section we review the S-matrix approach to nonrelativistic potential scattering, showing how the Regge poles are to be extracted and how they are related to the partial-wave N/D problem. The final section discusses possible Regge poles in the relativistic $\pi\pi$ amplitude.

II. CALCULATION OF REGGE POLES IN NONRELATIVISTIC POTENTIAL SCATTERING

It has been shown by Blankenbecler *et al.*[9] that, for nonrelativistic scattering by a superposition of direct

[6] The cut in the full amplitude satisfying the double-dispersion representation begins at a point $z=z_c$, where $z_c>1$. The contribution from the interval $1<z<z_c$ is canceled by the residual Sommerfeld-Watson integral.

[7] M. Froissart, Department of Physics, Princeton University, invited paper at the International Conference on the Theory of Weak and Strong Interactions, La Jolla (1961) (unpublished).

[8] G. F. Chew and S. C. Frautschi, Phys. Rev. **124**, 264 (1961).

[9] R. Blankenbecler, M. L. Goldberger, N. N. Khuri, and S. B. Treiman, Ann. Phys. (New York) **10**, 62 (1960).

Yukawa potentials, the double-spectral function is determined by the following equation, first derived in Ref. 2:

$$\rho(q^2,t)=\frac{1}{2\pi}\frac{1}{q}\int\int dt'dt''\frac{\tilde{D}^*(t',q^2)\tilde{D}(t'',q^2)}{K^{\frac{1}{2}}(q^2;t,t',t'')}. \quad \text{(II.1)}$$

The integration is restricted to that part of the region $t^{\frac{1}{2}}>t'^{\frac{1}{2}}+t''^{\frac{1}{2}}$ for which

$$K(q^2;t,t',t'')=t^2+t'^2+t''^2 -2(tt'+tt''+t't'')-(tt't''/q^2) \quad \text{(II.2)}$$

is positive. The function $\tilde{D}(t,q^2)$ is the discontinuity in the amplitude in crossing the positive t axis with q^2 fixed; it is related to the potential and to the double-spectral function by

$$\tilde{D}(t,q^2)=v(t)+\frac{1}{\pi}\int dq'^2\frac{\rho(q'^2,t)}{q'^2-q^2}, \quad \text{(II.3)}$$

where $v(t)$ determines the configuration space potential $V(r)$ through the formula

$$V(r)=-\frac{1}{2\pi M^2}\int dt\, v(t)\frac{\exp[-t^{\frac{1}{2}}r]}{r}. \quad \text{(II.4)}$$

Generally speaking there is some positive threshold t_0, such that $v(t)$ vanishes for $t<t_0$. We shall speak of $t_0^{-\frac{1}{2}}$ as the "range" of the potential.

As has been explained in reference 2, the pair of equations (II.1) and (II.3) uniquely determines $\tilde{D}(t,q^2)$ since the nature of the integration region in (II.1) ensures that n iterations give a result exact for $t<(n+1)^2t_0$. In other words the Born series for $\tilde{D}(t,q^2)$ certainly converges (although not necessarily uniformly in t) regardless of the occurrence of resonances or bound states. It is well known, on the other hand, that the Born series for the scattering amplitude $A(q^2,t)$ does not always converge, a circumstance that at first sight is puzzling if one expects the unsubtracted dispersion relation

$$A(q^2,t)=\frac{1}{\pi}\int dt'\frac{\tilde{D}(t',q^2)}{t'-t} \quad \text{(II.5)}$$

to be meaningful. In Eq. (1.7) above, however, we have seen that when Regge poles occur with $\text{Re}\alpha\geqslant 0$ the integral (II.5) is not defined in the elementary sense but only through analytic continuation; so precisely when the first resonance or bound state appears the possibility of expanding $\tilde{D}$ in a power series no longer implies that A similarly can be expanded.

Nevertheless, a knowledge of $\tilde{D}(t,q^2)$ implies a knowledge of $A(q^2,t)$, as we shall now show, so the iteration of Eqs. (II.1) and (II.3) actually forms the basis for a practical method of calculation—with or without bound states or resonances. The essential point is that, according to Regge,[3]

$$A(q^2,t)=A'(q^2,t) +\sum_i \frac{\beta_i(q^2)}{\sin\pi\alpha_i(q^2)}P_{\alpha_i(q^2)}\left(-1-\frac{t}{2q^2}\right), \quad \text{(II.6)}$$

where $A'(q^2,t)$ is the background term that vanishes as $t\to\infty$ (we may also allow A' to contain Regge poles with $\text{Re}\alpha_i<0$). Then by reference to (I.7)

$$\tilde{D}(t,q^2)=\tilde{D}'(t,q^2)-\sum_i \beta_i(q^2)P_{\alpha_i(q^2)}\left(1+\frac{t}{2q^2}\right), \quad \text{(II.7)}$$

with the integral

$$A'(q^2,t)=\frac{1}{\pi}\int dt'\frac{\tilde{D}'(t',q^2)}{t'-t}, \quad \text{(II.8)}$$

defined in the elementary sense. Thus if it is possible to decompose $\tilde{D}(t,q^2)$ according to (II.7)—so that one has a separate knowledge of $\tilde{D}'(t,q^2)$, $\beta_i(q^2)$, and $\alpha_i(q^2)$—then one can construct the amplitude $A(q^2,t)$.

An elementary method for determining $\alpha_i(q^2)$ and $\beta_i(q^2)$ may be based on the dominance of the Regge poles over the background term for large t. Suppose that there is only one pole for which $\text{Re}\alpha\geqslant 0$; then, for sufficiently large t, this pole will be dominant in formula (II.7), and one may calculate the position $\alpha_i(q^2)$ and the strength $\beta_i(q^2)$ by equating, at large t, the calculated $\tilde{D}(t,q^2)$ with $-\beta_i P_{\alpha_i}[1+(t/2q^2)]$. One then subtracts out this pole term at all t to obtain the background term $\tilde{D}'(t,q^2)$. If there is more than one pole, the one for which $\text{Re}\alpha_i$ is largest can be determined first and subtracted; the remainder will then be dominated by the pole with the next largest $\text{Re}\alpha_i$, and the procedure can be repeated until all pole parameters are determined. In an actual numerical calculation one may wish to use a more elegant approach, but there seems nothing in principle to prevent the extraction of the necessary information from the iterative solution for $\tilde{D}(t,q^2)$.[10]

Note that when the potential problem is approached in this way there is no need to treat any partial waves separately. In principle an alternative to separating and identifying the Regge poles is to calculate individually by N/D method all waves for $l\leqslant(\text{Re}\alpha)_{\max}$. When these low-partial waves are subtracted out of formula (II.5) the remainder of the integral (containing all high waves) converges in the elementary sense. The necessary ingredient for the N/D partial-wave calculation is the discontinuity across the left-hand cut; this is given for

---

[10] It is reassuring to note that iteration of the behavior $\tilde{D}(t,q^2)\propto t^{\alpha(q^2)}$ at large t in (II.1) leads to the consistent result $\rho(q^2,t)\propto t^{\alpha(q^2)}$ if $\alpha(q^2)$ has a nonzero imaginary part for $q^2>0$ This consistency is most easily established using a transformation of (II.1) due to M. Froissart (to be published).

the lth wave by

$$\operatorname{Im} A_l(q^2) \underset{q^2<-t_0/4}{=} \frac{1}{4q^2}\int_{t_0}^{-4q^2} dt\, P_l\left(1+\frac{t}{2q^2}\right)\tilde{D}(t,q^2), \quad \text{(II.9)}$$

and presents no difficulty of principle if, as conjectured in Sec. I, the Regge poles all retreat through the vertical line, $\operatorname{Re} l=-\frac{1}{2}$, for large $|q^2|$. In this case $\operatorname{Im} A_l(q^2)$ vanishes sufficiently rapidly as $q^2\to-\infty$ so that the N/D integral equations are nonsingular. In practice, however, for all $l>0$, delicate cancellations must occur between the right and left cuts to produce the correct threshold behavior, $A_l(q^2)\propto(q^2)^l$, near $q^2=0$. The N/D equations then become awkward from a numerical standpoint, so an approach that does not separate partial waves is preferable.

III. REGGE POLES IN RELATIVISTIC $\pi\pi$ SCATTERING

We now illustrate by a discussion of $\pi\pi$ scattering our conjecture that Regge poles occur quite generally in the relativistic strong-interaction S matrix. Consider the three amplitudes $A^I(s,t)$ which represent pure I scattering ($I=0$, 1, 2) in the s channel. Two of the authors have defined a "generalized potential," here to be denoted by $v^I(t,s)$, which is to be used in equations of the type (II.3) and (II.1) in place of the nonrelativistic potential $v(t)$.[8] The "long-range" part of the generalized potential, exact for $t<16m_\pi^2$, is associated with 2-pion exchange, and is given by

$$v_{2\pi}^I(t,s)=\sum_{I'=0,1,2}\beta_{II'}D_{\text{el}}^{I'}(t,s), \quad \text{(III.1)}$$

where the crossing matrix β has the form,[11]

$$\beta_{II'}=\begin{bmatrix}1/3 & 1 & 5/3\\ 1/3 & 1/2 & -5/6\\ 1/3 & -1/2 & 1/6\end{bmatrix}, \quad \text{(III.2)}$$

and $D_{\text{el}}^I(t,s)$ is the elastic absorptive part for isotopic spin I scattering in the t channel. As discussed below, the imaginary part of $v_{2\pi}^I(t,s)$, which develops at large s, produces inelastic scattering in the s channel that is not properly bounded by unitarity. An approximation which replaces v^I by $v_{2\pi}^I$ then leads to inconsistencies in the case of actual physical interest. Contributions from $v_{4\pi}^I$, $v_{6\pi}^I$, etc. must be added to correct this deficiency, but it will be argued below that the low-energy effects of these shorter-range potentials are probably repulsive, so we should be able to discuss qualitative questions on the basis of (III.1).

If Regge poles in fact dominate asymptotic behavior in the relativistic amplitude, as discussed above for the nonrelativistic case, then for the interval in s such that a small number of poles are consistently to the right of all other singularities (and within the region of analyticity in l), it follows that

$$\left.\begin{matrix}A^I(s,t)\\ \tilde{D}^I(t,s)\end{matrix}\right\} \underset{t\to\infty}{\propto} t^{\alpha^I(s)}, \quad \text{(III.3)}$$

if $\alpha^I(s)$ is the position of the pole farthest to the right in the l plane and $\tilde{D}^I(t,s)$ is the discontinuity in $A^I(s,t)$ in crossing the positive t axis. An appropriate general definition of the "strip" region discussed earlier in a qualitative way by two of the authors would be just this interval in s.[12] (The earlier definition of the "strip" was linked to the approximation $v^I\approx v_{2\pi}^I$. We now wish to dissolve this link.) If the analogy with nonrelativistic potential-scattering holds, we expect $\alpha^I(s)$ to increase with the strength of the generalized potential $v^I(t,s)$, when v^I corresponds to attraction; furthermore, we expect $d\alpha^I/ds$ to be positive for $s<4$. For $s>4$, $\alpha^I(s)$ becomes complex, but the real part is continuous and should reach a maximum value at some moderate value of s, eventually falling to a negative value for s sufficiently large.

From the elements of the crossing matrix (III.2) one sees that all contributions to $v_{2\pi}^{I=0}$ are attractive and stronger than (or at least as strong as) in the other two I-spin states. Thus if any Regge poles develop, the one standing farthest to the right in the l plane at a given s should be in the $I=0$ state. If $\alpha^{I=0}(s)$ is still positive for some range of negative s then in the crossed channel (where t corresponds to energy and s to momentum transfer) the high-energy behavior at fixed (low) momentum transfer evidently will be controlled by the $I=0$ Regge pole. We now examine the connection between this possibility and constant limits for high-energy total cross sections.

From the optical theorem it follows that

$$D^I(t,s=0)=(q_t t^{\frac{1}{2}}/16\pi)\sigma_{\text{tot}}^I(t), \quad \text{(III.4)}$$

where $D^I(t,s)$ is the complete absorptive part in the t channel and σ_{tot}^I is the total cross section, both quantities for isotopic spin I in the t channel. Then, since

$$\tilde{D}^I(t,s)=\textstyle\sum_{I'}\beta_{II'}D^{I'}(t,s), \quad \text{(III.5)}$$

a glance at the elements of $\beta_{II'}$ in (III.2) shows that no cancelation can prevent a behavior

$$\tilde{D}^{I=0}(t,0)\propto t, \quad \text{as} \quad t\to\infty, \quad \text{(III.6)}$$

if each total cross section σ_{tot}^I approaches a constant. Such asymptotic behavior, pointed out in an earlier paper by two of the authors,[12] implies that

$$\alpha^{I=0}(s=0)=1. \quad \text{(III.7)}$$

At first sight this last requirement seems to predict a bound-P state of zero total energy, but symmetry requirements eliminate all odd l waves with $I=0$. Because of the presence of exchange as well as direct forces, the

[11] G. F. Chew and S. Mandelstam, Phys. Rev. **119**, 467 (1960).

[12] G. F. Chew and S. C. Frautschi, Phys. Rev. **123**, 1478 (1961).

potential determining even physical values of l is different from that determining odd values of l. Nevertheless we must ask the question: Is it reasonable to expect a direct potential equal to $v^{I=0}$, if it were effective in both odd and even l states, to be sufficiently attractive as to bind a P state? We believe the answer to be affirmative because qualitative arguments have shown that a "bootstrap" mechanism probably can sustain an $I=1$ P-wave resonance in terms of itself.[13] In other words, a potential

$$v_{2\pi}{}^{I=1}(t,s)\approx\beta_{11}D_{\rm el}{}^{I=1}(t,s), \quad \text{(III.8)}$$

when $D_{\rm el}{}^{I=1}$ contains a P-resonance contribution, is attractive and has roughly the required strength to produce the $I=1$ P resonance in question. Now $\beta_{01}=2\beta_{11}$, so the corresponding contribution to $v^{I=0}$ is twice as attractive as (III.8) and might well produce a *bound* P state.

The above argument implies that

$$\alpha^{I=1}(s=0)<1, \quad \text{(III.9)}$$

which is consistent with the experimental requirement that $\text{Re}\alpha^{I=1}(s\approx 28)=1$,[14] and the theoretical expectation that for $s<28$, $d\,\text{Re}\alpha/ds$ is positive. Since $\beta_{21}=-\beta_{11}$, the potential $v^{I=2}$ is probably repulsive and no Regge pole will even appear in the $I=2$ state. Thus, we expect

$$\frac{1}{t}\tilde{D}^{I=1,2}(t,0)\underset{t\to\infty}{\longrightarrow}0, \quad \text{(III.10)}$$

and in view of the relation

$$\sigma_{\rm tot}{}^{I}(t)=(16\pi/q_t t^{\frac{1}{2}})\textstyle\sum_{I'}\beta_{II'}\tilde{D}^{I'}(t,0), \quad \text{(III.11)}$$

there follows from (III.5) the expectation that

$$\lim_{t\to\infty}\sigma_{\rm tot}{}^{I=0}=\lim_{t\to\infty}\sigma_{\rm tot}{}^{I=1}(t)=\lim_{t\to\infty}\sigma_{\rm tot}{}^{I=2}(t). \quad \text{(III.12)}$$

By such a mechanism, therefore, one expects to achieve *both* Pomeranchuk conditions.[15]

It may appear strange at first sight that the Pomeranchuk relations should depend on the detailed structure of the crossing matrix. When one realizes, however, that coherent elastic scattering is uniquely associated with states in the crossed channel that have the quantum numbers of the vacuum, then a select role for $I=0$ in asymptotic considerations is no longer surprising. Pomeranchuk's second condition, after all, is equivalent to the assertion that completely coherent elastic scattering predominates in the forward direction at high energy.

We now remark on two consequences of the assumption that $d\alpha^{I=0}/ds>0$ for $s<4$. The first is that in view of (III.7) we expect $\alpha^{I=0}$ to vanish at some negative value of s, a circumstance which would correspond to an unphysical bound S state of imaginary energy. Gell-Mann has pointed out to us that if the residue of such a pole were to vanish there would be no conflict with unitarity.[16] If the residue does not vanish we cannot determine the $I=0$ S wave from $\tilde{D}^{I=0}$, but must use the N/D method.

The second consequence of the positive derivative of $\alpha^{I=0}$ with respect to s is that the width of the high-energy elastic diffraction peak will shrink indefinitely with increasing energy—albeit only logarithmically. Since the first Pomeranchuk condition ensures that the real part of the amplitude near the forward direction is negligible with respect to the imaginary part, we have

$$\frac{d\sigma^I}{ds}\underset{t\to\infty}{\propto}\left[\frac{1}{t}D^I(t,s)\right]^2, \quad \sim f(s)t^{2[\alpha^{I=0}(s)-1]},$$
$$s=-2q_t{}^2(1-\cos\theta_t). \quad \text{(III.13)}$$

If $\alpha^{I=0}$ is a slowly varying function of s, we may write for small $|s|$

$$\alpha^{I=0}(s)\approx 1+\epsilon s, \quad \epsilon>0, \quad \text{(III.14)}$$

and thus deduce the small momentum-transfer behavior

$$\frac{d\sigma^I}{ds}\underset{t\to\infty}{\longrightarrow}f(s)t^{2\epsilon s}=f(s)\exp(s2\epsilon\ln t). \quad \text{(III.15)}$$

Integration of (III.15) over the elastic diffraction peak yields the related prediction

$$\sigma_{\rm el}{}^I/\sigma_{\rm tot}{}^I\underset{t\to\infty}{\propto}(\epsilon\ln t)^{-1}. \quad \text{(III.16)}$$

Evidently, the rate of shrinkage is small; nevertheless, precision experiments at very high energy should detect such an effect.[17] It is possible to argue, as pointed out by Lovelace,[18] that experiments already are giving support for the form (III.15) through the observed-exponential behavior of the tail of diffraction peaks. Such behavior is difficult to understand in any classical model but follows immediately from the Regge pole-hypothesis.

As discussed by two of the authors, *all* forward diffraction peaks (πN, NN, $\pi\pi$, KN, etc.) are controlled by the Regge pole under discussion here, if any are.[19] The universal character of the slope ϵ (and of course higher derivatives if they can be measured) is another striking feature of our mechanism. One must keep it in mind, of course, that the diffraction peak may well be produced by a more complicated mechanism than envisaged here. Experiments to test the characteristic features of

[13] G. F. Chew and S. Mandelstam, Nuovo cimento **19**, 752 (1961); F. Zachariasen, Phys. Rev. Letters **7**, 112 (1961).

[14] A 2π $I=1$ resonance has recently been experimentally observed at an energy of $5.3m_\pi$ or $s_r=28$. For a list of references to the many independent experiments, see E. Pickup, D. K. Robinson, and E. O. Salant, Phys. Rev. Letters **7**, 192 (1961).

[15] I. Pomeranchuk, J. Exptl. Theoret. Phys. (U.S.S.R.) **3**, 306 (1956) and **34**, 725 (1958) [translation: Soviet Phys.—JETP **34**(7), 499 (1958)]. Also I. Pomeranchuk and L. B. Okun, JETP **3**, 307 (1956).

[16] M. Gell-Mann (private communication).

[17] We are indebted to K. Wilson, Dept. of Physics, Harvard University, for pointing out that the decrease in the elastic cross section is only logarithmic.

[18] C. Lovelace (to be published).

[19] G. F. Chew and S. C. Frautschi, Phys. Rev. Letters **7**, 394 (1961).

formula (III.15) are therefore of crucial importance. The predictions discussed above are so startlingly nonclassical in nature that their confirmation would provide convincing evidence for the Regge pole hypothesis.

We return finally to discuss the inconsistency in the equations, as they are at present formulated with $v^I=v_{2\pi}{}^I$, in the case where there is a P-wave resonance. The difficulty arises essentially from the equation

$$\rho_{\mathrm{el}}{}^I(s,t)=\frac{1}{\pi q_s(q_s{}^2+1)^{\frac{1}{2}}}\times\int\int dt'dt''\frac{\tilde{D}^{I*}(t',s)\tilde{D}^I(t'',s)}{K^{\frac{1}{2}}(q_s{}^2;t,t',t'')},\quad\text{(III.17)}$$

which is the relativistic analog of (II.1). Here $\tilde{D}^I$ is given by

$$\tilde{D}^I(t,s)=v^I(t,s)+\frac{1}{\pi}\int ds'\frac{\rho_{\mathrm{el}}{}^I(s',t')}{s'-s},\quad\text{(III.18)}$$

the analog of (II.3), and v^I is in turn given in terms of $D_{\mathrm{el}}{}^{I'}(t,s)$ by the crossing equation (III.1). Now, $D_{\mathrm{el}}{}^{I=1}(t,s)$ will behave like $\beta_1(t)s^{\alpha_1(t)}$ as s approaches infinity and, if there is a P-wave resonance, the α_1 will be greater than 1 for some values of s. We have indicated that the same may well be true for D^0. From (III.17) one may deduce that if $\tilde{D}^*$ and $\tilde{D}$ behave like $s^{\alpha(t)}$ at large s the contribution to the integral for ρ_{el} from $t'=t''=t_1$ will behave like $s^{2\alpha(t_1)-1}$. This value of t' and t'' will contribute if $t\geqslant 4t_1$. If $\rho_{\mathrm{el}}(s,t)$ behaves like $s^{2\alpha(t_1)-1}$ for $t>4t_1$, it follows from (III.18), even if subtractions are made, that $\tilde{D}(t,s)$ has the same behavior for such values of t. On putting this behavior of $\tilde{D}$ into (III.17), we find that ρ_{el} behaves like $s^{4\alpha(t_1)-3}$ when $t>16t_1$. The procedure can be repeated and, if $\mathrm{Re}\alpha(t_1)>1$, it appears that the asymptotic behavior of ρ and D as a function of s becomes worse and worse as t increases.

It is unlikely that the oscillatory behavior of D will decrease the asymptotic behavior of ρ given by (III.17). The simplest way of seeing this is to make a Froissart transformation by which the integral in (III.17) is replaced by another containing a δ function,[10] so that, for any value of t', only one value of t'' contributes. The asymptotic behavior is unchanged by this transformation. Writing this functional relationship as $t''=t''(t')$, and denoting $\alpha[t''(t')]$ by $\gamma(t')$, we observe that the contribution to the integral on the right-hand side of (III.17) from a particular value of t' behaves like $s^{\alpha^*(t')+\gamma(t')}$. The integral of such a function over t' will ordinarily be dominated by that value of t' for which $\mathrm{Re}\alpha+\mathrm{Re}\gamma$ is greatest, and cancellations will in general not occur.

If one seeks the physical origin of the inconsistency of our equations, the most likely culprit is the failure of the approximation $v^I\approx v_{2\pi}{}^I$ to put a unitarity bound on inelastic scattering. The trouble develops as soon as the real part of any α^I becomes greater than unity, and Froissart has shown that unitarity requires $\alpha^I(s\leqslant 0)\leqslant 1$,[1] a constraint that is lacking in our approximation. To cure the disease one must take some account in the inelastic processes of multipion exchange. An exact treatment is, of course, out of the question, but it may be possible somehow to impose the correct unitarity bound. In terms of our generalized potential, $v^I(t,s)$, the required unitarity damping in the inelastic part comes about through 4π, 6π, etc. contributions; it seems plausible that such contributions appear as repulsive forces, since their effect has to limit the magnitude of $\alpha(s)$ at low energy. One may speculate, in fact, that there may be a universal repulsive core in *all* two-body forces due to exchange of multiparticle systems with the quantum numbers of the vacuum. It is for these quantum numbers that the Froissart limit is most closely approached, so the compensating reaction of multiparticle contributions should here be the strongest.

The reader's attention is also drawn to a recent paper by R. Blankenbecler and M. L. Goldberger,[20] which we received in preprint form after completion of this manuscript. These authors treat from a somewhat different standpoint a number of the same questions that have interested us.

ACKNOWLEDGMENTS

We wish to acknowledge the many important contributions of Dr. M. Froissart to the ideas discussed here.

[20] R. Blankenbecler and M. L. Goldberger, Phys. Rev. **126**, 766 (1962).

PROC. PHYS. SOC., 1962, VOL. 80

Regge Poles and Diffraction Scattering

By P. T. MATTHEWS

Imperial College, London

Review Lecture presented at the High Energy Conference of The Institute of Physics and The Physical Society at Imperial College, London, 26th March 1962; *MS. received* 10*th April* 1962

Abstract. A review lecture on the possible application of Regge poles to the analysis of high energy elementary particle diffraction scattering.

§ 1. INTRODUCTION AND NOTATION

WE shall be discussing the theory of high energy collisions, by which we mean energies accessible to present-day machines. This implies the range of roughly 2–20 GeV/c^2 kinetic energy in the laboratory. Within this energy range I propose to be highly selective and a great deal of what I have to say will be concerned with elastic scattering at these energies. I shall be concerned with processes which can be represented by a four-line graph (figure 1) and shall use the Mandelstam variables

$$s = (p_1+p_2)^2, \qquad t = (p_1+p_3)^2, \qquad u = (p_3+p_2)^2 \tag{1.1}$$

which satisfy the relation

$$s+t+u = \sum_{i=1}^{4} m_i^2 = M^2 \tag{1.2}$$

where m_i are the appropriate masses.

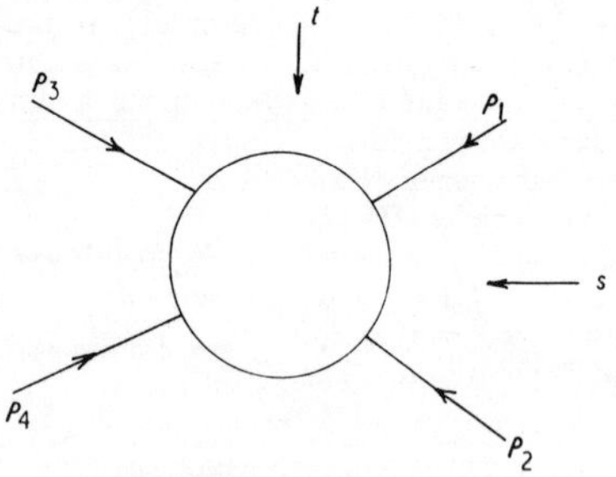

Figure 1. The diagram of a four-line scattering matrix element, indicating the four momenta of the particles and the Mandelstam variables.

We are interested in elastic scattering in the s-channel (p_1 and p_2 being the initial particles) so that we can restrict the discussion to the case

$$m_1 = m_3, \qquad m_2 = m_4. \tag{1.3}$$

Then

$$E_s^2 = s \tag{1.4}$$

$$\cos\theta_s = \left(1+\frac{2t}{s-M^2}\right) = -\left(1+\frac{2u}{s-M^2}\right) \tag{1.5}$$

where E_s and θ_s are the energy and scattering angle in the centre-of-mass system. We also use q to denote the centre-of-mass momentum.

In discussing the t-channel, in which p_1 and p_3 are the initial particles, the roles of s and t are interchanged, and it is this 'crossing' relation which enables us to correlate low energy phenomena in the t-channel with high energy (large s) and low momentum transfer (small $|t|$) phenomena in the s-channel. This is the most powerful tool we have in our kit.

Since we are more concerned with new ideas than with numbers we shall ignore any complications which may arise due to spin.

§2. TOTAL CROSS SECTIONS

Pomeranchuk (1958) has conjectured two theorems about the high energy limits of total cross sections: namely

(i) $$\sigma_{ab} \to \sigma_{a\bar{b}} \quad \text{as} \quad s \to \infty \tag{2.1}$$

where a is any particle target and b and $\bar{b}$ are particle and anti-particle beams.

(ii) $$\sigma_{ab}{}^{I} \to \sigma_{ab}{}^{I'} \quad \text{as} \quad s \to \infty \tag{2.2}$$

where $\sigma_{ab}{}^{I}$ and $\sigma_{ab}{}^{I'}$ are the total cross sections for any collision (a, b) in the i-spin channels I and I', respectively.

The first theorem was based on dispersion relations and the assumption of a finite radius for the interaction, which implies that total cross sections approach constants at high energies. The theorem has since been refined by a number of authors, particularly Weinberg (1961), and established under wider conditions. The second conjecture is physically reasonable when many inelastic channels are open, but is based on less precise mathematical arguments, and has received much less attention from theoreticians.

Experimentally (Peyrou 1961) σ_{pp} is constant at about 40 mbn from 10 GeV/c (lab) up to the highest known energies including cosmic ray results. The K^+p cross section also appears constant. On the other hand $\pi^{\pm}p$, K^-p and $\bar{p}p$ cross sections are all falling slowly in the experimentally available region and at the highest energies still fail to satisfy Pomeranchuk (i) by several millibarns.

For pion–nucleon scattering the two conjectures are equivalent so that the prediction

$$\sigma_{1/2} = \sigma_{3/2} \tag{2.3}$$

is also not satisfied by about 7%. However, the latest data from Dubna show that above 10 GeV/c

$$\sigma_{pn} = \sigma_{pp} \tag{2.4}$$

so that for the nucleon–nucleon system Pomeranchuk's second conjecture is satisfied.

In spite of these discrepancies, in what follows we shall assume as a working hypothesis that at sufficiently high energies all cross sections do become constant and that both Pomeranchuk conjectures are satisfied.

In discussing total cross sections, we also have the optical theorem for the imaginary part of the forward scattering amplitude:

$$\mathscr{I}T(s, 0) = 2qE\sigma_{tot} \simeq s\sigma_{tot}. \tag{2.5}$$

At high energies the angles involved become very small and it is much more convenient for both the theoretician and the experimentalist to work in t. Thus

$$\frac{d\sigma}{dt} = \frac{4\pi}{s}\frac{d\sigma}{d\Omega} = \frac{1}{\pi}\left|\frac{T}{4s}\right|^2. \tag{2.6}$$

The optical theorem (ignoring possible complications from spin) then asserts

$$\left(\frac{d\sigma}{dt}\right)_{t=0} \geqslant \frac{q^2}{4\pi s}\sigma_{\text{tot}}^2 \tag{2.7}$$

where equality implies a pure imaginary amplitude. The great majority of the data are consistent with the equality, and any discrepancies (Azimov *et al.* 1960) can be explained as spin effects, so again as a working hypothesis we shall assume that the amplitude is pure imaginary at high energies.

§ 3. INELASTIC PROCESSES AND PERIPHERAL COLLISIONS

It appears that in a large proportion of the inelastic production processes only a small fraction of the available energy goes into particle production and such collisions may be described in terms of the peripheral model, in which the interaction between the colliding particles takes place through the exchange of the lightest available particle, usually a π-meson. This is an extremely promising approach, but I do not propose to say much about it, since the situation was recently well summarized by Peyrou (1961) and has not changed appreciably since. There are certain obvious correlations which arise from this model, which seem to be qualitatively correct, and a lot of quantitative information may be expected within the next two years.

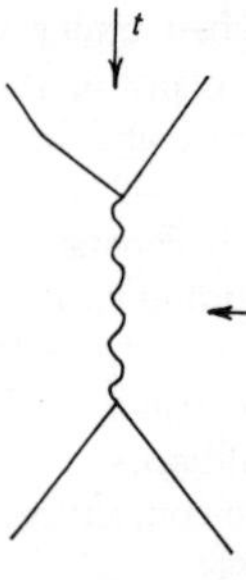

Figure 2. One-particle exchange term giving rise to a Mandelstam pole. In the Regge theory this is replaced by a Regge pole term representing the exchange of a family of particles. See equation (6.5).

The model is typical of the method of 'polology', which is based on the selection of graphs with single particle intermediate states, which are expected to dominate in physical regions near to the pole corresponding to the intermediate particle. A particularly well-known example of this is the one-pion exchange in nucleon–nucleon scattering, which gives rise to a term in the amplitude of the form (figure 2)

$$T_{\text{B}} = \frac{g^2}{t-t_{\text{B}}} \tag{3.1}$$

where

$$t_B = m_\pi^2. \tag{3.2}$$

This is found to give the long range (small momentum transfer) part of the elastic scattering at energies low enough for the process not to be dominated by diffraction.

A fundamental difficulty arises in this approach, if intermediate particles of spin greater than zero are involved. Suppose the 'pion' has spin l, then the pole term in the t-channel will have the form

$$T_B = \frac{g^2 P_l(\cos\theta)}{t - t_B} = \frac{g^2 P_l(1 + 2s/\{t - M^2\})}{t - t_B}. \tag{3.3}$$

In the s-channel, for large s and small $|t|$, this behaves like

$$T_B \simeq \frac{gs^l}{t - t_B} \tag{3.4}$$

which will give a cross section which rises in a quite unphysical manner with energy if $l \geqslant 1$. I shall come back to this point later. (For a more detailed discussion see Chew, Frautschi and Mandelstam 1962, to be published).

§ 4. OPTICAL MODEL OF DIFFRACTION SCATTERING

At the energies we are considering the elastic scattering is almost entirely diffraction. This used to be expressed in the language of classical optics and everyone thought they understood it. But the work of Lovelace (1962, to be published) (reported briefly by Drell (1961) at the Aix Conference) on the application of Regge (1959, 1960) poles has changed all that, and my main objective is to try to render intelligible to the common man the new language which is now being used for the description of diffraction scattering, and its relation via Regge poles to the low energy resonances discussed by Lynch (1962) and Salam (1962).

Let me start by summarizing the classical optical description. The differential cross section can be expanded in partial waves.

$$\frac{d\sigma}{d\Omega} = \frac{1}{q^2} \sum_{l=0}^{l_{\max}} \left| (l + \tfrac{1}{2}) \frac{-1 + \exp[2i(a_l + i\beta_l)]}{i} P_l(\cos\theta) \right|^2. \tag{4.1}$$

The first parameter to be introduced is the radius of the interaction R, which determines the maximum value for scattering through the relation

$$l_{\max} = qR. \tag{4.2}$$

This is just the classical condition that the particles collide. If the interaction is 'black', β_l is large, the exponential is then negligible, and the amplitudes for all $l < l_{\max}$ are

$$\frac{-1 + \exp[2i(a + i\beta)]}{i} \simeq i. \tag{4.3}$$

If the interaction is not 'black', then the non-vanishing amplitudes are again taken to be pure imaginary and equal, but of magnitude a. This is the opacity parameter, which measures the degree of blackness of the target. By replacing the sum over l by an integral over impact parameter one arrives at the standard formulae

$$\frac{d\sigma}{d\Omega} = a^2\left|\frac{RJ_1(qR\sin\theta)}{\sin\theta}\right|^2 \tag{4.4}$$

$$\sigma_{el} = (\pi R^2)a^2, \qquad \sigma_{tot} = (2\pi R^2)a \tag{4.5}$$

the final relation following from the optical theorem. The angular distribution gives the well-known forward peak within an angle given by

$$\theta_0 \simeq \frac{3{\cdot}8}{qR} \tag{4.6}$$

followed by a series of subsidiary peaks. This two-parameter optical theory gives a reasonable fit (Matthews and Salam 1961) to the main peak for π–p and p–p collisions with (μ is π-meson mass)

$$R \simeq \frac{1}{\mu} \tag{4.7}$$

and

$$a = \frac{2\sigma_{el}}{\sigma_{tot}} \simeq \tfrac{1}{3}. \tag{4.8}$$

The value of t corresponding to the outer edge of the main diffraction peak is

$$t \simeq -25\mu^2. \tag{4.9}$$

There are three main reasons for being dissatisfied with this formulation. Firstly, the subsidiary diffraction peaks are a direct consequence of the sharp edge, which we have attributed to the interaction region. This is clearly quite unrealistic, but there is no obvious way to modify our assumptions about the dependence of the scattering amplitude on t without introducing additional parameters. Secondly, even if an average value is taken for the wide angle scattering it is given far too large by the simple optical formula and it proves difficult to reduce it sufficiently by more field theoretic ideas (Amati *et al.* 1961), based on the peripheral picture. Thirdly, the assumption that the amplitude is purely imaginary implies that it has certain analytic properties imposed by the Mandelstam representation. These are not satisfied by the form assumed in the optical approximation. The work of Lovelace remedies all three of these failings, by using the notion of Regge poles. These ideas also show a way out of the difficulties associated with polology of spin 1 particles mentioned in the previous section.

§ 5. REGGE POLES

Consider elastic scattering of a particle in a potential, at an energy E, through an angle given by

$$\cos\theta = x. \tag{5.1}$$

Then the scattering amplitude can be written

$$A(E, x) = \sum_{l=0}^{\infty} A_l(E)P_l(x)$$
$$= \frac{1}{2i}\int_C \frac{A(\alpha, E)P_\alpha(-x)}{\sin\pi\alpha}d\alpha \tag{5.2}$$

where the contour C is that shown in figure 3. This rewriting of the familiar angular momentum expansion is just a mathematical device, making use of the fact that $(\sin \pi\alpha)^{-1}$ has poles at integer values of α with residues $(-1)^l\pi$ and

$$P_l(-x) = (-1)^l P_l(x). \tag{5.3}$$

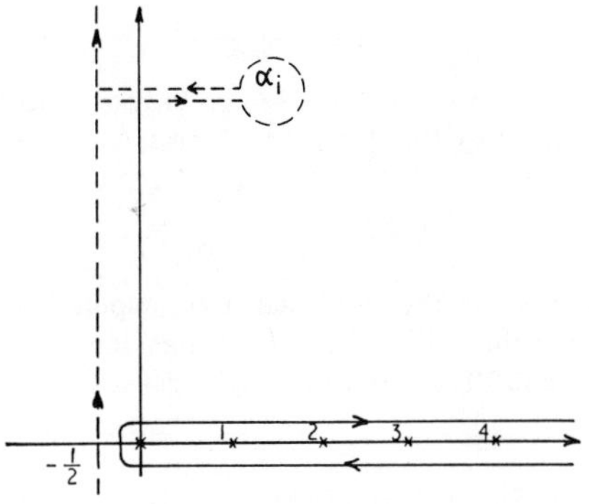

Figure 3. The contours of the Regge integral.

Using the analytic properties of the $P_\alpha(x)$, the contour may be distorted into a straight line parallel to the imaginary axis from $-\frac{1}{2}-i\infty$ to $-\frac{1}{2}+i\infty$. Additional terms arise from poles α_i in the function $A(\alpha, E)$ which have to be written explicitly. Thus

$$A(E, x) = \frac{1}{2i}\int_{-\frac{1}{2}-i\infty}^{-\frac{1}{2}+i\infty} \frac{A(\alpha, E)P_\alpha(-x)}{\sin \pi\alpha} d\alpha + \sum_i \frac{g_i(E)P_{\alpha_i(E)}(-x)}{\sin \pi\alpha_i(E)}. \tag{5.4}$$

Here $g_i(E)$ are the residues at the (Regge) pole α_i, which like the $\alpha(E)$ themselves, may be functions of E. For negative E (corresponding to bound states) $\alpha_i(E)$ are real. For $E < 0$, the positions of the poles $\alpha_i(E)$ in the (complex) angular momentum space determine the points where the amplitude becomes infinite (as in (3.1)), and consequently where the system has a bound state. Physically the angular momentum must take on a non-negative integer value so that the equation

$$\alpha_i(E_l) = l \qquad (l = 0, 1, 2, \ldots) \tag{5.5}$$

is just an unusual way of writing the energy eigenvalue equation. For values of E near to E_l, we can make an expansion of the appropriate Regge pole term in (5.4) to give

$$\frac{g_i(E)P_{\alpha_i(E)}(-x)}{\sin \pi\alpha_i(E)} \simeq \frac{g_i(E_l)}{\pi\alpha_i'(E_l)} \frac{P_l(x)}{E-E_l} \tag{5.6}$$

which is just the (non-covariant form of the) bound state term corresponding to a spin l, given in (3.3). If the energy is positive, $\alpha_i(E)$ is complex and (5.5) is replaced by

$$\mathscr{R}\alpha_i(E_l) = l \tag{5.7}$$

and gives rise to a resonance term in the amplitude

$$\frac{g_i(E_l)}{\pi} \frac{P_l(x)}{\epsilon[(E-E_l)+i\mathscr{I}\alpha_i(E_l)\epsilon^{-1}]} \tag{5.8}$$

where

$$\left[\frac{d\mathcal{R}\alpha}{dE}\right]_{E_i} = \epsilon. \tag{5.9}$$

In the (unphysical) limit of $x \to +\infty$,

$$P_\alpha(x) \simeq x^\alpha \tag{5.10}$$

and the integral in (5.4) can easily be shown to go to zero at least as fast as $x^{-1/2}$. The amplitude is then dominated by the Regge pole terms, so

$$A(x, E) \simeq \sum_i \frac{g_i(E)x^{\alpha_i(E)}}{\sin \pi\alpha_i(E)}. \tag{5.11}$$

This may be approximated by the single term corresponding to the $\alpha_i(E)$ which is greatest in magnitude for the value of E under consideration. These remarks are of great physical importance in the relativistic generalization of these ideas.

§ 6. DIFFRACTION SCATTERING AND REGGE POLES

We now consider the possible generalization of these ideas to a relativistic system. Suppose that the s-channel in figure 1 represents elastic scattering and, to be specific, that the particles represented by p_1 and p_3 are π-mesons.

Consider first the t-channel. If the π-mesons are in an isotopic spin state I, then the amplitude is even or odd for exchange of $p_1 \leftrightarrow p_3$ according to the evenness or oddness of I. But this exchange is equivalent to $s \leftrightarrow u$. Thus the scattering amplitude for this i-spin state can be written

$$T(s, t, u) = A(t, s) \pm A(t, u)$$

$$= \sum_l A_l(t) P_l\left(1 + \frac{2s}{t - M^2}\right) \pm P_l\left(1 + \frac{2u}{t - M^2}\right) \tag{6.1}$$

$$= \sum_l A_l(t) P_l\left(1 + \frac{2s}{t - M^2}\right) \pm e^{i\pi l} P_l\left(-1 - \frac{2u}{t - M^2}\right). \tag{6.2}$$

The P_l's appearing in (6.1) are just $P_l(\cos\theta)$ and $P_l(-\cos\theta)$ and the equation simply asserts that only even (odd) l-waves appear in the expansion according to the signature of $(-1)^I$.

If we now assume that the single particle and resonance states with the same quantum numbers (i) (apart from mass and spin) are dynamically related (through a Bethe–Salpeter equation for example), then it is reasonable to suppose that one can go through the same manipulations with (6.2) as with (5.2). The amplitude can then be expressed as an integral, plus additional Regge pole terms of the form

$$T_R(s, t, u) = \sum_i \frac{g_i(t)[P_{\alpha_i(t)}(1 + 2s/\{t - M^2\}) \pm \exp[i\pi\alpha_i(t)] P_{\alpha_i(t)}(-1 - 2u/\{t - M^2\})]}{\sin \pi\alpha_i(t)}. \tag{6.3}$$

The bound states are again given by the solutions of

$$\mathcal{R}\alpha_i(t_l) = l \tag{6.4}$$

where l must now be an odd or even integer for physically significant particle masses, t_l, according to the values allowed by the signature, $(-1)^I$. Somewhat fanciful plots of possible $\alpha_i(t)$ against t for some of the known particles and resonances, from a paper by Chew and Frautschi (1962), were shown by Lynch (1962).

If we now consider high energy scattering in the s-channel, we are interested in $T(s, t, u)$ in the limit

$$s \to \infty$$

$$t \to 0-$$

and hence, by (1.2),

$$u \to -\infty (\simeq -s).$$

In this limit the integral term in T goes to zero like $s^{-1/2}$ and we can approximate by the Regge pole terms:

$$T(s, t, u) \simeq T_{\mathrm{R}}(s, t, u) = \sum_i \frac{g_i(t)\{1 \pm \exp[i\pi\alpha_i(t)]\} s^{\alpha_i(t)}}{\sin \pi\alpha_i(t)}. \tag{6.5}$$

The ith term in this series can be regarded as the contribution to the scattering amplitude in the s-channel from the exchange of the *family* of particles associated with the Regge pole $\alpha_i(t)$, and replaces the Mandelstam pole term (3.4), corresponding to the exchange of a single particle (figure 2). Since Froissart (1961) has shown that for $t \leqslant 0$, $\alpha_i(t) \leqslant 1$, this shows the way round the difficulty of 'polology' of particles with spin.

We now consider the possibility of elastic scattering in the extreme high energy limit being described by a single term of the form (6.5). The Pomeranchuk limits imply that this will correspond to a pole, called $\alpha_{\mathrm{P}}(t)$, which gives rise to no exchange of quantum numbers between the colliding systems in the s-channel. Thus the pole must have $I = 0$, positive parity, and in general 'the quantum numbers of the vacuum'. In this Pomeranchuk limit we have then the amplitude

$$T_{\mathrm{P}} = g_{\mathrm{P}}(t)\left[\frac{1+\exp[+i\pi\alpha_{\mathrm{P}}(t)]}{\sin \pi\alpha_{\mathrm{P}}(t)}\right] s^{\alpha_{\mathrm{P}}(t)}. \tag{6.6}$$

From the optical theorem (2.5) and our assumption of constant cross sections at high energies it follows that

$$\alpha_{\mathrm{P}}(0) = 1. \tag{6.7}$$

This does not correspond to a particle, since for $I = 0$ only even values of the angular momentum are allowed in (6.4). From Froissart's result this is the maximum allowed value for any α_i, so it is quite consistent to assume that this is the dominant term in (6.5).

Using this result, the limit of the square bracket in (6.6) is just $+i$. Since the t dependence may be expected to come mainly from the final term, we arrive at the approximate expression for the amplitude at high energy (Frautschi, Gell-Mann and Zachariasen 1962, to be published, Chew and Frautschi 1962)

$$T_{\mathrm{P}} \simeq igs^{\alpha_{\mathrm{P}}(t)}. \tag{6.8}$$

Note that this has come out pure imaginary, which is again consistent with our comparison of forward scattering and total cross sections via the optical theorem.

This implies, by the optical theorem (2.5), that

$$g = \sigma_{\mathrm{tot}} \tag{6.9}$$

and by (2.6) that

$$\frac{(d\sigma/dt)}{(d\sigma/dt)_{t=0}} = s^{2(\alpha_{\mathrm{P}}(t)-1)}. \tag{6.10}$$

In the Pomeranchuk limit, (6.10) should apply to all elementary particle diffraction scattering (π–π, π–N, N–N, K–N etc.) with the same $\alpha_p(t)$, since in each case the same quantum numbers (those of the vacuum) are involved in the exchange. Formulae (6.9) and (6.10) have been employed by Wetherell (1962) in the analysis of the p–p scattering data, from which he has attempted to extract the dependence of $\alpha_p(t)$ on t (the Pomeranchuk trajectory). However, the assumption that this data can be interpreted in terms of the single Pomeranchuk pole through (6.10), and does not require the more general formula (6.6) is clearly open to question. (See also von Dardel *et al.* 1962.)

It is possible to carry the theoretical analysis a stage further by building in the analytic properties implied by the Mandelstam representation. Since the amplitude is pure imaginary it satisfies a dispersion relation for large s, which for the π–N amplitude, for example, is

$$T(s, t, u) = \frac{1}{\pi}\int_{4\mu^2}^{\infty} \frac{\rho_1(s, t')}{t'-t}dt' + \frac{1}{\pi}\int_{(\mu+M)^2}^{\infty} \frac{\rho_2(s, u')}{u'-u}du'. \qquad (6.11)$$

Forward scattering corresponds to $|t|$ small, $u \to -\infty$, backward scattering to $|u|$ small, $t \to -\infty$. Since no backward scattering is observed, one can assume that ρ_2 is small and consider only the first integral. Equation (7.1) then asserts that $T(s, t)$ is an analytic function of t in a plane with a cut running from $4\mu^2$ to infinity. Lovelace (1962, to be published) (see Drell 1961) has remarked that this can be ensured by introducing the variable

$$\eta = \frac{-t}{[2\mu+(4\mu^2-t)^{1/2}]^2} \qquad (6.12)$$

which maps the entire physical plane in t into the inside of the unit circle in η. Now (7.1) says only that $\alpha(t)$ must be analytic within this unit circle when expressed in terms of η. Lovelace takes as his form for $\alpha(t)$ the single parameter family

$$\alpha_p(t) = 1-\delta\eta^2(t) \qquad (6.13)$$

thus reducing (6.9) and (6.10) to a two-parameter (g, δ) theory, which should determine π–N scattering at all energies and angles (s and t) in the high energy region. A good fit to the data is obtained in the range under consideration. The same parameter δ should also apply to diffraction scattering for any pair of elementary particles in the Pomeranchuk limit (see Lovelace, preprint September 1961, to be published.)

We may now consider the qualitative predictions of this theory and at the same time compare the two new parameters with those of the simple optical model.

(i) Equation (6.10) can now be written

$$\frac{(d\sigma(s, t)/dt)}{(d\sigma(s, t)/dt)_{t=0}} = \exp[-2\delta \log s\eta^2(t)]. \qquad (6.14)$$

Thus the width of the main forward peak is determined by δ, which plays a similar role to R in the old theory. In fact

$$R \sim \delta \log s \qquad (6.15)$$

so that the Lovelace–Regge theory predicts a logarithmic sharpening with energy of the forward diffraction peak.

(ii) The total elastic cross section clearly depends on g^2, and at high energies, owing to the narrowing of the forward peak,

$$\sigma_{el} \sim \frac{g^2}{\log s}. \qquad (6.16)$$

By (6.9),

$$\sigma_{\text{tot}} = g. \tag{6.17}$$

Thus the opacity, if we take it to be defined by the formula (4.8), is

$$a \sim \frac{g}{\log s}. \tag{6.18}$$

The parameter g is thus closely related physically to the opacity parameter a. The logarithmic dependence implies that as the radius of the interaction region increases, the region itself gets less and less opaque.

(iii) The dependence of $\alpha_{\text{P}}(t)$ for negative t may in principle be taken direct from experiment (as has been attempted by Wetherell 1962) or by fitting the parameters of the expansion in η (as has been done by Lovelace). It may then be extrapolated to positive values of t. In any case there is the clear possibility of

$$\mathcal{R}\alpha_{\text{P}}(t_{\text{P}}) = 2 \tag{6.19}$$

for some positive t_{P} which would then imply a d-wave two-pion ($I = 0$) resonance (the Pomeron) $m_{\text{P}}^2 = t_{\text{P}}$, which would be closely linked with high energy diffraction scattering.

We have so far discussed only the extreme high energy limit in which it is assumed that the Pomeranchuk conjectures are satisfied. At lower energies (and present experiments clearly fall in this category), other Regge poles may be expected to play a role in (6.5).

In particular the forward scattering amplitude in the s-channel corresponding to isotopic spin I in the t-channel is

$$\mathcal{I}T^I(s, 0) = \sum_i G_i{}^I s^{\alpha_i(0)} \tag{6.20}$$

where the summation is only over those poles with isotopic spin I. If the known 2π and 3π resonances are associated with Regge trajectories $\alpha_i(t)$, the implications are straightforward and have been tabulated by Udgoankar (1962). For example, in π–N scattering the amplitude may be split in the usual way into

$$T^+ = \tfrac{1}{3}T^{1/2} + \tfrac{2}{3}T^{3/2}$$
$$T^- = \tfrac{1}{3}T^{1/2} - \tfrac{1}{3}T^{3/2}.$$

The Pomeranchuk trajectory contributes only to T^+; the trajectory to which the ρ meson belongs, $\alpha_\rho(t)$, contributes only to T^-. If only these two are considered, the optical theorem combined with (6.20) and (6.21) gives

$$\tfrac{1}{2}[\sigma(\pi^-\text{p}) + \sigma(\pi^+\text{p})] = g$$
$$\tfrac{1}{2}[\sigma(\pi^-\text{p}) - \sigma(\pi^+\text{p})] = G_\rho s^{\alpha_\rho(0)-1}.$$

According to the above ideas, it should be possible to obtain the t dependence of $\alpha_\rho(t)$ from a detailed study of accurate experimental data. But it may be that the situation is, in principle, more complicated. A study of the Regge representation of relativistic Coulomb scattering shows that there are cuts as well as poles in the α-plane (Virendrasingh 1962, to be published) and this may well be a general feature of the relativistic theory.

In any case the logarithmic sharpening of the forward peak, the likely presence of a d-wave resonance in the two-pion system and a common pattern for all elementary particle elastic scattering in the Pomeranchuk limit are very specific predictions of the

Lovelace–Regge theory. This will certainly provide the stimulus for a great deal of work, both theoretical and experimental, in this field in the next few years.

§ 7. PERIPHERAL-DIFFRACTION SCATTERING

In conclusion we should like to make some remarks on the inelastic nucleon–nucleon diffraction scattering reported by Wetherell (Cocconi *et al.* 1961), which has been interpreted by Drell and Hiida (1961) as the diffraction scattering of the beam proton off a meson in the cloud of the target proton (figure 4)—peripheral-diffraction scattering.

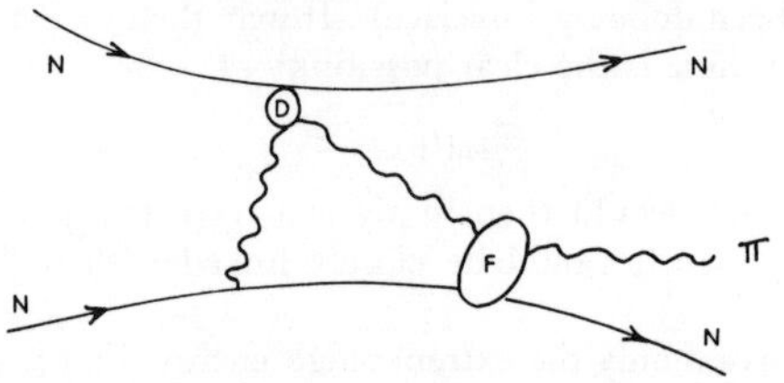

Figure 4. Feynman diagram of peripheral diffraction of nucleon–nucleon scattering, showing the diffraction scattering D off the virtual pion, and the final state interaction F between the pion and the target nucleon.

M. M. Islam (1962, to be published) has repeated these calculations. He makes the point that the bump in the inelastic cross section ($d^2\sigma/dEd\Omega$) at $p_L = 15{\cdot}89$ GeV/c corresponds to a momentum transfer of about $-t = 37 \sim 40\,\mu^2$. This is also the momentum transfer of the virtual diffraction scatter from the pion and lies considerably outside the main π–p diffraction peak. It is most important for the consistency of the model that the value put into the calculation is in agreement with the observed cross section, and care must be taken since all 'theories' other than that of Lovelace are very unreliable in this region. Islam claims that the value taken by Drell and Hiida is more than four times larger than the experimental value, which seems to destroy any quantitative agreement between the Drell–Hiida theory and experiment.

However there is evidently a strong final state interaction between the produced pion and the target nucleon, as shown by the bumps corresponding to the production of the two $I = \frac{1}{2}$ pion–nucleon resonances in the final state. Preliminary calculations by Islam suggest that the enhancement due to this final state interaction might produce the observed structure, and restore in part at least the missing factor of 4 in the overall magnitude.

REFERENCES

Amati, D., Fubini, S., Stanghellini, A., and Tonin, M., 1961, *Nuovo Cim.*, **22**, 569.
Azimov, S. A., *et al.*, 1960, *Proc. High Energy Conference, Rochester* (Saclay: C.E.N.), p. 91.
Chew, G. F., and Frautschi, S. C., 1962, *Phys. Rev. Letters*, **8**, 41.
Chew, G. F., Frautschi, S. C., and Mandelstam, S., 1962, *Phys. Rev.*, in the press.
Cocconi, G., Diddens, A. N., Lillethun, E., Manning, G., Taylor, A. E., Walker, T. G., and Wetherell, A. M., 1961, *Phys. Rev. Letters*, **7**, 450.
von Dardel, G., *et al.*, 1962, *Phys. Rev. Letters*, **8**, 173.

DRELL, S. D., 1961, *Proceedings of Aix-en-Provence Conference* (Saclay: C.E.N.), p. 125.
DRELL, S. D., and HIIDA, K., 1961, *Phys. Rev. Letters*, **7,** 199.
FRAUTSCHI, S. C., GELL-MANN, M., and ZACHARIASEN, F., 1962, *Phys. Rev.*, in the press.
FROISSART, M., 1961, *Phys. Rev.*, **123,** 1053.
LOVELACE, C., *Nuovo Cim.*, in the press.
LYNCH, 1962, *Proc. Phys. Soc.*, **80,** 46.
MATTHEWS, P. T., and SALAM, A., 1961, *Nuovo Cim.*, **21,** 126.
PEYROU, C., 1961, *Proceedings of Aix-en-Provence Conference* (Saclay: C.E.N.), p. 103.
POMERANCHUK, I., 1958, *Soviet Physics–JETP*, **7,** 499.
REGGE, T., 1959, *Nuovo Cim.*, **14,** 951.
—— 1960, *Nuovo Cim.*, **18,** 947.
SALAM, A., 1962, *Proc. Phys. Soc.*, **80,** 13.
UDGOANKAR, B. M., 1962, *Phys. Rev. Letters*, **8,** 142.
WEINBERG, S., 1961, *Phys. Rev.*, **124,** 2049.
WETHERELL, A. M., 1962, *Proc. Phys. Soc.*, **80,** 63.

INDEX*

Amplitudes, helicity, for spin-$\frac{1}{2}$ particles, 131
Analytic continuation of
  F, 31
  integrals, 22
  ϕ into left half-plane, 22ff.
  S, 35
Analytic potentials, consequences
    for f, 16
    for trajectory turning, 58
    for zeros of F_-, 52–54
  defined, 16
Analyticity,
  of S, as function of E, 34
  as function of k,
    for analytic potentials, 16
    branch points of f, 17
    of $f_\pm$, 15
    of $\lambda(k)$, 56
    for potentials of Yukawa type, 17
    of residue $\beta(k)$, 76–77
    of S, 34
  as function of λ,
    of $f_\pm$, 19
    of ϕ, 26
    of S, 35
  of potential, 15
Angular momenta, orbital and total, 135
Angular momentum coupling, ambiguity, 135
Asymptotic behavior,
  of amplitude, as function of momentum transfer (or of cos θ), 3, 7, 8, 37, 158
    as function of energy, 3, 12
  of Bessel functions, for large order, 38
  of f_-, as Im $\lambda \to \pm\infty$, 40–42
    as Re $\lambda \to \infty$, 42–43
    as Re $\lambda \to -\infty$, 44–45
  of Legendre functions, for large order, 5
    for large variable, 6
    of second kind, 11
  of S, as Im $\lambda \to \pm\infty$, 11
    as Re $\lambda \to \infty$, 6, 43, 44
Asymptotic distribution of zeros of f_- in λ-plane, 81ff.

Background integral, convergence of, 7
  elimination of, 11, 13
  pushing of, toward left, 10, 11
$\beta(k)$, defined, 76 (*see also* Residues of S-matrix poles)
Bessel functions, estimates, 162
  Hankel's integral, 161
Bessel's integral, 43
Born approximation, to $\underline{f}_\pm$ (*see* $\underline{f}_\pm$,

*Page numbers in italic indicate the principal reference.

Born approximation)
divergence of first, as evidence for higher orders, 80
Bound states, 10, 49, 51, 54, 57
scattering by, 135ff.
Boundary conditions, effect on analyticity, of f in k-plane, 17
of irregular solution, 14
of ϕ in λ-plane, 22
of regular solution, 14
Branch cut, of amplitude, 7, 8, 10
of f and ϕ in λ-plane, for r^{-2} potentials, 28
of f_+ in k-plane, 18
of Legendre functions, 6, 7, 13
Branch points, of amplitude, 4, 5, 7
dynamical, for three-body problem, 152ff.
in E-plane, 153ff.
of F, at k = 0, 30, 64
of f_+, 17
of Hankel functions, 17
of inverse of integral operators, 149ff.
kinematic, in three-body problem, 144
in momentum transfer plane, 7, 8
of ϕ and f for r^{-2} potentials, 28
of S, for particles with spin, 127, 131
for coupled channels, 133
Breit-Wigner formula, 9

C(λ), defined, 65
C-type poles, 66, *69–70*
for square wells, 95, 96
Carleman's theorem, 81
Carlson's theorem, 116
relevance in three-body problem, 158
Centrifugal term, as potential, 49
in coupled equations (for spin), 122
Channels, many (*see* Many-channel problem)
Circuit relation, of f_0, 17
of f, 17, 18
of $\bar{f}$, 19
of $\underline{f}$, 32
of F, 30
of Hankel functions, 17
of S-matrix, 34
Collision of zeros of F_-, or of poles of S (*see* Zeros of F_-, collision)
Complex conjugation properties, of f, 17–19
of F, 31
of $\underline{f}$, 32
of $\bar{\phi}$, 32
Continuous angular momenta, in contrast to complex, 2, 10
Core, hard, potential, 28, 36, 49, 55
Correlations, between partial wave amplitudes, 118
Correspondence, between ℓ-trajectory and E-trajectory, 110ff.
Crossing, 3, 12
Coulomb potential, negative energy poles of S, 54
pole trajectories, 86–87
regular solution, 27
S-matrix, 86
vanishing of $\bar{\phi}$, 27
Cut, dynamical (*see* Branch points, dynamical)
kinematical (*see* Left-hand cut, kinematical)
left hand (*see* Left-hand cut)
for particles with spin (*see under* Branch points)
right hand (*see* Right-hand cut)

Degeneracy, accidental, 128–129
Delay of particle flux, 9
Delay time, associated with retrograde pole motion, 58
Diagonalization of potential matrix, 123
Differentiability of potential, near origin, 24
Diffraction peak, shrinking, 12
Disconnected diagrams (*see* Graphs, unconnected)
Discontinuity, across cuts of inverse of integral operator, 150–151
of amplitude, 7–8
of Legendre function, 7

Dispersion relations, double, 1, 8
energy, 8
momentum transfer, 8, 116
Dynamical branch points (*see* Branch points, dynamical)
Dynamical interpolation, 2, 6

E-plane, related to k-plane, 34
E-trajectory, 110
Ellipse, Lehmann, 6
Energy scale, of motion of poles near E = 0, 67
Exchange forces, 103ff.
Exchange of trajectory tails (*see* Tail exchange)

$f_{\pm}$, bound in λ-plane, 39
for coupled equations, 122
defined, 14
reality, 18
relation between the two, 17–19
for three-body problem, 142
$\underline{f}_{\pm}$, behavior as Im $\lambda \to \pm\infty$, 40
for potentials of Yukawa type, 42
near k = 0, 65
as $|k| \to \infty$, 33, 61–62
as Re $\lambda \to +\infty$, 42–44
as Re $\lambda \to -\infty$, 44
Born approximation, 40
bound, 39
circuit relation, 32
complex conjugation property, 32
defined, 31, 32
finiteness at k = 0, 32, 36
growth rate, 45
integral representation, 32–33
for square wells, 94
symmetry in λ-plane, 32
$\overline{f}$, defined, 18
for spin-$\frac{1}{2}$ problem, 124
$\overline{\underline{f}}_{-}$, defined, 19
$\overline{f}_{\pm}$, for three-body problem, 144
$\overline{\underline{f}}$, defined, 45
f_{ϕ}, defined, 46
$F_{\pm}$, circuit relation, 30
complex conjugation property, 32
for coupled equations, 123
defined, 30
fixed poles (*see* Poles of F)
integral representation for three-body problem, 142
in k-plane, properties, 30
in λ-plane, 31
reality, 31
relation to $\underline{f}_{\pm}$, 31
symmetry in λ-plane, 31
$\overline{F}$, defined, 124, 144
$\overline{\overline{F}}$, defined, 129
Factorization, of residue, 128, 150
of discontinuity across cut, 151
Finite number of S-matrix poles, 7, 8
Fractions, partial (*see* Mittag-Leffler expansion)

Genus, of set of zeros of f in λ-plane, 83
Graphs, unconnected, 155–157
Green's function, 15, 122, 141, 161ff.

Hadamard's factorization (*see* Weierstrass factorization)
Half-integral values, negative, of λ, absence of poles of ϕ for square well, 27
poles of F, 31
poles of ϕ, 26
zeros of $\overline{\phi}$, 27
of ℓ (*see* Integral values, negative, of λ)
Hankel functions, in terms of Bessel functions, 40
estimates, 163
Hankel's integral, 41, 161
Hard core (*see* Core, hard)
Helicity amplitudes, 131
Hermiticity, lack of, of potential for spin case, 127

Indeterminacy points, 62
Inelastic processes, 135ff (*see also* Many-channel problem)
Infinite $|k|$, behavior of f, 15
$\underline{f}$, 33
ϕ, 28
S, 33

Infinite series, replaced by contour integral, 1
Integral equation, for irregular solution, 14, 122, 142
  for regular solution, 21, 122, 141
Integral representation, of $\underline{f}$, 32, 33
  of $F_{\pm}$ in three-body problem, 142
Integral values, negative, of λ, poles of ϕ, 26
  of ℓ (*see* Half-integral values, negative, of λ)
Interparticle distance, orbital angular momentum associated with, 136, 155
Interpolation, agreement with partial wave amplitudes, 118-119
  conditions on, 5, 6, *114*ff.
  dynamical, 2, 6, 115
  of Froissart and Gribov, 117
  of Schrödinger equation, uniqueness, 120
  uniqueness of (*see* Uniqueness)
Inversion, of integral operator, 149ff.
Irregular part of solution, 28
Irregular solution, *14*ff.
  boundary condition, 14
  for coupled equations, 122
  Green's function for, 15
  for three-body problem, 142
  zero order, 15
  (*see also under* $f_{\pm}$)
Isolated subsystem, 155

Jensen's theorem, 81
Jost function, 30 (*see also* $F_{\pm}$, $\underline{f}_{\pm}$)

k-dependence of, boundary condition for f, 15
  irregular solution f, 15
    F, 30
    $\underline{f}$, 32
  regular solution ϕ, 22
k-plane, analyticity in, of f, 15
  F, 30
  $\underline{f}$, 32
  ϕ, 22
  distinction between upper and lower, for f, 15
  pole trajectories of S, in, 106ff.

ℓ-trajectory, 110
λ defined, 14
  $|\lambda| \to \infty$, 37ff.
Laplace transform of potential (*see* Yukawa type, potentials of)
Left-hand cut, 17, 19, 30, 34
  of F_-, 56
  kinematical, 17, 34
  of $\lambda(k)$, 56
Left-hand half-plane, continuation to, of F, 31
  irregularity of ϕ, 22
  of ϕ, 22ff.
  reference to literature, 28
  relevance in three-body problem, 157
Legendre functions, asymptotic behavior, 11
  interpolation, 5, 13
  of second kind, 10

Many-channel problem, 121, 133
Mapping, defined by zeros of F_-, 112–113
  of ℓ- and E-trajectories, 110
Mass, reduced, 20
Matrix potential (*see* Potential, matrix)
Mittag-Leffler expansion of S-matrix, 84
Moments, absolute, of potential conditions, 15
  relation to Laplace transform, 20

Nonsense terms (*see* Sense and nonsense terms)

Order, defined, 46
Outgoing wave, ratio to incoming, 20

p, defined as a potential parameter, 24
  generalization to nonintegral values, 27
Parity, conservation, 138
  of triplet states for spin-$\frac{1}{2}$

particles, 121
Partial fraction representation (*see* Mittag-Leffler expansion)
Partial wave analysis, 2, *4*, 13
for spin-$\frac{1}{2}$, 121
Partial widths, 128–129
Phase shift, 4
difference, between contiguous ℓ-values, 166
downward passage of, 10, 58
for $\ell = -\frac{1}{2}$, 65
near resonance, 166–167
threshold behavior, 64
φ, defined, 41
for coupled equations, 122
$\overline{\varphi}$, defined, 124
ϕ, analytic continuation to left half λ-plane, 22ff.
bound in λ-plane, 38, 39
bound uniform, 38
complex conjugation property, 22
defined, 21
for three-body problem, 141
evenness, 22
high-energy behavior, 27–28
irregularity in left half λ-plane, 22
$\phi_{\pm}$, defined, 26
linear independence, Wronskian, 26
$\overline{\phi}_{\pm}$, defined, 26
for three-body problem, 144
linear independence, 27
vanishing, 27
Wronskian, 26
Physical S-matrix element, 8
Physical sheet, of E-surface, 34
Poles, of F, in left half λ-plane, 31, 51, 60–61, 107
fixed, lack of cancelation, 125
of ϕ, in left half λ-plane, 26, 51
absence for square wells, 27
of det F, fixed, 125ff.
effect of absence of, on C-type poles, 70
of potential, 123
of S, accumulation point of, 67
C-type, 66
distribution in λ-plane, 37
in E-plane, 10, 34, 108
near imaginary axis, 37
infinite number of, 55, 69
in k-plane, 106ff.
leading, 7–8
if on left, 11
0-type, 66
Pomeranchuk trajectory (*see* Vacuum trajectory)
Potential, analyticity of, 15
matrix, 122, 168–169
nonlocal, 58, 132
of r^{-2} type (*see* Singular potential)
Product representation, of $\underline{f}_{-}$, 83
of S, 83
Production of particles, 135

Quantization of angular momentum, 1, 2

R-function representation of S, 84–85
Radial Schrödinger equation, 14
coupled, for spin-$\frac{1}{2}$, 121
irregular solution of, *14*ff., 122
regular solution of, *21*ff., 122, 141
for three-body problem, 140
Reflection principle, Schwartz, 20
Regular part of solution, 28
Regular solution, *21*ff.
boundary condition, 21
of coupled equations, 122, 140
integral equation for, 21
zero order, 21
Representation of S, partial fractions, 84
product, 83
in terms of functions without kinematical left-hand cut, 84–85
Residues of S-matrix poles, 4, 5, 60, 72, *76*ff.
behavior as $|\lambda| \to \infty$, 79
of C-type poles, 78
definition for double poles, 79
factorization, 128
high-energy behavior, 78
left-hand cut of, 77
threshold behavior, 77
vanishing of, 77, 130
of 0-type poles, 77–78

Resonance, 9
phase shift near, 166–167
shift, 9
width, 9
behavior as function of ℓ, 74
as function of E, 109
negative width, 58
zero width, 59
Retrograde motion of poles, 10
Right-hand cut of S, 34
Rotational invariance, 2

$\bar{S}$, defined, 124
regularity near $j = -\frac{1}{2}$, 125ff.
for three-body problem, 144
S-matrix, analyticity in E-plane, 34
in λ-plane, 35
behavior as Im λ → ±∞, 42, 47
on imaginary axis, 35
as k → ±∞, 33
as Re λ → ∞, 43–44, 47
defined, 33
for coupled equations (spin), 123
for three-body problem, 142
in terms of $\underline{f}$, 33
in terms of $\bar{F}$, 35
poles in λ-plane, 48ff. (*see also* Zeros of F_-)
motion of poles, 56ff.
reason for distinction between k- and λ half-planes, 35
symmetry in λ-plane, 35
Schwartz reflection principle, 20
Second sheet, of S-matrix E-surface, 34
Sense and nonsense terms, 128, 130, 132, 138, 147
Series, infinite (*see* Infinite series)
σ-class, potential of, defined, 16
Signature, of pole trajectories, 104
Singlet states, 121
Singular potential, 28, 55
Singularity of differential equation, 15
Spin-$\frac{1}{2}$ ħ, particles with, 121ff.
Spin-orbit force, 132
Square well potential, absence of poles of φ at negative half-integral λ, 27
effect of absence on analyticity, 54, 55, 58
motion of poles as E → ±∞, 61–62
pole trajectories, 94ff.
Watson transform, 94
zeros of φ at half-integral λ, 27
Successive approximations to integral equations, of irregular solution, 15
of regular solution, 21
Symmetry, in λ-plane, of F, 31, 129
of $\underline{f}$, 32
of $\bar{S}$, 35, 129
of poles of S, or of zeros of F_-, 59–60
Symmetry of S-matrix, 123, 143

Tail exchange of trajectories, 71, 88, 93
Tensor force. 121
Three-body problem, 3, *135*ff.
Threshold behavior of S, 64
"anomalous," 62
branch point of $\underline{f}$, 64
caused by F, 56
in E-plane, 109
effect on poles, 55
in j-plane for spin-$\frac{1}{2}$, 127
of poles in λ-plane, *64*, 72–74
Trajectories of poles of S in k-plane, 107ff.
in λ-plane, 10, *56*ff.
crossing, 58
crossing imaginary λ-axis, 58, 59, 68
crossing real negative λ-axis, 59
continuity, 59
endpoints (*see* Zeros of F_- behavior as E → ±∞)
leading, 62
loops, 58
for negative energy, 57
turning, 58
Triplet state, 121
Type, defined, 46

Unconnected graphs (*see* Graphs, unconnected)

Uniqueness of interpolation, 2, *114* ff.
  of interpolation of Schrödinger equation, 120
Unitarity, generalized, 34, 151
  for particles with spin, 127
  for three-body problem, 145–147

Vacuum trajectory, 129–130

Watson transform, *4*, 37
  relevance for uniqueness, 115
  for spin-$\frac{1}{2}$ particles, 131
  if spin-orbit force present, 132
  for square well potential, 94
  for three-body problem, 157, 158
Weak potentials, effect on pole trajectories, 67, 70, 71
Weierstrass factorization of f_-, 83
Width (*see* Resonance, width)
Wronskian, defined, 19
  of $f_\pm$, 19
  of $\phi_\pm$, 26
  of $\overline{\phi}_\pm$, 26
  of ψ with $f_\pm$, 20
  of ψ with $\phi_\pm$, 28

Yukawa cut (*see* Left-hand cut)
Yukawa potential, simple, pole trajectories for, 87ff.
  modified by exponential potential, 88
Yukawa type, potentials of (Yukawa potentials, potential a superposition of), 6, 7, 11, 20

  consequences for f, 17, 19
    for analyticity of S in E-plane, 34
    for behavior of F as $|\lambda| \to \infty$ (*see under* F)
    for F, 30
    for trajectories as $E \to \pm\infty$, 61–62, 63
    for trajectory turning, 58
  defined, 16
  relation to differentiability, 24

0-type poles, defined, 66
  energy scale for, 67
  representation of, 69
  for square well, 95, 99ff.
  for Yukawa potentials, 95
Zero energy (or k) behavior of f, 18
  of $\overline{f}$, 19
Zeros of F_-, 48
  collision, 50, 59
  for $E \to 0$, 59, *64*, 66, 68
  for $E < 0$, 49, 54
  for $E < 0$, and $\text{Re}\,\lambda < 0$, 50
  for $E > 0$, 51
  in k-plane, 108
  in k-plane, as function of λ, 107ff.
  in left half λ-plane, 54–55
  limitation on position of $\text{Re}\,\lambda > 0$, 52–54
  motion as $E \to \pm\infty$, 59–63
  motion as function of E (*see* Trajectories of poles of S)
  number in right half λ-plane, 51, 52
  on real axis, 51
  simplicity, 50–51